PHEASANTS IN NORTH AMERICA

Reproduction from a painting by Bob Hines

PHEASANTS
IN NORTH AMERICA

Edited by

DURWARD L. ALLEN

Frontispiece and drawings by
BOB HINES

Frontispiece and drawing reproductions courtesy
of the Frederic C. Walcott Memorial Fund
of the North American Wildlife
Foundation

Published by
THE STACKPOLE COMPANY
Harrisburg, Pennsylvania

and the

WILDLIFE MANAGEMENT INSTITUTE
Washington, D.C.

1956

AUTHORSHIP AND CONTRIBUTORS

This book is a cooperative effort among biologists of federal, state, and private institutions. It supplements the first work of this kind, THE RING-NECKED PHEASANT AND ITS MANAGEMENT IN NORTH AMERICA, published in 1945. By design, authorship was not duplicated between the two books. Contributors to the present work are here identified. In a few cases, affiliation was changed while the book was in preparation, and both sponsoring institutions are given.

939016

CHAPTER I
Fred H. Dale, Biologist, Game Bird Investigations, U. S. Fish and Wildlife Service, Laurel, Maryland

CHAPTER II
J. Burton Lauckhart, Chief, Game Management Division, Washington Department of Game, Seattle
John W. McKean, Chief of Game Operations, Oregon State Game Commission, Portland

CHAPTER III
Chester M. Hart, Leader, pheasant research project, California Department of Fish and Game, Sacramento
Ben Glading, Chief, Game Management Branch, California Department of Fish and Game, Sacramento
Harold T. Harper, formerly Leader, pheasant research project, California Department of Fish and Game (later in armed services).

CHAPTER IV
Lee E. Yeager, Leader, Colorado Cooperative Wildlife Research Unit, Fort Collins
Jessop B. Low, Leader, Utah Cooperative Wildlife Research Unit, Logan
Harry J. Figge, in charge, Game Bird Survey, Colorado State Game and Fish Commission, Denver

CHAPTER V

James W. Kimball, Assistant Regional Supervisor, Office of River Basin Studies, U. S. Fish and Wildlife Service, Minneapolis, Minnesota

Edward L. Kozicky, Leader, Iowa Cooperative Wildlife Research Unit, Ames

Bernard A. Nelson, Federal Aid Coordinator, South Dakota Department of Game, Fish and Parks, Pierre

CHAPTER VI

Robert A. McCabe, Associate Professor of Wildlife Management, University of Wisconsin, Madison

Ralph A. MacMullan, Biologist in Charge, Houghton Lake Wildlife Experiment Station, Game Division, Michigan Department of Conservation, The Heights

Eugene H. Dustman, Leader, Ohio Cooperative Wildlife Research Unit, Columbus

CHAPTER VII

Allen W. Stokes, Assistant Professor, Department of Wildlife Management, Utah State Agricultural College, Logan; formerly Leader, Pelee Island pheasant research project, 1947-50, University of Wisconsin and Wildlife Management Institute.

CHAPTER VIII

Allan T. Studholme, Assistant Regional Director in charge of Wildlife, U. S. Fish and Wildlife Service, Boston, Massachusetts

Dirck Benson, Senior Wildlife Biologist, Bureau of Game, New York State Conservation Department, Albany

CHAPTER IX

Durward L. Allen, Associate Professor of Wildlife Management, Purdue University, Lafayette, Indiana; formerly Assistant Chief, Branch of Wildlife Research, U. S. Fish and Wildlife Service

Illustrator (frontispiece and chapter head sketches)
Bob Hines, Washington, D. C.

Drafting (maps, charts, graphs)
John T. Linehan, Biologist, U. S. Fish and Wildlife Service, Laurel, Maryland
Oscar Warbach, Illustrator, Game Division, Michigan Department of Conservation, Lansing; formerly Biologist, U. S. Fish and Wildlife Service, Laurel, Maryland

Editor's Acknowledgments

In the planning and compilation of this book, the editor received a multitude of favors, many of which cannot be mentioned here. Thanks are due, first of all, to the chapter authors whose willing cooperation and painstaking effort made the project possible. Photographs used are acknowledged individually, and they came from a wide selection generously contributed by the institutions and individuals named. There can be no substitute for the kind of skill and enthusiasm which Bob Hines brought to his task of illustration, and the meticulous care with which John T. Linehan and Oscar Warbach made final drafts of maps and charts from data furnished by the authors. I owe a particular debt to Fred H. Dale, who gave unstintingly of his time, good advice, and editorial skill in shaping up the entire manuscript. Similar favors were frequently had for the asking from Daniel L. Leedy and C. Edward Carlson, of the Fish and Wildlife Service.

Ira N. Gabrielson, President, and C. R. Gutermuth, Vice President of the Wildlife Management Institute, caused this book to be written and made helpful contributions to the editing. James B. Trefethen cheerfully assumed the onerous job of final editing and proofreading.

D. L. A.

Table of Contents

LIST OF PLATES

LIST OF FIGURES

INTRODUCTION

The history of wildlife conservation in North America has been marked by many attempts to introduce foreign game species. Most failed; a few, notably the chukar and Hungarian partridges, succeeded locally; but none has adapted itself so spectacularly to so large an area of this continent as the Chinese ringneck pheasant.

As the introduction of grain production in the prairies and plains destroyed the essential habitat of native game birds, it produced ideal living conditions for the gaudy Asiatic. In a period of time within the memory of many living Americans, the pheasant has risen from a zoological curiosity to a top-ranking game bird, familiar to and hunted by sportsmen from coast to coast throughout the northern states and much of southern Canada. In the West, from British Columbia to southern California, it has made a home for itself in the irrigated valleys. In the Northeast it has found suitable environment on the comparatively small farms of this diverse agricultural region.

Because of the far-flung and widely varying nature of the occupied range of the ringneck pheasant in North America, no one man could have authored this book, for no one man has intimate knowledge of the habits of the pheasant under all ecological conditions. Leading specialists in each region of the ringneck's range have contributed their observations and experience to the following chapters. In this respect the book follows the pattern of *The Ring-necked Pheasant and its Management in North America,* published by the Institute in 1945, but the information is far more complete because of the accelerated, broadened and improved research programs which have been developed since that time.

This book will provide the answers to almost any of the

questions of all those interested in this exotic, which actually has become the principal farm game bird in the northern states. It will be of particular interest to students of wildlife, fish and game technicians and administrators, game breeders, and sportsmen.

C R Gutermuth

Vice-President, Wildlife Management Institute

PHEASANTS IN NORTH AMERICA

CHAPTER 1

PHEASANTS AND PHEASANT POPULATIONS

By FRED H. DALE

WHEN the first cock pheasant in the Willamette Valley selected a "territory" and gathered a harem of hens around him, he brought something new and important to the North American wildlife scene. Hunting of the wily ringneck was to become a popular field sport and its management one of our most stirring issues.

By the first decade of this century, wing shooting for the average hunter appeared doomed on northern farms. The best soils were becoming too cleaned-up for quail. The passenger pigeon was nearly counted out. Prairie grouse never could be expected to compete with intensive agriculture and provide shooting for a large host of hunters. Waterfowl would continue to yield outsize bags for several years, but principally for the specialist.

Intensive farming was creating new conditions for a game bird that could take advantage of them. In filling this gap, the pheasant helped continue the sport of shooting for vast numbers of farmers and city workers who needed to find their recreation nearby.

People had tended to think of game as belonging to the wilderness, but the coming of the pheasant helped emphasize that the good lands which grow our food have a high potential yield of crops for the gun. This was the land to which sportsmen turned, and hunter demands soon highlighted a need for more management know-how. When the biologist got well into his studies of the ringneck, he found that it offered something unique in an opportunity to discover and understand certain principles basic to management of all game species. In all the restless tampering with exotic wildlife, the pheasant stands out as the greatest gain.

The Nature of the Bird

The pheasant is a gallinaceous bird. This tell something of its relatives and characteristics. Other gallinaceous birds include grouse, wild turkeys, quail, and the introduced partridges, all of which are like the pheasant in many ways. But for the nearest of kin we need look no farther than the barnyard. Fundamentally the ringneck cock resembles the domestic rooster more closely than he does any native bird.

Our North American pheasant lays no claim to racial purity. The original Willamette Valley stock probably was pure Chinese ringneck, but it would be a formidable task to trace introductions by state agencies and private clubs to learn how this strain has been modified. In the veins of today's ringneck on this continent flows the mingled blood of several Old World birds, variously considered as geographic races or even separate species. Most important are the Chinese ringneck, Mongolian, Japanese, and common English pheasant. The latter came from Caucasian stock with additions of other strains.

Hens of these races are much alike, but the more gaudy cocks present a variety of color patterns. All have the brilliant metallic sheen, but certain combinations of hues in the North American bird attest to its hybrid character. Pheasants from Asia Minor, and also the Mongolian, have strong coppery-red tones over the breast, sides, and back. In Eastern Asiatic races, like the Chinese ringneck, the red color is more restricted to the breast, while the flanks are yellowish and the back is mottled with browns and buff. So distinctive is this color difference that, until recently, pheasants of eastern Asia were considered to constitute a separate species, *Phasianus torquatus,* the name *P. colchicus* being restricted to western types.

A third color variation comes from the Japanese green

pheasant, *Phasianus versicolor,* a bird with green breast, back, and underparts. Although this species has had little direct success in North America, some traces of it have crept in through mixed game-farm stock or introductions of English pheasants with some Japanese blood.

Added to this mingling of Asiatic races and their Western descendants is the melanistic mutant, a dark bird that arose as a mutation, or "sport," from mixed English stock in the

PLATE I.—Like us, he's an alien in a man-made habitat (R. M. Cady, Pennsylvania Game Commission).

late 19th century (Delacour 1945). This color phase has further complicated the picture in some parts of our pheasant range. Most North American pheasants resemble the Chinese ringneck, and in parts of the Northwest they frequently are called "Chinese pheasants," but the observant hunter often finds evidence of other ancestral strains.

The name "pheasant," or sometimes "native pheasant," has been misapplied to ruffed grouse in parts of the Southeast. Although this use of names is unfortunate, it seldom causes much confusion, since the true pheasant is a rarity in most states south of the Mason-Dixon Line. Within its principal range the name now is restricted almost entirely to the introduced bird. In this book, the term "ringneck" is used, for despite the fact that certain ancestors did not have the white collar, this feature is almost universal in pheasants of the New World.

Like the barnyard fowl, pheasants are heavy, short-winged birds. This has been learned the hard way by many a motorist who has had one come through the windshield of his car. The ringneck has sturdy legs and feet with claws useful for scratching. The beak is short and strong. Although much of its food comes from the ground or from low-growing plants, the pheasant is well equipped to scratch beneath the surface for worms or insect larvae or to uncover food beneath the snow (Weston 1950, Leedy and Hicks 1945).

Cock pheasants are larger and heavier than hens. Average fall weights are about $2\frac{3}{4}$ pounds for cocks and $2\frac{1}{4}$ pounds for hens. These averages are computed roughly from records for Ohio, Michigan, Nebraska, Utah, South Dakota, and New York. Mongolian pheasants are larger and Chinese ringnecks smaller than this.

The stout tarsal spurs of cocks resemble those of game cocks and serve the same purpose. They are short and blunt during the first few months but may reach adult size by early winter. Usually they are not developed fully in texture and shape until the next summer (Linduska 1943, 1945).

Game technicians make use of spurs in distinguishing older

cocks from birds of the year. Although a few young cocks in late fall will have spurs as long as some adults, most specimens can be separated by length of spur alone. It has been found in South Dakota that almost all young cocks can be identified

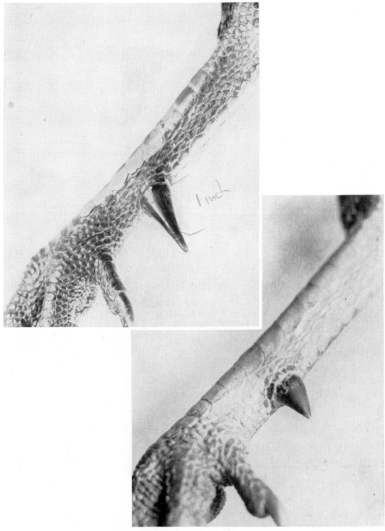

PLATE II.—Spur of an old cock pheasant in October (*above*) compared with the spur of typical bird of the year (J. P. Linduska).

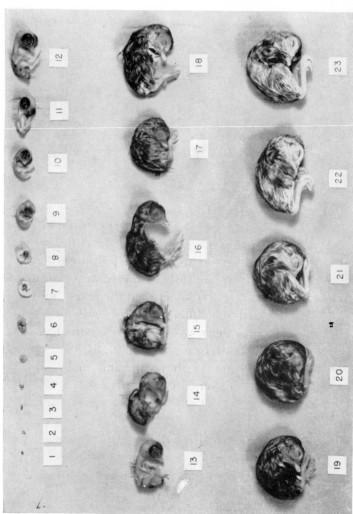

PLATE III.—The daily development of a pheasant chick to hatching time. When field men check broken-up or abandoned nests, they use this chart to estimate the beginning date of incubation (Colorado Cooperative Wildlife Research Unit).

in this way in mid-October but that some young birds have
spurs as long as adults by November. The spurs of most juveniles are less than 19 mm. (about ¾ inch) in length, while
adult spurs usually are longer, sometimes more than an inch
long (this measurement is from the tip of spur to the opposite
side of the "leg," or tarsus). Spur length is a rapid way of judging pheasant age, and doubtful specimens can be checked by
other characters.

During fall and winter, cocks have small bare patches of
red skin around the eye. In early spring these begin to enlarge,
and by the mating season become bright red wattles that practically cover the sides of the head.

How young pheasants develop

The pheasant chick is precocial. In other words, it is completely clothed with down and can leave the nest soon after
hatching. By the end of the second week it is capable of short
flights. The downy coat soon is replaced by juvenile feathers,
which, in turn, are exchanged during the post-juvenile molt
for adult garb. Young birds are fully feathered at 5 or 6 weeks
and there are plumage distinction between the sexes, but there
is little hint of the striking differences that will be seen in
mature birds. As soon as the young pheasant gets its first complete plumage, the process starts all over again. By 8 or 9 weeks,
the adult feathering begins to show up, and males can be
distinguished both by greater size and suggestions of color
about the neck. From that time on they change rapidly until
they reach adult appearance.

Close examination is needed to distinguish between young
cocks 17 or 18 weeks of age and fully adult birds, and many
a hunter will be surprised to learn that most of the brilliantly
colored cocks bagged in October are young birds of the year
that only recently have acquired their adult appearance.

Wing feathers are most useful in studying the age of young
birds, although feathers over the entire body are changed during the molt. The ten outermost flight feathers, the primaries,
are lost and replaced according to a fairly reliable time

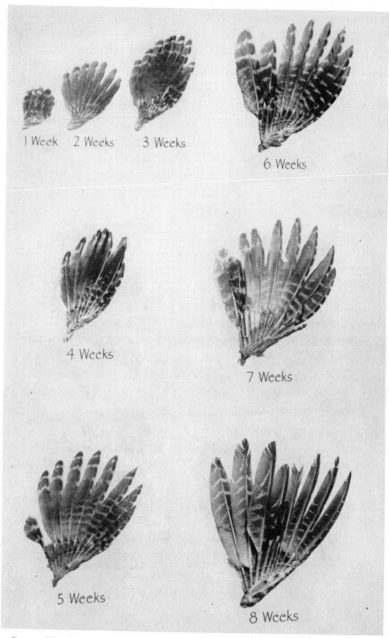

PLATE IV.—Progressive feathering of the wing of a young pheasant. A reference chart from which approximate age of juvenile birds may be determined

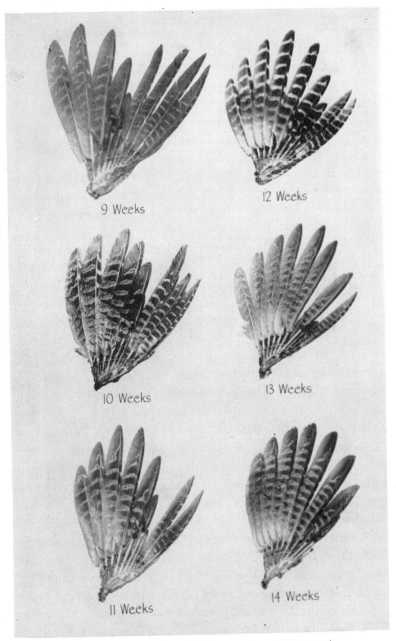

(From Buss, 1946, courtesy Wisconsin Conservation Department).

schedule. This begins when the chick is 4 weeks old and continues for about 12 weeks. The innermost primary is lost first, and others follow in regular order, until the tenth feather is dropped at about 16 weeks (Trautman 1950).

The age of young pheasants from 4 to 16 weeks can be estimated to the nearest week by noting the progress of this feather exchange. Since feathers grow at about the same rate for all young pheasants, age in older birds, from 16 to about 21 weeks, can be estimated by measuring the length of the outer primaries and comparing them with the length of feathers of known age. With this information the biologist counts back to learn hatching dates and to piece together other details of the nesting season.

Another change in the growing bird is of interest mainly to the researcher. Like almost all other birds, pheasants in their first year have a small pouch leading off the intestine near the anal opening. This pouch, known as the bursa of Fabricius, can be found on the upper wall of the cloaca just inside the anal opening, and an experienced worker can measure its depth by probing with a blunted nail or similar instrument. By the second summer the bursa disappears or becomes shallow. In the fall a pheasant is either less than 7 or more than 14 months old, and the depth of the bursa serves to separate young of the year from older individuals.

California workers have reported exceptions that question the reliability of this method of aging pheasants. Pheasants known to be a year of age have been found to have bursas 8 or 10 millimeters deep, and under standards accepted by midwestern biologists would be classified as young of the year. The California exceptions may reflect the lack of stress under which these birds live. The bursa of Fabricius, as lymphoid tissue, regresses under the influence of adrenal hormones. The size of this organ in poultry can be used as a measure of the responses of the bird to stress conditions (Garren and Shaffner 1954). Possibly it can be used as an indicator of age only in northern areas where severe winter conditions exist.

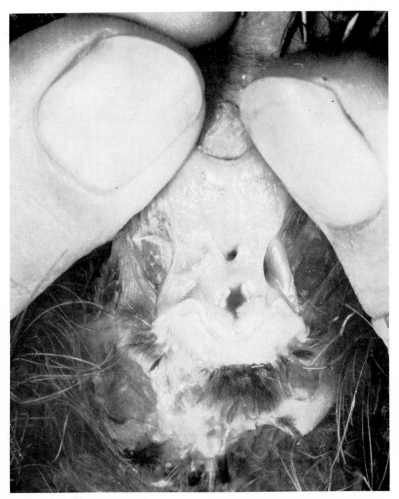

PLATE V.—The anal opening of a juvenile cock pheasant in the fall. The sides have been slit and the upper wall laid back to expose the opening of the bursa. In an old bird this opening would be missing or very shallow (J. P. Linduska).

Pheasant foods

The pheasant is hardly more restricted in its diet than the domestic chicken. It shows a leaning toward vegetable matter and especially toward grains and seeds, but almost anything from the tiny seeds of panic grass to snakes and mice may be

PLATE VI.—Over much of the eastern range, corn is first on the pheasant's menu. It is high in vitamin A but low in calcium (*above:* South Dakota Dept. Game, Fish and Parks; *below:* D. L. Allen).

reported at some time as pheasant food. Since the principal pheasant concentrations are in grain-producing areas, cultivated crops usually predominate.

Corn is first on the menu over the greater part of the ringneck's range, but it is not essential where there is a good substitute. Yellow corn is a good source of vitamin A, but this vitamin is found in most green plants, and there has been no evidence of deficiency where other grains replace corn. It will come as something of a shock to many persons to learn that corn may be less than a perfect diet for the pheasant. Studies completed in 1953 indicated that the pheasant has considerable difficulty in obtaining an adequate supply of calcium. Corn is the poorest source of this element in the diet, and where the pheasant depends on corn for the major part of its food supply it must have some rich source of calcium to enable it to exist. This may be the reason why the heart of the corn belt is not among the best of the North American pheasant ranges (Dale 1954).

Dalke (1945) found more than 110 plant species to serve as food for pheasants in Michigan, and about the same situation seems to prevail elsewhere. Nevertheless, it is evident that only a few foods make up the basic diet. Corn, lesser ragweed, acorns, and pigeon grass appear to be mainstays in Iowa, and pheasant nutrition in that state seems to depend largely on annual production of these plants (Errington 1936). In South Dakota, about 80 percent of the pheasant's summer food consists of corn, wheat, oats, and barley (Trautman, 1952).

The ringneck is adaptable and seems to do well with whatever foods are at hand. It was found in Utah by Rasmussen and McKean (1945) that small grains comprised about 60 percent of the diet in one area and 81 percent in another, but in the Sandhill region of Nebraska, where the pheasant gets by in grassland without much help from farm crops, cultivated grains amounted to only about 5 percent of the total (Sharp and McClure 1945). Skunk cabbage seems to be relished when available, and seeds of this plant made up 43 percent of the food in 70 fall pheasant crops examined in Massachusetts; corn amounted to less than 20 percent (Wandell *et al.* 1942).

The ringneck has a liking for greens, and in Massachusetts it was estimated that 11.6 percent of the annual diet was leaves and grass. In Michigan, there seemed to be an increase in the use of green material late in winter, which Dalke (1945) thought might be associated in some way with requirements of the approaching breeding season. An experiment on penned pheasants in Oregon (Uhlig 1948) showed that the birds could subsist, and even gain weight, over a three-month winter period on green herbage alone.

Fruits are eaten in season and at times make up a fairly substantial part of the pheasant's diet. In the Massachusetts study, fruits were estimated to comprise 10 percent of the total annual food supply.

PLATE VII.—The pheasant is adaptable and makes good use of what is at hand. Here the birds dug through a light snow for greens and possibly weed seeds (D. L. Allen).

As every farm wife knows, insects are especially important for growing chicks. Such a diet is rich in protein (Norris 1934), and young pheasants in the wild appear to eat little vegetable matter for the first few weeks. In Utah, about 75 percent of the food of pheasant chicks 3 to 8 weeks old seemed to be insects, but such food made up only 2 percent of the diet of 10- to 13-week-old pheasants (Rasmussen and McKean, 1945).

In California, too, practically 100 percent of the first week's diet proved to be insects, but vegetable matter gradually increased in importance. In the 11- to 12-week group, animal matter made up 30 percent of the diet, but in the 12- to 16-week birds this dropped off to 3.3 percent (Ferrel *et al.* 1949).

Insects seem to be important also as a source of moisture for young pheasants. Chicks in South Dakota deprived of both insects and water died quickly, even though they received mash that was high in protein, but those having access either to water or insects survived (Harris 1950).

Under some conditions, adult pheasants also eat large numbers of insects. Examples in a South Dakota study included a ringneck with 38 cutworms in the crop and 25 in the gizzard, one with 103 grasshoppers in the crop, and a third with 115 crickets in the crop and 8 in the gizzard (Severin 1933).

The ringneck is not a purist in its food habits, a fact that enables it to use crop residues of many kinds and to prosper in the face of intensive farming. In California's Sacramento Valley, rice does fully as well as corn (Ferrel *et al.* 1949), and on Pelee Island, waste soybeans became the number-one food item. In irrigated valleys of the Southwest, such grains as sorghums and Sudan grass are acceptable. The chief requirement seems to be that food be plentiful and nutritious. Pheasants seldom are found away from fertile agricultural areas.

Ringneck Country

Pheasants seem most at home in our best northern farm lands. In the East, they show Yankee affinities and are a rarity south of the 39th parallel, which is near the southern boundary of Pennsylvania. Even in the West, the principal populations are north of a line connecting San Francisco and southern Colorado, although a few occur southward even across the Mexican border.

By no means can all the area within these extremes be classed as pheasant range. South Dakota has long been the Mecca of avid pheasant hunters, and the largest continuous block of ringnecks is found in the northern Great Plains States of North Dakota, South Dakota, Minnesota, Iowa, and Nebraska. But even in those states there are large blank areas.

To the south and west of the prairie pheasant range, water controls the destinies of both men and pheasants. Dryland farming is precarious even for the farmer, and in arid regions the pheasant gives way to the cow, sheep, and jackrabbit. Nevertheless, soils of arid lands usually are rich in minerals, and where irrigation is possible crop-yields are high. Pheasants are abundant in many of the irrigated valleys of western United States. All states west of Arkansas have some pheasants, but there are no large regions of high population south of Colorado. Few western areas, except parts of Washington and Oregon, support pheasants away from irrigated lands.

Pheasant distribution in the eastern half of the country is even less easily explained. The Lake States and all eastern states north of Maryland have pheasants, but distribution is spotty. There are fair to good populations in parts of Wisconsin, Illinois, Michigan, Ohio, Pennsylvania, and New York. The New England states boast a few in fertile valleys, and northern New Jersey has some shooting, but there are few pheasant populations in the Northeast comparable with those of the better western valleys. In the Midwest, Indiana and southern Illinois present unusual problems, for, despite fertile soil and high production of corn, pheasants never have become abundant there.

Although there has been much speculation and some research on reasons for the spotty distribution of the pheasant in North America, no single explanation so far seems to give a complete answer to the problem.

Pheasants and weather

The northern distribution of pheasants in eastern United States strongly suggests that climate is what bars the spread of ringnecks into the South, but complications arise when considering the arid West. There the ringneck has been able to endure the intense heat of the Imperial Valley and contiguous areas in Lower California. From this distribution, it seems that high temperatures alone do not constitute a barrier. If climate controls the spread, then it seems to be the combination of high temperature and high humidity in the Southeast that is unfavorable. Ringnecks have demonstrated their ability to withstand high humidity in parts of the Northwest and Northeast, but there temperatures are moderate.

Pheasants can be reared in pens all over the country, and adult birds can survive in the wild in some southern states. A small local population has been maintained in central Florida for several years with the aid of annual stocking. This seems to suggest that limitations to pheasant distribution work by hampering normal breeding or rearing of young. If so, then climate during spring and early summer must be more important than in other seasons.

Summer temperatures and rainfall in the southeastern United States are unlike those in good pheasant country, or in the Asiatic range of the ringneck (Cahn 1938, Graham and Hesterberg 1948). However, this fact does not necessarily explain the ringneck's failure in the Southeast. The climate of California's Sacramento Valley is different from that of the Lancaster Valley in Pennsylvania, yet both these valleys are good pheasant areas.

One clue as to the way temperature might work is the fact that high temperatures lower the hatchability of pheasant eggs. Pheasant eggs stored at 88 degrees in an Illinois study failed to hatch, while quail eggs were not injured by this temperature (Yeatter 1950). More research on problems of this sort may provide the answer to the riddle of climate and ringneck production. Studies of critical ground temperatures in potential pheasant range might be still more significant.

In this, as in many other pheasant problems, the key to the future is in the hands of the researcher.

Glaciers and pheasants

When Aldo Leopold surveyed game conditions in the Lake States, he was impressed with the fact that most successful pheasant establishments were in glaciated areas. He speculated that this might be explained on a nutritional basis, since glaciated soils in these states generally have lime near the surface (Leopold 1941). In Pennsylvania, pheasants do well on unglaciated soils, but this could be due to the limestone underlying most of the unglaciated range there. If glaciation is a requirement of pheasants in the Lake States, the relationship does not hold everywhere; they also thrive in several unglaciated valleys of the far West.

Thus, although the correlation between pheasant distribution and glaciation is strong enough to be suggestive, there are exceptions that complicate the picture.

What about soils?

Soil fertility is important in determining good pheasant range, but no one is sure why. Good soils usually are farmed differently from poor soils. Not only do they produce more weeds and crops (Baumgras 1943), but the plants grown on them are different. Furthermore, animals make better gains on foods from fertile soils than on those grown on deficient soils (Albrecht and Smith 1941, Albrecht 1946, Crawford 1950).

In general, soils of arid lands are richest in minerals. Higher rainfall in other lands is attended by more leaching of nutrients from the topsoil, a process that is speeded up in warmer climates. Northern soils are protected by snow and freezing weather during winter months, but in the South the topsoil is continuously subjected to percolation of water and loss of plant nutrients. In addition, plant residues in hot, humid areas are broken down rapidly. Consequently, soils of the Southeast tend to be low in nitrogen as well as minerals.

In some northern areas, loss of minerals has been offset in

part by glaciation, which resulted in a redistribution of minerals within the soil and the bringing of limestone from places farther north. In some localities, soils have been formed directly from beds of limestone. Such areas, as in Pennsylvania's Lancaster Valley, usually are highly fertile.

Studies at the Patuxent Research Refuge, in Maryland, on requirements of pheasants for calcium, offer a plausible explanation for the apparent dependence of the ringneck on calcareous soil. In these studies, pheasants given a natural diet but confined to granite grit failed to produce viable eggs, whereas others on the same diet, but with limestone grit, laid eggs that hatched normally (Dale 1954, Dale 1955). This demonstrated need for calcium supplement, coupled with the observed distribution of the pheasant in areas with high calcium availability, suggests an answer to a problem that has long puzzled biologists.

It is apparent that there has been relatively little progress in explaining the distribution of the pheasant. Soils and climates are so intricately involved that it is unrealistic to consider them separately. Not only does climate control development of the soil, but it also influences the quality of foods produced. The climate of Kansas produces wheat containing more protein and potash on soil transported from Maryland than the Maryland climate on either Maryland or Kansas soil (Browne 1938).

About all that can be said with confidence at this stage of knowledge is that the pheasant requires fertile soil, and that it is not found in hot, humid parts of the continent. Southeastern United States, whether because of climate, soils, or some factor as yet unsuspected, appears to offer little promise for ringnecks.

Mating and Reproduction

The ringneck cock is a harem master, and judged by Western standards performs this role with remarkable efficiency. The hunter often worries about unbalanced sex ratios, but those factors present no problem to the cock pheasant. Harems of as many as 18 hens have been reported, and in experiments with penned birds, one cock has mated successfully with 50 hens. Spring sex ratios of about 8 or 10 to 1, which are seldom exceeded in the wild, are well within the capabilities of the cock.

The harem is a matter of convenience, lasting only through the courting and nesting periods. The cock has no part in the care of young, although there have been a few reports of cocks accompanying half-grown broods. Winter flocks may be of either sex, or both hens and cocks.

Evidence of the approaching mating season may be seen while ringnecks are in their winter flocks, with cocks showing the first outward signs of sexual development. As early as January 18, in 1951, wattles of penned cocks at the Patuxent Research Refuge, Maryland, were beginning to enlarge. Dominant cocks begin to challenge less aggressive members of their flocks. Some courting and possibly actual mating may occur before flocks break up, and males begin to leave their winter concentrations by late February and March and move out to take up crowing areas or territories (Taber 1949a). Where cover is well dispersed, spring movements may be minor, but in Iowa and South Dakota, pheasants move as far as 7 to 10 miles from winter cover to breeding areas (Kimball 1948, Weston 1950).

The "territory" is a somewhat indefinite area which the ringneck cock stakes out and claims as his personal property to be defended against trespass by other cocks. This prohibition does not apply to hens. Within a territory there may be several places from which he crows regularly, probably for the dual purpose of warning other cocks away and advertising his presence to hens. Property boundaries are not exact and seem to shift as the season progresses. Boundary disputes often arise between neighboring cocks. In such instances the more domiant cock usually wins by default, but occasionally there are battles to the death.

Hens crossing a territory are courted by the cock. The pheasant harem is not like those of polygamous mammals such as seals, where females are herded into a family group and are under constant guard. The hen pheasant seems free to go or come at will. The cock displays to her but does not use force to hold her. The Schwartzes, writing of their observations in Hawaii (Schwartz and Schwartz 1949), say that the cock attracts hens "by crowing, by emitting low clucking calls, and by offering choice bits of food." The territory is the center for courting, mating, and feeding, but some hens may make nests outside. In such instances they normally return while off the nest (Taber 1949a).

It once was believed by some biologists that the number of territories, or "crowing areas," might limit the size of the population (Wight 1933). In more recent years, biologists have been less inclined toward this view. Although a shortage of such sites might prevent some cocks from collecting harems, there is no evidence to indicate that hens ever go unmated for this reason. Where sex ratios are near even, the bulk of the hens appear to be preempted by a minority of the cocks (Allen 1942), but an actual shortage of locations suitable for crowing has not been demonstrated.

Hen affairs

The time for beginning of nesting varies from year to year, and in different parts of the range. Mating activities in the wild seem to be influenced by early spring temperatures, although pheasants in pens can be made to breed even in late fall and winter by manipulating periods of light and darkness (Bisonette 1938). Workers in several states have reported that the peak of breeding activities may be shifted as much as two or three weeks by spring weather. In the cold, wet spring of 1950, most states in the Midwest found pheasant nesting to be nearly three weeks later than in 1949 or 1951, when early conditions were more favorable.

Biologists in Wisconsin report that some hens do not drop their first egg for as much as a month after the earliest hens have started (Buss *et al.* 1951). Just how this ties in with weather conditions still is not clear. The earliest egg found by Randall (1940) in Pennsylvania was on April 6. Baskett

(1947) estimated March 20 as the date of nest establishment for the earliest nest found by him in Iowa. The Schwartzes say that in Hawaii pheasants begin laying early in March, and possibly much earlier for some individuals.

Construction of a nest is no major enterprise for the pheasant. Hamerstrom (1936) found most Iowa nests to be

PLATE VIII.—*Above.* Her success in the nesting season is the key to abundance (Illinois Natural History Survey). *Below left.* This cluth of nine eggs is about complete. If the hen loses it before incubation starts, she probably will try again (R. M. Cady, Pennsylvania Game Commission). *Below right.* Evidence of a successful hatch.

in scooped-out or natural depressions, but some were on the surface or even on slight elevations. Lining material varies with what is readily available, but the nest seldom shows evidence of careful construction.

Wight (1950) reported 63 of 77 nests found by him in Pennsylvania to be in hayfields. In Wisconsin, also, pheasants use hayfields more than other cover for nesting, and older alfalfa fields seem to be preferred over new seedings (Buss 1946). Randall (1940a) found 51 percent of Pennsylvania nests in hayfields, but when he adjusted this to the amount of each kind of cover available, there were fewer nests per acre in hay than in roadsides and fencerows.

Alfalfa is one of the most important nesting cover types for pheasants in most states because of its large acreage and relatively high rank in preference. Grain fields usually are passed up in favor of hay, although nests seem to be safer in grain. Woody or brushy cover is not essential for nesting Where hay is mowed early there may be serious losses, yet some of the best populations of pheasants are in alfalfa-producing areas.

Beginnings of nesting are gradual. Often a few eggs are dropped at random before a nest site is selected. This may be the result of a need to lay before nesting cover has developed, but possibly it represents only the first step in the annual nesting cycle (Buss et al. 1951). It may be significant that in a California study fertility of dropped eggs was found to be only 61.5 percent, while 96.6 percent of eggs from nests were fertile (Twining et al. 1948). By delaying nesting, the hen may avoid incubating many infertile eggs.

The pheasant hen is far from meticulous as to the places in which she lays her eggs. Pheasant eggs have been found in duck nests (Bennett 1936), and field biologists often report "dump nests" used by two or more pheasants. An average pheasant nest early in the season may have a full clutch of about 15 eggs, but these dump nests often contain more than 30 (Einarsen 1945, Hamerstrom 1936, Baskett 1947).

Dump nests seldom occur except in areas of high concentration and do not seem to be important in influencing production.

Hens often appear reluctant to settle down to the serious business of rearing a family. Not only are the first few eggs dropped at random, but the hen may make several false starts at laying a clutch. It is noted that many nests are deserted early in the season with no more than two or three eggs in them. Some of those desertions may result from disturbances, but from the large number of early-season desertions it seems likely that this is a normal part of the pattern of establishing nests.

Voluntary abandonment of nests in early stages probably has had much to do with the low rate of success reported for pheasants, but even when allowance is made for this, the fact remains that the probability of success is not very high for any nest. In common with other ground-nesters, the pheasant is exposed to many hazards, and failure can be expected in as high as 60 or 70 percent of nests (Buss and Swanson 1950, Eklund 1942). Fortunately, the pheasant hen is persistent and will continue to try again so long as she is able, or until time runs out. Thus there is a good chance that she will bring off a brood eventually. It has been found by studying pheasant ovaries that many more eggs usually are laid than would be necessary if the hen successfully incubated her first clutch (Buss et al. 1951). If a hen loses her brood, however, or if the nest is destroyed when the eggs are about to hatch, it is doubtful that she will make further attempts.

In 1933-35, Errington and Hamerstrom (1937) computed that from 70 to 80 percent of Iowa hens produced broods, despite a high percentage of nest failure. Leedy and Hicks (1945) estimated that a similar proportion of the hens surviving until fall in Ohio had been successful in rearing broods.

Clutch and brood size

Early clutches are consistently larger than those late in the season. The average size of April clutches is about 12 or 13 eggs, but there is a decline each month to a July average of about 8.5 (Hamerstrom 1936). This seasonal decrease has been observed by several investigators and seems to occur generally in different parts of the pheasant range.

The number of young per brood varies more than clutch size. Like clutches, broods decrease in size as the season advances. In Pennsylvania, Randall (1940) found the average number of chicks hatched to vary from 13.5 in early July to 7.0 in late August. Because of losses among chicks, broods are reduced considerably by fall, and the average size in September seems to be about six young. Michigan observations over a number of years suggest that fall brood size is fairly constant, but there are indications from other states that the average varies from year to year and from place to place.

Eggs that count

Fertility of eggs under field conditions seems to vary from about 85 to almost 100 percent. Evidently this variation has nothing to do with the relative numbers of cocks and hens in the population, since some of the highest fertility has been found where there were few cocks in proportion to hens.

Of 141 eggs taken from abandoned nests in California all were fertile (Twining *et al.* 1948). In this same study, 95.1 percent of 1,559 eggs from various sources were fertile. Fertility of eggs in South Dakota varied from 87 to 97 percent (Nelson 1950), while in Pennsylvania a fertility of 94.6 percent resulted from a sex ratio of 6 hens per cock (Randall 1940).

Not all fertile eggs hatch. In Iowa, there were dead embryos in from 1.5 to 14 percent of the eggs examined (Hamerstrom 1936). In Pennsylvania, hatchability was 90 percent and fertility 94.6 percent, so there must have been a loss of about 5 percent of the fertile eggs (Randall 1940).

Hatching schedule

Since the average early clutch is about 13 eggs, and the incubation period about 23 days, it seems that 40 days would be near the minimum length of time between the laying of the first egg and the hatching date. Later in the season, as clutches become smaller, less time may be required for laying. One rule of thumb is to multiply the number of eggs by 1.3 to compute the average number of days required to lay a clutch (Buss *et al.* 1951).

Thus the first week in May would be about the earliest for hatching of pheasants in the United States. South Dakota hatching dates, as estimated from ages of young birds killed during the 1948 hunting season, ran from about the first week in May to the first week in September (Nelson 1949). Less than 10 percent of the 1948 hatch, however, occurred before the last week in May, and around 90 percent was completed by the last week in July.

Randall (1940) estimated that 75 percent of the successful nests in Pennsylvania were started in May. This would indicate about the same hatching time as that shown for South Dakota. In Washington, 77 of 100 successful nests observed over a two-year period hatched by July 7 (Knott *et al.* 1943).

Hatching dates vary in different years, not only in the time of first appearance of broods, but in the pattern throughout the summer. In "normal" years, the rate of hatching increases rapidly from late May until a peak is reached sometime between mid-June and early July, after which it drops off sharply to late July or early August. When there are interruptions in the breeding season (as by weather extremes), there may be two hatching peaks, but best production seems to be in years when the rate builds up regularly to a single peak and then drops off.

What Happens in a Population

From the game manager's point of view, the purpose of the pheasant flock is to produce an annual supply of harvestable birds. Except for a few heavily populated areas, the harvestable surplus is limited to cock birds, since all young hens usually are needed to replace natural losses in the breeding stock.

The production line

Under all known wild conditions in North America, the proportion of cocks to hens has been high enough to insure fertile eggs. The most realistic approach to pheasant population studies is to consider hens as a basic resource or captial stock. As long as a stock of productive hens is maintained, the flock is in condition to produce its annual crop. Cocks can be ignored except under conditions more extreme than have yet been found. This can best be illustrated by a simple hypothetical case.

The fall population is made up principally of birds of the year. Percentages vary with the success of the nesting and rearing season, but in good years young birds should make up about 70 percent of the hen population. This bespeaks the high annual rate of turnover in the pheasant, a characteristic shared with other species. Turnover probably varies with local factors, such as severity of winter and quality of nesting cover, but 70 percent is the rate found on a Wisconsin refuge (Leopold *et al.* 1943), and it fits well with other known facts on population dynamics.

Thus, from a fall sample of 1,000 hens only about 300 should be expected to survive until the following fall. The other 700-odd birds will have succumbed to hazards of winter and nesting and rearing seasons. Various factors account for losses in different parts of the country, but the end result seems to be surprisingly constant.

From 75 to 85 percent of these 300 surviving hens should have been successful in rearing broods. Again, there is variation in hatching success, but in a good breeding year most of the hens finally come through. If 78 percent are successful, about 234 broods will be brought into the fall population.

Early broods are larger on the average than those produced late in the season, but this is offset partly by summer loss of chicks, and an average fall brood should be about 6 young. If the 234 broods attain this average, the production for the year will be 1,404 young, or about 700 each of hens and cocks.

At this rate of mortality and production, the hen population has replaced its losses. The 1,000 hens of the second fall include 300 adults and 700 young. In order for the population to increase, at least one of three things must happen: (1) Hen mortality must be less than 70 percent; (2) more than 78 percent of the surviving hens must produce broods; or (3) the average size of fall broods must be greater than 6 young.

What happens to the cock population is unimportant so long as a small number persist to provide for fertile eggs. Probably one or two hundred old cocks will have survived from the previous fall. These added to the 700 young cocks will give a hunting-season population almost as large as that of the hens. Most of them can be harvested without harming the potential breeding capacity of the flock.

The above figures are for illustration only. In any specific year mortality and production rates might differ significantly from those cited, but in a stable population of hens the rate of production must be equal to the losses. On Pelee Island, Ontario, where in good years losses are considerably below 70 percent, and well over 80 percent of the hens have broods in the fall, the result is a striking annual increase in hens. There, some hens as well as cocks can be harvested and the production is enough to replace all losses. In most areas, however, the balance between natural losses and gains is too fine to permit hen shooting.

The above illustration explains why failure of pheasants in an area does not necessarily indicate that individuals of the species cannot live and breed there. If the rate of production is even slightly below natural losses, the birds cannot survive over a long period.

With some similar formula in mind the biologist samples the pheasant population at critical times to get indices of the condition of his capital stock as well as the current harvestable surplus.

Much popular interest in sex ratios arises from a misconception. The hunter, in particular, is likely to view the slaughter of cocks with alarm and to voice fears that not enough are left to mate with the hens. Undoubtedly every game administrator in pheasant states receives letters from well-meaning persons asking for the release of cocks, because "there are some hens on my farm, but the cocks were all shot last fall."

Results of game research have dispelled this fear among most biologists. Sex ratios that once were considered to be critical now are known to be adequate for high egg fertility, and few technical men believe that ratios are likely to reach a dangerous state of unbalance as a result of normal heavy shooting.

The annual balance

The average sportsman may picture the heavily hunted pheasant population as a static resource from which each year more cocks are removed, with the inevitable result that after a few years nothing is left but hens. The fact that this does not happen usually is somewhat of a mystery to him.

Actually, a long-time balance is maintained by a fairly simple process. Pheasants, even on sanctuaries, are birds of short life span. In the absence of hunting there are innumerable natural hazards to cut down any surplus, and production is geared to replace annual losses of better than 70 percent.

This high production means that, no matter what has happened to reduce the proportion of cocks in the adult population, a reasonable balance will be restored by the addition of a new crop of young birds.

A specific example may indicate how this works. Take an unbalanced spring flock of 90 old hens and 10 old cocks. In a high production year, these hens might produce 450 young birds (225 of each sex). The total fall population then would be 315 hens and 235 cocks, a ratio of about 1.34 hens per cock. If the production is low, however, and the average is only one young bird per hen, the fall population might be 135 hens and 55 cocks, or a ratio of about 2.45 hens per cock.

As pointed out elsewhere, unbalanced spring populations are likely to be accompanied by high production, so that the tendency toward balancing the fall population becomes stronger as the need for it increases. Where production ordinarily is low, spring sex ratios seldom are more divergent than two or three hens per cock. Even a small production of young birds will suffice to bring such a population into fair balance by fall.

The favorable sex ratio

Early students often spoke of "unfavorable" sex ratios in breeding birds. This usually was taken as anything greater than 4 or 5 hens per cock. It is known however, that where pheasants are hunted hard, those high winter and spring sex ratios indicate good range, high production, and a heavy harvest of males. Winter sex ratios of only two or three hens per cock mean either poor range or failure to shoot surplus cocks.

Examples of high production and high winter sex ratios (expressed as hens to cocks) include Lehigh County, Pennsylvania——7:1 (Randall 1940); Wood County, Ohio——5:1 (Dustman 1950); Prairie Farm, in Michigan——7:1 (Shick 1947); Pelee Island——10:1 (Stokes 1948); and the better pheasant counties of Wisconsin——8:1 (Buss 1946). In these same states, low-quality range has fewer hens in proportion to cocks, and in poor range there may be as many cocks as hens, even where hens are protected. In the northern prairie region, this relationship does not hold. There, the low sex ratio results from failure to harvest surplus cocks rather than from low production of birds.

The wide divergence in sex ratio frequently observed in good pheasant areas is brought about by the fact that (1) high populations attract heavy hunting, and (2) in a high population it is easy to shoot a high *proportion* of the cocks, even with ordinary gun pressure, (3) large numbers of hens are present to mate with the thinned out males.

Where there are lots of ringnecks, a high proportion of the cocks can be killed with only moderate hunting pressure. For example, on Pelee Island in 1948 it was fairly easy to remove 90 percent in a two-day shoot (Stokes 1948). Although there was a hunter for every 10 acres, the total pressure in gun-hours was not excessive. Probably the heavy kill of cocks was accomplished with fewer than 100 gun-hours per 100 acres. In sparsely stocked areas, it may be difficult to harvest 50 percent with much heavier pressure. At Michigan's Rose Lake Wildlife Experiment Station, in medium quality pheasant habitat, more than 250 gun-hours per 100 acres removed only about 75 percent of the cocks (Allen 1947). In low concentrations of ringnecks a great amount of hunting is required to find the few that are present, and the relative kill will be correspondingly lower.

From the standpoint of breeding success, it makes little difference whether 50 or 90 percent of the cocks are killed, as long as an adequate flock of hens remains. However, the game manager needs to know the sex ratio of winter and spring flocks. This knowledge is basic for interpreting crowing cock censuses and bag checks during the hunting season.

Annual variations

Sex ratios vary widely through the year. At the close of hunting the proportion of hens to cocks is at its highest point. It is then that sex ratios of "10 to 1" and "12 to 1" are reported. However, from that time on almost all population changes are in the direction of equalization.

Work in Wisconsin showed that the sex ratio dropped gradually through the winter in such a way as to suggest that hens were more vulnerable than cocks (Buss 1946). Such selective losses might come about in a number of ways. Possibly some predators not strong enough to kill adult cocks are able to prey successfully on hens. In South Dakota, starvation appears to cause greater losses among hens than cocks (Nelson and Janson 1949), and there is evidence that even accidental deaths tend to strike hens more often than their relative numbers would warrant (Norstog 1948, Gubser 1942).

Possibly a slight reversal of this trend occurs in early spring, when cocks become more aggressive, but any advantage gained by the hen at this time soon is lost. Nesting losses in some areas once again swing strongly against them, especially in hayfields where many are killed by mowing. In Ohio, as many as 58 percent of hayfield-nesting hens have been killed, while total mortality of nesting hens in all situations was estimated at 42 percent (Warvel 1950, Leedy and Hicks 1945). Hayfield losses in Pennsylvania have been estimated at 33 percent (Wight 1950).

While the fact-finder can demonstrate that pheasant hens lead a more precarious existence than cocks, he has difficulty in finding out exactly what the sex ratio is. Hens and cocks do not always react in the same way, and he seldom is sure that what he has seen is a fair sample.

For example, cocks and hens do not flush at the same rates at the close of the hunting season. Many hunters report that cocks flush at greater distances than hens, while in some heavily hunted areas cocks seem to hide rather than flush. In some places cocks may take refuge in dense cover to a greater extent than hens. In the winter, the two sexes often segregate into flocks composed predominantly of one or the other sex. Unless the observer knows that all flocks in an area have been checked, he never can be sure of the true picture. Later on, there are differences in movements. Cocks are the first to leave wintering flocks, and in early spring they are more conspicuous than hens. Roadside counts at such times may be biased in favor of cocks.

Sex ratio counts made in Michigan by conservation officers in 1946 illustrate the difficulty in interpreting field data. In early February, the ratio of hens to cocks seen was 6.1:1. This increased during the month and by late February was 7.3:1. Thereafter the proportion dropped steadily until by early April it was 2.1:1 (Linduska 1947).

Some of this change in observed sex ratio may have been a result of differential loss of hens from February to April, but this scarcely could have accounted for so great a change over this short time. Undoubtedly the greatest factor was change in habits and ranges of the two sexes at that time.

One way to estimate spring sex ratios is to locate crowing areas and count the number of hens in each harem. This method is subject to two important errors: (1) Not all cocks establish territories or collect harems, and (2) not all the hens in a harem may be present at one time to be counted.

In South Dakota, it has been found that sex ratio counts during the nesting season are most reliable between the hours of 6 and 7 a. m. Later in the day, hens are likely to be on the nests, and a biased picture results (Janson 1946). Intensive studies on small areas make it possible to work out these problems and make good use of harem counts, but the method is not entirely satisfactory for extensive surveys.

Different methods of estimating sex ratio may give widely differing results. This is illustrated by Wisconsin winter estimates derived from three sources. In Fond du Lac County the ratio observed by cooperators along regular routes during the winter was 12.6:1; that observed at feeding stations maintained by clubs was 3.8:1; while the sex ratio of live-trapped birds in that county was 4.2:1 (Buss 1946).

From this it can be seen that sex ratios reported from surveys usually should be considered as observed rather than actual ratios. They are useful chiefly for comparison with observed ratios of other years. In comparing results, it is important that estimates be made in the same manner and at the same stage of the breeding cycle each year.

Learning from the broods

If the exact age of every bird killed during hunting season were known, it would be possible to count back to the date on which its incubation had begun and just about when the nest was established. Still more important, it could be ascertained which weeks in the spring had the best records for establishment of successful nests and when the bulk of the harvestable crop originated.

It probably would be found that a few birds had hatched about the first week in May. If there were no interruptions during hatching season, then each succeeding week should have contributed a larger number of broods until the peak hatch, about mid-June. From then on to the end of the season, production should have dropped, with few broods coming off after the last week in July.

Observers cannot check all birds killed during the hunting season, except in small areas, and must depend on random samples, taken through hunter cooperation, to reconstruct the breeding-season picture. In that way it can be determined when successful nesting got under way and whether there were any serious interruptions in brood production.

The same sort of information can be obtained from summer brood studies. From sight records, an experienced field man can judge the age of broods within about one week. Some errors may creep into his estimates, but where large numbers of broods are involved, such results give a good picture of the season's production. In South Dakota, where workers make many brood observations during the season and compare results with extensive checks of birds killed during hunting season, techniques of aging birds by sight have been improved considerably.

Although ages of broods seen in the field cannot be estimated as accurately as those of birds killed in hunting, there are some advantages to field estimates. The slight loss in accuracy is offset by the advantage of being able to count individual broods. Hunting-season checks can give a clue to relative numbers of young birds produced by weeks, but they do not indicate the size of individual broods. By field observations through summer the technician can compute the relative number of hens producing chicks each week of the season, and also the average size of each week's broods. This is possible in top-quality pheasant range, but the observer has to see lots of broods during the summer to make his observations mean anything.

A third indication of breeding success is the relative number of hens with broods. Nest destruction and desertion is high, and throughout the summer hens continue to renest unless they are successful in hatching a brood. Consequently, counts taken early in the season will show but a small percentage of successful hens. This percentage then increases to a peak in August or September.

There is reason to believe that field counts of hens with broods do not always give a true picture of the situation. Toward the end of summer there is a tendency for broods to combine and for some to become independent of the hen. At this time they are seen more easily than in early summer when chicks are small. When broods are young, an observer is likely to see the hen rather than the chicks, while in August and September many broods are located by seeing the young rather than the hen. For this reason, in late summer an observer probably records a greater percentage of the broods present than he does in July.

Although few clutches hatch after the last week in July, the percentage of hens seen with young continues to increase for another 5 or 6 weeks. This increase must result from more favorable conditions for observation in August and September. It raises doubts as to the value of estimating hatching success from the percentage of hens seen with broods in mid-summer.

In South Dakota the rate of hatching usually follows a regular curve. In some states, however, there is evidence of two peaks in the establishment of successful nests (Buss 1946, Hamerstrom 1936). The second peak may be caused by re-nesting after early nests are destroyed during spring plowing. In the Northern Great Plains the relative amount of good nesting cover plowed under during the nesting season probably is slight, a fact that may explain the more regular production in South Dakota.

What age ratios can mean   **939016**

Age ratio is the proportion of young to old birds. This is important to the game manager because is gives him a clue to the rate of turnover in the population. Ordinarily young birds will predominate in bag checks, and when there is an unusually high proportion of adults in the kill he knows that something has happened to production of young in that year.

In order to arrive at a standard for measuring productivity it is necessary to interpret age ratios in terms of production *per hen*. Otherwise, when age ratios of different regions are compared, the results may give a biased picture.

A comparison of bag checks from Michigan's Prairie Farm from 1940 to 1943 with that for South Dakota in 1947 will illustrate the problem involved. At the Prairie Farm the number of young cocks per adult cock in the bag ranged from 13.4 to 23.4, and the average for the three years was 18.5. (Allen 1947). In contrast, the South Dakota figure in 1947 was 2.98. (Kimball 1948). At first glance it might be assumed from these figures that production at the Prairie Farm was six times as great as that in South Dakota.

Closer inspection shows, however, that the breeding population at the Prairie Farm was approximately 7 hens per cock for these three years. (Shick 1947), while in South Dakota in 1947 the numbers of cocks and hens were about equal. (Kimball *op. cit.*). Thus for every Prairie Farm cock there must have been 7 hens, producing an average of 2.6 young cocks each, while in South Dakota the single hen per cock produced on the average of 2.98 young cocks. Since cocks represent only half the young birds produced, then the average production of young birds *per hen* seems to have been about 5.2 at the Prairie Farm and 5.9 in South Dakota.

In sampling hunters' bags, allowance must be made for the fact that young birds are less wary than adults early in the season. In South Dakota the age ratio of cocks killed changed progressively through six weeks of the 1947 hunting season from 5 young per adult the first week to 1.2 per adult the last week.

In 1945, the age ratio computed for South Dakota pheasants was only 1.06:1. This increased the following year to 1.53:1, and in 1947 to 2.98:1. In other words, in 1945, there were about as many adults as young in the bag, and production had fallen far below the critical point. Evidently there was a high carry-over from the 1944 population, because the 1945 kill remained high. By 1946, when production still was below normal, the kill fell off severely, and in 1947, despite a good hatch, it reached bottom for the 1940's.

The picture of what happened in South Dakota is not altogether clear, but some important points stand out. Most significant is the fact that the big decline from 1945 to 1947 was ushered in by failure of the annual crop of young pheasants. This illustrates what game technicians have recognized for a long time. *Pheasant populations are determined fundamentally by annual production of young and not by shooting.*

How many?

The first successful release, in 1881, in Oregon's Willamette Valley comprised only 28 ringnecks (Einarsen 1945a), yet from this small initial stocking the birds spread over an area 40 miles wide and 180 miles long and became so abundant that the first open season was declared in 1891. There may have been additional releases of imported birds during this period, but, in the absence of game farms, they would have been small. After the first two or three years, any additional introductions would have been insignificant in comparison with the newly established wild population.

There is a lesson in this early history of the ringneck in North America that frequently has been overlooked. The increase was on the mainland, where birds were subjected to normal predation. It was accomplished in the face of human interference, for the Willamette Valley is a fertile farming area. Reports of poaching were heard then, as now, an indication that there has been no great change in human nature. Yet, despite these influences, which probably were no more serious than hazards in their Asiatic habitat, pheasants must have approached their maximum productive potential in the first few years after introduction.

Similar accounts could be given for many other introductions, for this behavior is so well known to the ecologist as to be considered typical when a species is introduced into favorable environment. Fundamentally, the almost phenomenal increase following some island introductions is similar, except that where the birds cannot spread to new areas the same rate of increase causes a more rapid build-up in local density.

Just as typical is the fact that populations level off after a few years, sometimes seeking stable levels below their peak. The highest level reached is not the same for all places, and stability is relative. There are annual or long-time fluctuations after the initial curve of increase levels off, but these tend to vary around an average population level for the area in question.

The fact that populations expand rapidly when there are few birds but slow down in rate of increase as they approach the long-time level indicates that the chief barrier to further expansion is the carrying capacity of the habitat. Sometimes, of course, the land will not support as many birds as the sporting public wants. Then, there usually is a clamor for the adding of game-farm birds to the wild population. Game farms may offer some relief to the game administrator, especially when attention can be focused on the number of birds produced and liberated rather than on those harvested, but they have failed utterly to increase carrying capacity and, consequently, have had little effect upon wild populations.

Ringneck population levels may reach astonishing heights. The Sand Lake Waterfowl Refuge in South Dakota was reported to have had as many as five pheasants per acre at one time (Nelson 1946), and the Protection Island population reached 470 birds per 100 acres in 1942 (Einarsen 1945). Pelee Island in Lake Erie may have supported that many, and some parts of the island probably had even more. This 10,000-acre island had a legal kill of more than 22,000 birds in 1950 (220 per 100 acres), and the total losses must have exceeded that figure (Stokes 1954).

Statewide populations, of course, are much lower. The pheasant population of South Dakota's 50,000-square-mile range was estimated at from 30,000,000 to 40,000,000 birds in 1945 (somewhere in the neighborhood of a bird per acre) (Nelson 1946). This probably is the highest population for such an extensive area that has occurred in North America and it represents a peak density. (The 1948 estimate was about 30 birds per 100 acres.)

Michigan's pheasant range, of approximately 26,000 square miles, produced an estimated kill of 1,400,000 pheasants in 1944. This suggests a total fall population of some 4,000,000 pheasants, an average density of about 23 birds per 100 acres. In that year, however, the population probably ranged from about 75 pheasants per 100 acres in Genesse County to a low of 5 or 6 per 100 acres in the six poorest counties of the pheasant range.

The Wood County, Ohio, kill of 1937 was about 14 cocks per 100 acres, which suggests a population density of some 40 pheasants per 100 acres (Leedy and Hicks 1945).

In the fall of 1948, on the McManus Ranch, in California's Sacramento Valley, there was an estimated population of approximately 125 pheasants per 100 acres (Ferrel et al. 1949). This represents superior range for that state, and it is surrounded by less productive land.

From these examples, taken somewhat at random but covering some of the best pheasant areas of the United States, it can be seen that localities differ greatly in their capacity to produce ringnecks. Any sizable area (upwards of 100 square miles) with a fall population of 50 or more pheasants per 100 acres probably should be classed as superior. Such a population could be expected to have a minimum of 20 cocks per 100 acres. Subjected to a 75 percent kill, it should yield a bag of at least 15 cocks per 100 acres. Judged by this standard, relatively little pheasant range east of the Mississippi River is superior.

Ups and downs

Although the first open season was held in Oregon in 1891, pheasants did not reach national significance until much later. Pennsylvania had some open seasons, without daily or seasonal bag limits, as early as 1902 (Gerstell 1937), but the kill was insignificant until after 1915. Several states had abundant populations in some localities in the years from 1915 to 1920, but for the country as a whole the trend was upward during the second and third decades of the present century.

Despite differences in the time required for establishing pheasants in various parts of the range, the underlying pattern of increase has been quite consistent. In a few places the birds took hold almost at once, as in the Willamette Valley, Protection Island, Washington, and the area southwest of Salt Lake City, Utah (Rasmussen and McKean 1945). In other areas, there was a long period between first releases and the time when pheasants demonstrated their capacity for rapid expansion. This delay, in some instances, probably resulted from the low carrying capacity of the localities where birds were first introduced. In practically all states, however, once a start was made in favorable areas, populations built up rapidly to a peak.

Failure to recognize this basic pattern has led to some confusion as to the part played by the state game farms. In looking back on the period of introductions, it now seems evident that the game farms served their most important function by introducing pheasants to all habitats of the states. In a few states, the original releases were in favorable sites, and peak populations were reached without large release programs. The first-ranking pheasant state of the nation, South Dakota, achieved success without a game farm, and with relatively small releases. A few, such as Pennsylvania and Michigan, trace pheasant success from the establishment of game farms. Some states have added game farms after the pheasant was established, but the effect, if any, on population levels of wild stock has been slight.

Kill records for Pennsylvania from 1915 to 1950 illustrate the way in which populations often react following establishment. Pheasants were introduced there about 1892 and succeeded moderately well in a few places until the first game-farm releases in 1915 (Bennett 1945). In that year, the estimated kill was 796 pheasants (both sexes were legal game). The next few years, following large-scale releases, represented the period of establishment, and by 1922 the kill was estimated at 20,000 birds. From that point onward expansion was rapid, and the succeeding seven years saw the annual kill increase tenfold.

During this period, the increase was hampered but little by lack of living places. As some habitats became full, others were invaded, until all suitable range was occupied. The rate of expansion undoubtedly was helped by releases which continued to introduce birds into new and untried habitats.

By the late 1920's, some resistance to expansion became apparent. Either the pheasant had reached the carrying capacity of Pennsylvania's range or there was an unfavorable period for production. At that time, there was no way to decide which of these possibilities was correct, and it generally was assumed that Pennsylvania's pheasants had reached a stable level (Gerstell 1937). At any rate, expansion was halted for the first few years of the 1930's, and the annual kill fluctuated between 250,000 and 290,000.

Beginning about 1937, there was another upsurge. Increases continued, with some variation, until 1941, when a peak kill of 537,990 pheasants was computed for the state. After 1941, in common with many other states, Pennsylvania experienced a pheasant decline, the kill reaching a low of some 213,000 in 1946. Then, repeating the experience of a decade earlier, the birds started upward again. By 1954, the estimated kill had risen to approximately 453,000.

It now seems that the halt in growth during the early 1930's could not have been caused by pheasants' reaching the range carrying capacity. Since the population about doubled later, it is evident that there was room to expand. There must have been unfavorable conditions for the reproduction of pheasants during those years.

Viewed in this light, is seems that there were two unfavorable periods between 1930 and 1950 in the history of Pennsylvania pheasants. The first was in the growth stage of the population and resulted in holding the increase back for about five years. The second struck after pheasants had reached a high level in all good habitats and caused a decline to about half the former peak.

Most biologists are not inclined to say with assurance that the pheasant is a cyclic species, but it is at least suggestive that both these "unfavorable" periods occurred during the downswing of the small-game cycle. Pheasant workers will be watching population trends with increased interest to see whether future fluctuations coincide with the rhythmic swing of ups and downs characteristic of some other game species.

Not all pheasant population trends have seemed to follow

the game cycle. Colorado's annual kill of pheasants increased regularly through the 1940's, while the "crash decline" was distressing hunters farther east. Einarsen is quoted as saying that Oregon had no major fluctuation during the period from 1943 to 1947 (Kimball 1948), but there was evidence of declines in some areas. In the Willamette Valley, the population density dropped from 28 to 12 birds per habitat acre between 1942 and 1946 (Uhlig 1948).

To the hunter, the year of maximum population usually sets the standard. Subsequent populations are compared with this peak, and the hunter wants to know "what has happened to the pheasant." Actually, the low point of a population fluctuation is just as normal as the peak. Successions of favorable years, whether they be considered as results of "cycles" or not, cause peaks above the level at which any game species can be maintained perpetually. Whatever the "average carrying capacity" of an area may be, mathematics as well as biology decree that there must be years below as well as those above that level.

C H A P T E R 2

CHINESE PHEASANTS IN THE NORTHWEST

By J. Burton Lauckhart and John W. McKean

The majestic volcanic peaks of the Cascade Mountains overlook a region of extremely diverse climate and topography that is characteristic of northwestern United States and southwest Canada. From this north-south mountain range, dense coniferous forests extend westward to the sea, while on the east an arid, sparsely vegetated inter-mountain plateau stretches to the western slope of the Rocky Mountains.

Probably the dryest and wettest pheasant ranges in North America are found in this part of the country. The western rain forests are interspersed with fertile valleys and deltas where the moist, moderate climate creates a veritable "evergreen region." Here the principal land use is dairy farming to supply the needs of larger cities of the coast. In sharp contrast, east of the mountain range open pine forests of high elevations give way to arid grasslands of the valleys and virtual deserts of sagebrush and sand in much of the Columbia Basin plains.

Earliest Birds

It is more than 70 years since the Chinese pheasant was introduced into the northwestern states. The liberation of Shanghai-trapped birds by Judge Denny (Einarsen 1945a) into the Willamette Valley in Oregon in 1881 apparently was the first successful establishment of pheasants on the North

43

American continent. From this small beginning, and with much help from subsequent introductions, these birds have spread through all available habitat in northwestern United States. Most pheasants in this region are the direct result of the Denny introduction, since they were trapped and transplanted widely from the Willamette Valley.

Records of early transplanting are scarce because this work was done largely by farmers and interested sportsmen who merely wanted to get this exotic game bird established in the vicinity of their farms and homes. At that time, game management and game administration were in an embryonic stage. Limited game work was handled by elected county commissioners or by game commissioners appointed by them. They saw little need to keep records of their efforts in spreading Chinese pheasants. Available records show that a few of these birds were planted on Vancouver Island, British Columbia, in 1883 and in the lower Fraser River Valley in British Columbia in 1890.

The State of Washington received its first pheasants in 1883, and the birds were planted widely from Oregon into western Washington shortly after 1890. Eastern Washington stocking started between 1898 and 1900. The planting at Kemiah, Idaho, in 1903 was the first recorded introduction into that state, although the Idaho State Legislature had made it illegal to kill pheasants in 1899. First southern Idaho releases were made in 1907 in the vicinity of Buhl. Most of the State of Oregon was stocked with pheasants transplanted from the Willamette Valley release site prior to 1900.

The first open season in North America was in 1891 in the Williamette Valley, Oregon. Southern British Columbia's first open season was held in 1896 followed closely by one in Washington. Idaho did not start to hunt pheasants until 1916.

A game farm for pheasant propagation was authorized in Idaho in 1908, but it was discontinued after one year of poor results. In 1909, the first planting of pheasants was done by the British Columbia Game Commission, and in 1910, the Province took over and started operating its first game farm.

Gene Simpson of Corvallis, Oregon, began raising pheasants commercially in the early 1900's and sold many for stocking neighboring states. In 1911, his farm was leased by the State of Oregon and probably was the first large-scale, state-operated game farm. Mr. Simpson pioneered the artificial propagation of pheasants and supervised the Oregon game farm from 1911 to 1939.

The Province of British Columbia is the only area where hen pheasants were protected from the time the season was first opened, shortly before 1900. In Oregon, a closure on hens in most areas was adopted in 1937, and Washington established a complete closure in 1941. Idaho was the last state to adopt a regulation protecting hens, making it effective in 1945. In all areas, allowance has been made for the taking of hens in open seasons to control local damage problems.

Crop Lands and Pheasant Ranges

Nowhere are the hardiness and adaptability of the ringneck more evident than in the Pacific Northwest. Probably the northern-most established colony of pheasants in this hemisphere is the one on Graham Island, off the coast of British Columbia (Fig. 2). Ringnecks were introduced into the Matanuska Valley of Alaska, near Palmer, in 1939. They hung on for a few years, but by 1947 there were few left, and it was evident that they would not succeed.

In the Northwest, birds may be found from sea-level on the diked delta of the Fraser River of British Columbia to above 5,000 feet elevation in the Upper Klamath Basin of southern Oregon. They subsist alike under conditions ranging from 116 inches of annual rainfall at the town of Forks, on Washington's Olympic Peninsula, to a scant 5 inches of annual precipitation at Yakima in central Washington. At one point in the Sinlahekin Valley of north central Washington, the ranges of the pheasant and the mountain goat actually meet and overlap!

Agricultural lands of this region may be grouped into three fairly well-defined types, and birds may be found in densities from abundance to scarcity in all three.

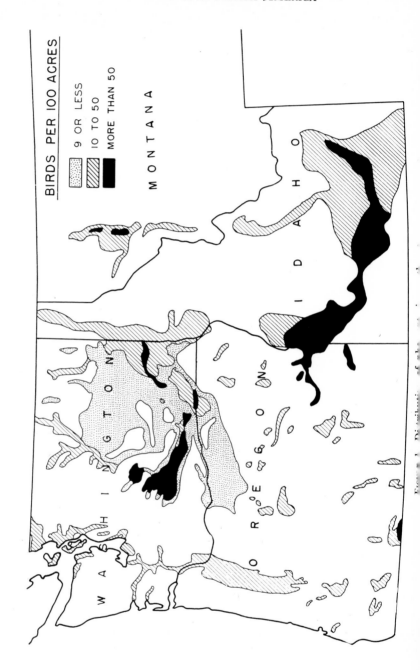

BIRDS PER 100 ACRES

9 OR LESS
10 TO 50
MORE THAN 50

MONTANA

IDAHO

WASHINGTON

OREGON

Figure 1. Distribution of the pheasant

As moisture-laden winds from the ocean rise over a mile to pass the jagged barrier of the Cascades, they release from 40 to 50 inches of annual rainfall on the fertile lowlands along Puget Sound and the river valleys farther south. Here the pheasant makes its way amid a rich and intensive agricultural economy. This probably is the most humid ringneck range on the continent; but in this respect it does not approach that found in Hawaii where the Schwartzes (1949) found pheasants in country that receives 300 inches of annual rainfall.

As winds are pressed eastward across the interior, they descend and deposit a mere 5 to 12 inches of rainfall on a vast area of central Washington and Oregon, and in the Snake River Valley of southern Idaho. There, in irrigated valleys, a man-created microclimate and mineral-rich soils of formerly arid lands combine to produce pheasants along with such crops as alfalfa, wheat, sugarbeets and corn. In some of that region a scattering of ringnecks get by without the aid of irrigation in what is perhaps the simplest and most barren of its North American habitats.

As the general air movement continues eastward, the clouds are forced to rise again and deposit more moisture as they approach the mountains of northern Idaho and the Blue Mountains in northeastern Oregon and southeastern Washington. This results in a vast checkerboard of wheat and fallow fields on the drifted soils of the Palouse region covering eastern Washington south of Spokane and extending into northwestern Idaho and northeastern Oregon. There again both wheat and pheasants grow without the aid of irrigation.

Humid coastal areas

When the white settlers first arrived in this region, a little over 100 years ago, the coastal valleys supported a magnificent stand of fir, hemlock, spruce, and cedar, which had to be removed before the soil could be tilled. The woodsman's ax soon produced a small clearing around each homestead where crops of oats and hay were raised. Unknowingly they were preparing a new habitat for pheasants. Lands cleared for agriculture were confined largely to the rich alluvial soils of the flood plains and deltas of the numerous rivers draining this humid region.

Annual rainfall varies widely depending on local topography, but usually ranges between 30 and 60 inches. Typical examples of the moderate range of temperature are Eugene, Oregon, with a record high of 104 degrees and a record low of minus 4 degrees, and Seattle, Washington, with an all-time high of 98 degrees and a low of 3 degrees. The larger units of agricultural land are found in the Willamette Valley of Oregon; the Cowlitz, Chehalis, and Skagit Valleys of Washington; and the lower Fraser River Valley in British Columbia. The principal crops are grass and clover, hay, oats, and pasture, with limited amounts of wheat, potatoes, corn, berries, fruit, and truck crops.

After the first introduction in the Willamette Valley, pheasants were transplanted widely and yielded good hunting for a number of years; however, most of the region has not recovered from the sharp decline that occurred in the early 1930's. Since that time, good pheasant populations have been maintained in a few isolated areas in the Willamette Valley, on San Juan Island in Puget Sound, and in the Ladner section of British Columbia's Fraser Valley, but most of the region supports a wild population of less than 10 birds per 100 acres and probably should be classed as submarginal.

Undoubtedly, the more intensive farming of recent years, the trend away from cereal crops, and the increased emphasis on dairying have resulted in habitat deterioration for pheasants. The regrowth of timber on the much logged but uncleared pasture land also has reduced the usable range for birds. However, there are indications that a prolonged series of years with heavy spring precipitation may be responsible for recent low populations. Hunter success seems to indicate that dry years produce a better bird crop.

This area never is exposed to extremely cold conditions, but occasional damaging ice storms do occur. Mild winter weather causes waste grain to sprout and decay rapidly, resulting in a shortage of cereal foods. Succulent green material is available

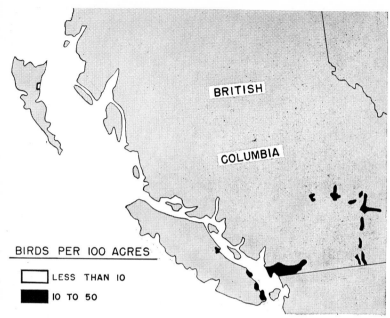

FIGURE 2.—Occupied pheasant ranges in British Columbia.

throughout the entire winter, but that alone does not seem to be adequate to maintain birds, as winter losses apparently are heavy. It now appears that these coastal areas may be outside the optimum range for pheasant production, but there may be dry weather cycles when natural propagation can operate successfully.

Since these ranges are close to large metropolitan centers, they are subject to heavy hunting pressure. The states of Washington and Oregon are stocking them with cock birds in the fall for what might be considered "gun fodder." A large percentage of the hens are released in the spring to escape heavy winter losses.

Watered lands

Irrigation, which transforms parched wastelands into productive agricultural areas, also builds pheasant habitat. Irrigated lands are the most productive ranges in this region. They vary in quality depending on the crops raised, but all the land having more than 50 birds per 100 acres is found in this type.

These ranges also are most consistent from the standpoint of year to year production. Irrigation guarantees abundant water and succulent green feed, which seems to be necessary for good egg production. The low annual rainfall, usually from 5 to 12 inches, results in a consistently warm, dry spring and summer, optimum for nesting and raising broods. The habitat association offers many ditchbanks and waste and drainage areas, which produce weeds and marsh plants that are both food and cover for pheasants. Often the edge of irrigated lands is most favorable, since birds utilize the farmed areas for food and water, while the adjoining sagebrush range constitutes excellent cover. Land contours frequently result in an irregular pattern of irrigation, providing considerable edge and interspersion of plant types.

From the standpoint of value to pheasants, irrigated ranges may be divided into three classes:

Most favorable for upland birds are diversified farming areas where the principal crops are alfalfa, wheat, potatoes, sugarbeets, and corn. Row crops usually are abundant producers of weeds. In addition to being the best type of irrigated range, this is by far the most abundant, comprising about 70 percent of what is being watered now, or in excess of a million acres.

The principal units of this kind of range are found in the Upper Snake River irrigation projects of southern Idaho, in the Ontario area of eastern Oregon, and in the Yakima River areas in central Washington. These areas are the best pheasant range of the Northwest. Additional reclamation projects that are planned or currently being developed will add materially to this excellent ringneck range. The greatest expansion will occur in Idaho's Snake River country and in Washington's Columbia Basin. This is by far the most encouraging feature in prospects for better ringneck hunting.

A somewhat poorer type of irrigated range is land used chiefly for livestock production. Here the principal crops are hay and irrigated pasture. It is obvious that this type would lack much of the game-bird food and cover found in the

PLATE IX.—Pheasant habitat in Whatcom County, Washington; typical of the better range in the humid coastal region (Washington Dept. of Game).

previous class of range. Yet, many of these beef-cattle areas do
provide some good pheasant hunting, with birds utilizing
brush-lined water courses and marshy drainage areas. Such
lands are scattered throughout the diversified farming type,
but they are found chiefly in the smaller irrigation projects
of the region. Along smaller streams and minor river valleys,
water is diverted to nourish a narrow band of farm land and
support a livestock economy that also utilizes adjacent mountain ranges. Many of these shoestring valleys support a fair
population of upland birds. A little less than 20 percent of
the irrigated lands of the region are of this character.

Fruit-producing orchards constitute a third kind of irrigated crop grown extensively in some parts of the Northwest.
Arid valleys of central Washington and south central British
Columbia are covered with almost solid stands of fruit trees,
chiefly apple. When pheasants were introduced, these orchards
were excellent bird producers, but since that time they gradually have lost their value for wildlife. This is the result of
several factors. As insect pests became more persistent, the
spray program had to be increased from one or two sprays a
year prior to 1930 to as high as eight to twelve applications
per season in the early 1940's. This summer activity greatly
reduced the value of orchards for nesting. At the same time,
the spray then in use so impregnated the upper layer of soil
with lead and arsenic that many orchards no longer grow a
cover crop and must be clean cultivated. With the increase
in value of fruit, most of these lands were closed to hunting
to prevent damage to trees and to protect workers and pickers.
What may have been the beginning of the end for pheasants
in orchards occurred in 1946 when a revolutionary change
took place in the spray program. In that and the following year
there was a complete change-over from lead and arsenic to
DDT and organic poisons developed for chemical warfare and
released after the war. A study of these sprays is described
later in this section, but the conclusions generally indicate that
they are killing many pheasants.

From the standpoint of management, these apple orchards

are no longer considered to be usable habitat for birds. However, it is true that some scattered orchards still yield a good
crop of birds, and some less extensive fruit-growing districts
along the Snake River in Idaho produce excellent hunting. In
most instances, these orchards are farmed less intensively or
sprayed less heavily. Fortunately this orchard type or irrigated
land amounts to less than 10 percent of the reclaimed arid
lands of the Northwest.

Wheat-land pheasant range

Dune-like hills of fertile wind-deposited soil, interspersed
with a network of brushy draws and small streams characterize
the "Palouse Region" extending south from Spokane along the
eastern limits of Washington and including a small portion of
northwestern Idaho and northeastern Oregon. Geologically,
these lands apparently were formed from wind-blown soils
swept from the southern extremity of the great glacier. This is
one of the best pheasant-producing regions of the Northwest
and is the only extensive grain-growing area where pheasants
thrive without irrigation.

Wheat is almost the sole crop in this region except in a
few areas where peas are substituted. Rainfall ranges from a
low of 10 or 12 inches to over 20 inches annually. The better
game-bird habitat is confined to areas having more than 15
inches of rainfall. With less than this, there is a shortage of
permanent cover and an insufficient supply of water during
summer months.

These wheat lands are cropped only on alternate years, being
summer-fallowed (clean cultivated) in intervening years to
store moisture. Most of the wheat is planted in the fall on
fallowed lands. Harvested fields are plowed in the spring and
left idle for the season. This kind of land management renders
only half the land usable for game birds at any one time.
Farms are large, averaging 500 acres or more, with most individual fields more than 100 acres in extent. This results in few
fence rows and little cover for birds.

Spring burning of stubble and late plowing of summer fallow were quite destructive to game-bird nests. However,

PLATE X.—The "palouse" of eastern Washington—deep, wind-blown soils presenting a mosaic of wheat and summer fallow (D. L. Allen).

recent trends toward soil conservation to prevent the serious gullying that often occurs in this region have eliminated most burning. The use of large crawler-type tractors and gang plows also has speeded up farming operations to the extent that most plowing is completed now before the peak of the nesting season.

Feed for birds is plentiful in this region. Samples checked in the vicinity of Pullman, Washington showed an average of 190 pounds of residue wheat per acre left after harvest (Ball *et al.* 1941). This grain is available most of the winter, except on rare occasions when it is covered with crusted snow.

The principal factor limiting pheasants in the Palouse is shortage of brushy winter cover and grass for nesting. Permanent cover is confined chiefly to stream banks and steep draws, while most grass is found on slopes too steep to cultivate. Both types are quite limited. The better areas in this range carry from 20 to 30 pheasants per 100 acres and readily could support more if all of the land were cropped each year. However, recent high prices for wheat, combined with government payments for farm improvement, have accelerated the removal of permanent cover. This poses a serious threat to the pheasant population. In the 5-year period from 1945 to 1950, government payments were made to assist in the clearing of 1,326 acres of woody cover from the draws and streams of Whitman County, Washington. Many additional areas were cleared without government aid. In the same period, the Washington Game Department's program to restore pheasant habitat was able to replace only about 500 acres of cover in the entire state, and that at a considerable cost in game funds. If this trend continues for another 10 years, there may be serious effects on the pheasant population.

Recent Population Trends

The rapid increase that often follows the introduction of a species into a new and favorable environment was apparent in all the Northwest following the initial stocking of the Chinese pheasant. There are no accurate records that make it possible to compare those initial populations with the number of pheasants in subsequent years, but it is believed that the early populations far exceeded any since that time.

The period of initial abundance lasted until 1929; 1927 and 1928 were outstanding years in most of the northwestern states, and in the Province of British Columbia. A "crash decline" occurred in 1929 and 1930, and the low lasted until the middle 1930's. In 1938, 1939 and 1940, there was some recovery and then another decline from 1941 to 1945. In 1946, another period of increase began and the high point was reached in 1949. Apparently, the birds were considerably more abundant during the late 1940's than during the high of the late thirties. In 1950 there was another reduction in numbers.

From this general information it appears that pheasant populations have fluctuated in a fairly regular series of 10-year cycles, but it is debatable as to whether or not the pheasant may be classed as a truly cyclic game species. The tremendous increase following the first introduction never has been explained adequately. There are theories that it may be associated with freedom from disease or with favorable predator relationships. Subsequent fluctuations also are difficult to account for, partly because of the incompleteness of the records of varying abundance.

Unquestionably, habitat deterioration has contributed to the general downward trend in pheasant numbers. The rail fences still common in the coastal regions in the 1920's were replaced by barbed wire in the 1930's, and they in turn, have been replaced largely by electric fences in the 1940's. The horse was supplanted by the tractor, fields were enlarged, and brush removal and weed control became generally accepted farming practices.

Although a general reduction in bird populations is apparent and explainable, wide fluctuations within this pattern are difficult to account for. There are many indications that they are correlated with weather cycles or variations in temperature and rainfall during the nesting season.

The recent fluctuations in the pheasant population have

PLATE XI.—Examples of better cover types in the palouse region *(above:* Washington Dept. of Game; *below:* D. L. Allen).

been observed most closely by game technicians and reveal this correlation with weather. The 1946 and 1947 seasons were about average, showing general improvement after the low of 1945. The spring of 1948 was one of the coldest and wettest ever experienced in this region. These conditions were followed by record floods in late May. Plant growth was retarded about two weeks and Buss and Swanson (1950) found that the pheasant hatching peak also was about two weeks late. It was generally assumed that pheasant production would be very low, and a poor hunting season was anticipated. The subsequent season confirmed that the crop of birds was down but probably not as low as anticipated. In contrast to 1948, the spring of 1949 was both warmer and dryer than normal and apparently was one of the best pheasant-producing seasons on record. The 1949 hunting season kill was the best recorded during the past ten years.

The spring of 1950 was unusually cold throughout April and May, but there was little precipitation. Near-drought conditions in late May were terminated by general rains starting about the 5th of June, which is about the peak of the usual hatching season as determined by Knott, Ball and Yocom (1943). It was not considered a good breeding season, but the magnitude of the population decline came as a shock to technicians working throughout the region. In many instances they were not aware of the real scarcity of birds until the hunting season was about to open. Studies by biologist Carl Swanson of the Washington Game Department showed that this season had two hatching peaks. The first occurred about June 12, and a second, only slightly less pronounced, around July 15. Birds hatched in the latter period still were in juvenile plumage at the start of hunting in mid-October.

This great difficulty encountered in determining the actual crop of birds produced is one of the biggest problems facing game managers at the present time.

Foods and Feeding Habits

Although traces of nearly every plant family available have been identified in the crops, gizzards, and droppings of pheasants in the Northwest, all studies indicate that seeds of the grass family (Gramineae) provide the bulk of the pheasant food. This condition undoubtedly is weighted by the fact that cereal crops are common in the Northwest, and an abundance of waste grain normally is available seasonally. In the absence of domestic cereals, the pheasant makes heavy use of wild grass and weed seeds.

The versatility of the pheasant is demonstrated further by wide differences in food habits in different habitats. In the more arid upper Sonoran and transition zones, domestic and wild seeds normally remain available throughout most of the winter, but in humid coastal sections seeds commonly germinate in the fall and provide only green feed through the winter. Morse (1941) found that on Protection Island grass leaves provided the bulk of the pheasant food from January 1 to April 15.

In the livestock-producing, meadow type of habitat, domestic cereals are not abundant, and we find the pheasant making primary use of grass and weed seeds. These areas usually are at an altitude of 2,000 to 4,000 feet, and, with livestock competition and heavy snowfall, natural sources of food frequently become scarce. Under these conditions, pheasants are dependent upon livestock feedlots where seeds shatter from alfalfa and grass hay, and residues of grains and concentrates usually are available.

In Palouse wheatlands, Ball and Knott (Ball *et al.* 1941) found that in March, April, and May, the food of pheasants consisted of 85 percent spring-planted grains, 5 percent grass and weed seeds, 5 percent insects, and 5 percent green matter. In June, July, and August, there was a substantial increase in the consumption of insects, especially by young birds, followed by a return to cereals and weed seeds as they matured and became available. Small grains continued to provide more than 80 percent of the food in the fall, being supplemented with seeds and fruits of a wide variety of weeds, shrubs and trees. It was found that during fall and winter months pheasants make use of Russian thistle, rose, thorn apple, chokecherry, snowberry, and other exposed woody and herbaceous plants, but those sources were of importance only during emergency periods when other foods were not available.

Studies by the Oregon Cooperative Wildlife Research Unit demonstrated that pheasants were able to survive for three winter months on green alfalfa and kale but that a supplement of either weed seeds or small grains provides for a slightly greater gain in weight (Uhlig 1948). Chemical analysis of those green foods in winter indicated a crude protein content of 20 to 27 percent. The studies revealed that pheasants required a much greater volume and weight of green food. Those with access to unlimited supplies of green food and weed seeds consumed only 16.4 ounces per week while those having only green herbage required an average of 59.9 ounces per week.

Although corn and other sorghum crops are not as popular in the Northwest as in central states, they do occur on diversified farm lands and provide a preferred source of food during the fall and winter months. Sudan grass and Proso millet also rate high on the list of preferred foods but do not occur in sufficient volume to be of great importance. Wheat, barley, and oats are the principal cereal crops in the Northwest and have shown predominance in nearly all food studies.

Grains and weed seeds appear in crop and fecal samples as soon as they reach the dough stage but are consumed in greatest volume after the seeds have ripened and have been harvested.

There is little evidence that food is a direct limiting factor for pheasants in the Northwest. Normally, the birds are vigorous and in good flesh throughout the year, except during occasional extreme winters at higher elevations. The highest pheasant densities occur on the most fertile agricultural lands, which, in turn, are diversified and provide food, water and cover in close proximity.

As reported by Dalke (1945) in Michigan, pheasants in the Northwest feed most actively during early morning and late evening hours. The length of feeding periods is governed primarily by availability of food. Pheasants are adaptable feeders and, although they show some signs of confusion when the first snows fall, they soon learn to dig through snow or seek out exposed foods around farmsteads and livestock feedlots.

Pheasant feeding stations of many types have been used with varying degrees of success in the Northwest, but they are of questionable value on all but the most extreme climatic ranges.

During periods of heavy and prolonged snowfall, there is evidence that a supplement of grit may be of greater value to pheasants than other foods. In many sections, grit is available only along primary highways, and the exposed fine gravel is used heavily by birds in spite of acute traffic hazards.

Population Principles

Before discussing management practices, some of the principles affecting bird populations should be reviewed and discussed. For instance, artificial propagation would be far more important if it could be shown that bird populations are not generally at the carrying capacity of the range. To plant birds in an already "full" habitat is like pouring water into a full bucket. Any consideration of the hunter harvest of hens also is dependent upon the relation of the population to its habitat. If hens are going to die down to a certain capacity number, it should be possible to allow the hunter to take some; but if losses are merely a steady or normal drain regardless of the population level, the number starting into the winter would determine directly the number surviving in the spring.

It is an accepted principle of ecology that most introduced species increase rapidly to the carrying capacity of their range, then level off, with annual losses that equal annual increment. Any species that is incapable of reproducing adequately to maintain its number when the population is below the carrying capacity undoubtedly would be in danger of becoming extinct. It seems reasonable to assume that habitat capacity may change materially from year to year depending on winter weather conditions and on the growth of annual vegetation.

In the Northwest, pheasant numbers appear to be limited by winter carrying capacity. This is evident to anyone comparing a bleak snow-covered winter habitat with the same piece of range during the lush summer season.

Spring population counts made on established census areas in the states of Washington and Oregon (Table 1) show considerable stability in pheasant numbers over a period of years. These spring counts do not reflect the fluctuations found in fall populations as indicated by the kill figures for Washington (Table 2). Fall, or hunting season, numbers fluctuate widely depending on reproductive success, while spring supplies nearly always are bound within the narrow limits of winter capacities.

TABLE 1.   Pre-nesting season census.

Sample Plots	Acres	Area	Birds Per Hundred Acres				
			1947	1948	1949	1950	1951
177	10,998	Western Oregon	14.0	19.5	16.0	10.5	10.0
271	17,745	Eastern Oregon	30.0	28.5	25.3	27.0	24.1
12	2,386	Central Washington	10.7	14.3	21.9	16.3	13.1
24	21,108	S. F. Washington	4.7	6.4	6.1	6.8	6.0
11	7,160	N. E. Washington	6.6	7.5	5.2	5.2	

TABLE 2.   State of Washington pheasant kill.
(From hunter reports)

Year	Pheasant Hunters	Total Kill	Season Kill Birds Per Hunter
1946	148,600	341,800	2.25
1947	150,000	346,000	2.30
1948	105,000	249,900	2.38
1949	142,500	404,600	2.84
1950	115,000	283,500	2.46

Taylor's (1950) studies in southern British Columbia showing a 70 percent to 80 percent annual turnover in the pheasant population, and earlier work by Buss (1946) in Wisconsin, with similar results, also are interpreted to show that there is a carrying capacity limit. All of these figures seem to substantiate the assumption that habitat can support only a certain number of pheasants on a given piece of range, and that the number of birds found there in the spring generally represents its winter carrying capacity.

Management should attempt to retain just enough birds to

stock the range completely and utilize the remainder for a maximum hunter harvest.

The Reproduction Riddle

Why is one nesting season successful while another is unsuccessful? This is the question that plagues those whose responsibility it is to manage and produce pheasants for sportsmen to hunt. Until this "why" is known, it will continue to be difficult to predict the crop available for harvest.

There are many indications that prolonged cold, rainy weather immediately after hatching causes a heavy loss of young birds due to exposure. This is known to be true on game farms where pheasants are propagated artificially and has been considered a possible cause for unsatisfactory production in the wild. There seems to be some direct correlation between cold and wet weather and poor reproductive success (Allen 1950), yet the relationship is not defined clearly because some wet seasons yield a fairly good crop of birds while seasons appearing to be similar are very poor.

In an attempt to solve this riddle, research has been directed toward determining the factors that govern various phases of reproduction. Buss, working in Wisconsin, found that egg-laying dates are quite consistent from year to year, and this was confirmed in Washington by Carl Swanson of the Washington Game Department (Buss and Swanson 1950). Undoubtedly the onset of egg-laying is controlled by the length of day, as shown by many previous studies. However, yearly hatching peaks vary as much as two to three weeks, and it has been suggested (Buss et al. 1951) that the stimulus to incubate may be controlled by some other factor. Observations by Carl Swanson in Washington appear to correlate incubation with a certain stage in the vegetative growth. He found incubation usually starting when grass and weeds were grown sufficiently to conceal the setting hen.

A summation of findings gives the following approximation of the reproductive cycle of eastern Washington pheasants (Ball et al. 1941, Buss and Swanson 1950):

Laying starts about April 8, while, on the average, incubation does not commence until May 10, with the peak of hatching about June 3. In the period from April 8 to May 10, from 20 to 25 eggs are dropped or deposited in nests, many of which are deserted apparently due to some lack of incubation stimulus. The final nests average from 10 to 12 eggs, indicating that most hens lay about 15 eggs before starting on the nest that eventually will be incubated. This was confirmed by Buss and Swanson (*op. cit.*) who examined ovaries from a sample of wild eastern Washington pheasants and found that they laid an average of about 30 eggs each. From this it seems possible that a late spring such as that of 1950 might have caused many birds to lay their complement of eggs without receiving the stimulation to incubate properly.

Swanson (unpublished) also found that the number of eggs laid may be controlled by the soil type. A series of individual pens for experimental birds was constructed over a knoll topped with poor gravelly soil. Although all birds were supplied with grain, the one confined on the poorest soil laid only two eggs in mid-April and started incubating an empty nest on May 9. Those on the best soils laid most consistently, and the intervening birds laid lesser numbers of eggs in direct relation to soil quality. It was assumed that the poorer soils yielded an inadequate supply or quality of green feed to furnish the vitamins or other nutriment necessary for reproduction. This is far from a conclusive test, but if the assumption is correct it indicates that drought conditions might reduce the laying season greatly by influencing growth of green feed and in that manner limit production.

These are but a few of the possible explanations for nonproductive pheasant years and none of them seems to fit all conditions. It can be presumed that more than one factor could be operating against bird production at one time. For example, one area could be too wet while at the same time another might be too dry. However, this does not seem to be true because the "highs" and "lows" throughout the entire region, from the humid coastal to the very arid sections, all coincide (Table 3).

TABLE 3. Hunting kill fluctuations by range type, Washington.

County	1947	Pheasant Kill 1948	1949	1950
Humid Coastal:				
Whatcom	12,694	5,161	9,712	4,839
San Juan	4,928	3,792	5,180	2,856
Irrigated:				
Yakima	76,843	66,068	81,824	72,276
Walla Walla	23,012	11,175	17,239	16,737
Wheat Land:				
Whiteman	47,281	28,409	52,769	26,316
Spokane	14,296	9,053	29,460	16,929

The riddle of reproduction remains unsolved and must await a more accurate pin-pointing of the various climatic factors affecting birds.

Ringneck Predators

Two studies designed to measure the effect of predation on a pheasant population were conducted in this region. Biologist Carl Swanson of the Washington Game Department attempted to control winged nest predators on a study plot in southeastern Washington. However, when the production of this plot was compared with others there was no discernible benefit from these activities. Another study by Arthur Einarsen of the Oregon Cooperative Wildlife Research Unit, in 1949 and 1950, duplicated experiments with and without predator control. The studies were conducted on Eliza Island in the northern Puget Sound area of Washington State. Even though the area was small (158 acres) and the control efforts were intensive, it was found that their effectiveness was limited. Predators still took a number of the birds but production and survival increased. The results may be considered inconclusive because the samples were small, but the various experiments did show from 20 to 50 percent better survival when control was carried out.

Undoubtedly, effective predator control would increase pheasant survival and in doing so would enlarge the carrying capacity of most ranges. Carrying capacities are determined by environmental pressures and predators are one factor in that environment. A unit of pheasant range must have food, water, and cover, but there are few if any areas that have a perfect combination of these three. If predators were eliminated, or greatly reduced, it is logical that the cover factor would be of less importance. Cover-deficient habitat might be made to produce on a par with that having an ample supply. On the other hand, habitat having an abundance of cover in the proper relationship to food and water might receive little benefit from predator control.

This consideration of "effective" predator control is somewhat hypothetical in that it is virtually impossible to accomplish on anything but a small unit of land. A game keeper on a small hunting preserve or a superintendent on a game farm may accomplish some true control, but most programs amount to nothing more than "predator cropping." We may assume that this group also has the capacity to reproduce well in excess of its carrying capacity limits and that cropping actually may benefit some preying species. The yearly surplus of predators is taken much in the same manner that the annual crop of game is harvested without impairing the supply for the future. The intensive 1080 poisoning work now being done on coyotes is one exception, but to be effective most control must be intensive and localized, and reductions are only temporary. Excessive costs in relation to benefits received usually make predator control a poor management tool for any agency administering large areas.

Orchard Spray Menace

Sprays used to control agricultural pests have long been considered a possible cause of wildlife losses. Apple and pear trees in the State of Washington were treated for many years with lead arsenate to control the codling moth. Applications were increased until as much as 17 million pounds of this chemical were used on Washington crops in a single year. Yet there was no obvious lethal effect from this program.

In 1946 and 1947, lead arsenate was replaced by new sprays

developed during the war. Products such as HEPT, DDT, TEPP, DN-111, and Parathion became standard spray materials. They resulted in a tremendous saving to horticulturists in that they gave almost complete control of the codling moth with only two or three applications a season as compared to the eight or ten applications of lead arsenate required. Use of the new sprays, however, brought immediate complaints that both game and songbirds were being killed.

To study this problem, the Washington Game Department and Washington Agricultural Experiment Stations started a special study in 1947. Field work was done by game biologist Ralph Mohr (Mohr *et al.* 1951), and laboratory work and tests were conducted by personnel of the Experiment Station and the State College. In the course of three years' study, Mohr found in orchards 750 dead birds of which 494 were Chinese pheasants. It was concluded that both DDT and Parathion, the most commonly used insecticides, were capable of killing birds, but apparently DDT alone was responsible for most of the loss. Studies by Robbins and Stewart (1949), of the Fish and Wildlife Service, showed that anything in excess of 5 pounds of DDT per acre may cause damage to wildlife. Orchardists often utilize from 45 to 55 pounds of DDT per acre per season and rarely is there a single application of less than 5 pounds per acre.

A similar study conducted by the British Columbia Game Commission in the upper Okanogan Valley showed comparable results, except that they found Parathion to be somewhat more toxic to birds.

There is little that can be done to alleviate this difficulty because of the tremendous economic benefit from the use of these new insecticides. The saving in spray cost and increased value of crops may be as much as $1,000 per acre per year in some instances. The problem is confined chiefly to apple and pear orchards because soft fruits such as peaches, apricots and cherries do not require the heavy application of DDT. However, this problem will require continued study as new insecticides are being developed each year to combat new pests and overcome the immunity that insects develop to presently used materials.

Management Practices

As in other regions of the country, there are three main approaches to pheasant management in the Northwest: regulation of the kill, artificial propagation and stocking, and habitat improvement. It will be evident that this is a field in which, to date, there has been nothing approaching a reliable and clear-cut definition of what to do or what not to do. Nevertheless, progress is being made and the long record of experience in the Northwest is of particular value when compared with that of other regions.

Controlling the harvest

The oldest type of pheasant management in the Northwest is that of regulating the kill, having been inaugurated with the first closed season over 60 years ago. History of subsequent seasons and bag limits depicts the highs and lows of past pheasant populations. Periods of abundance had seasons of 30 to 45 days duration and bag limits of five birds per day, while periods of low populations had either closed seasons or 10-day seasons with limits of two birds per day. From an early date, British Columbia hunting was restricted to cocks, but other regions in the Northwest usually allowed one hen in the daily bag.

The first intensive study of pheasant populations in this region (Ball *et al.* 1941) resulted in the adoption of a hen closure in the State of Washington in 1941. This work, done in 1940, gave a complete kill check on a 33,000-acre area near Pullman, and on a 4-square-mile census plot at Colton. The results showed that hunters were harvesting 69 percent of the pheasant population and, in spite of the limitation of one hen in the three-bird daily limit, the over-all kill of hens amounted to 45 percent of the total bag. The effects of the hen closure also were studied by Knott and Ball (unpublished) who found them to be somewhat varied, some areas having a substantial pheasant increase, whereas other areas showed little response.

At that time, annual counts were made in only two areas of eastern Washington: The Colton plot, and another 4-square-mile plot near Rosalia. On the Colton area, which is excellent pheasant range, wintering populations increased 370 percent in the five years following closure. The Rosalie plot, a somewhat less productive pheasant range, had a 96 percent increase in the same period. The over-all bird population of the state made no such phenomenal increase, however.

Apparently hunting had resulted in the greatest over-cropping on the best ranges. The fact that average or poor range is so much more common than good-to-excellent range probably accounted for the poor general response to protection of hens.

The states of Oregon and Idaho reported similar experience when straight cock seasons were adopted in 1937 and 1945 respectively. Populations showed some local improvement, but there was no large increase in pheasants throughout the region. Unfortunately no kill data are available for these states before this regulation was adopted.

In order to evaluate the hen closure properly, it would be necessary to know how much the increase in cocks harvested exceeded the number of hens that had previously been included in the hunter's bag. For example, in Whitman County, where hens had constituted 45 percent of the annual harvest, an increase of 82 percent in the kill of cocks would be required to maintain the same yield of birds. In other words, it would be necessary nearly to double the kill of cocks before the total hunting harvest would be increased. It seems logical to assume that some hens could be harvested in seasons following good periods of pheasant production. At such times, carrying capacity limitations doom a large part of the hen population before the following spring.

In the early period, when hens were being hunted, game sanctuaries were established for pheasants in several states. After adoption of the seasons on cocks only, those closures gradually were reduced or eliminated, as it was found that ample cocks were left after the hunting season. In fact, most studies have shown that the harvest of cocks could and probably should be heavier than it is now. The better pheasant range in Washington, Oregon, and Idaho has spring cock-hen ratios from 1:1.5 to 1:3, with a few heavily hunted areas going as low as one cock to five hens. Since it has been shown quite definitely in this country, and in Europe, that one cock to ten hens is ample for breeding purposes, it is evident that the hunter harvest could be much greater in this region.

If it is true that ranges have a definite carrying capacity for pheasants, the removal of more male birds would, in turn, increase the survival of females and thus make the yearly production greater. For example, a unit of range having the capacity to carry 100 pheasants over the winter may have 50 hens and 50 cocks, or 66 hens and 33 cocks, or 90 hens and 10 cocks. It is obvious that the 90 hens could lay more eggs and produce more young than would be secured from either the 50 or 66 hens.

These same considerations apply to discussions of the length of hunting seasons. If the crop of game is not being harvested adequately, there should be no thought of shortening the hunting season, and undoubtedly it could be made longer. It is found, however, that the law of diminishing returns usually determines the amount of game that will be killed. When the productivity of hunting gets to a certain low point, the hunting effort drops sharply even though the season still is open. It is quite possible that longer shooting hours or earlier shooting in the morning period with later shooting in the evening would do more to increase the kill than would a mere lengthening of the hunting season.

Pheasant propagation and stocking

The Northwest region inaugurated pheasant propagation about 1910, and since that time probably has raised and stocked more birds than any other section of the country. From 1933 to 1951, the State of Washington liberated 1,398,000 pheasants, and many were stocked before 1933. Oregon is a close second with 1,091,500 birds liberated since 1911. Idaho and British

Columbia also have planted substantial numbers, but considerably fewer than the above named states.

At this time, Washington operates 10 state game farms, Oregon 4, and Idaho 2, while British Columbia relys on birds purchased from private game breeders. In 1950, over 250,000 pheasants were liberated from those sources, but there are indications that this program will be reduced gradually in future years. The public generally is becoming enlightened to the fact that promiscuous heavy stocking benefits the game population very little.

In the Northwest, pheasants still are raised largely by the so-called "old" or "field rearing system," using domestic chickens as foster mothers. This system has been retained primarily because it was believed that field-produced birds are better adapted to survive in the wild, and secondly because of the high capital investment involved in incubators and brooder farms.

Contrasted with the complete confinement of brooder or "pen-reared" pheasants, the field-rearing system allows them almost complete freedom until they are trapped at 8 to 10 weeks of age. The young pheasants are placed, 20 chicks to the hen, in small coops scattered throughout fields surrounded only by 8-foot poultry netting fences. By the time the birds are half-grown, they can fly in and out of the brood fields, but they return for food and water and to roost with the hen at night. At 8 to 10 weeks of age they are trapped and distributed to release sites chosen by Game Department personnel.

In spite of its so-called advantages, the hen system gradually is being replaced by incubator and brooder farms because it is becoming more difficult to secure setting hens. If the present trend continues, the poultry industry eventually will have the brooding instinct bred out of chicken flocks completely.

For a number of years there was strong public pressure to plant more pheasants, and at the same time, there was rivalry among game farmers to see who could raise the largest number of birds. This resulted in an almost complete emphasis on numbers without regard for quality. In the last ten years, this has changed entirely, and emphasis has been placed upon the quality of birds produced. Improvements in farm management and the development of better feeds, including the use of antibiotics, have resulted in the release of healthier and larger birds than were produced formerly. Some of the low returns reported from the study of pen-reared birds in the past undoubtedly have been the direct result of planting poor-quality birds.

The technique of liberation also has been studied and improved considerably. The old method of flushing birds from crates on trucks has been replaced by gentle release methods and also by night releases. A gentle release is accomplished by quietly placing a crate of birds in good bird cover and allowing them to walk out unmolested and in something comparable to a family group. The gentle release also reduces accidents resulting from birds flying into objects, or drowning in lakes or streams. A night release accomplishes the same thing, in that it tends to prevent wide dispersal, but it is rather difficult to accomplish and it appears that the same results can be secured with a well-planned gentle release during daylight hours. In British Columbia, Taylor (1950) found that night-released birds produced a better return in the hunter's bag. Ball *et al.* (1941), found that, in Washington, wide dispersal from release sites was nearly always accompanied by a low percentage of kill, while birds which remained where they were liberated produced the best returns.

The choice of proper habitat has an important bearing on stocking results. The common practice of releasing birds where there are no others usually results in low returns, since the fact that there are few or none is proof that the habitat is inadequate. Best results are secured by planting pheasants in good habitat where a wild population already is established.

The proper age at which to release young pheasants has been studied in a number of areas. In Massachusetts, Pushee (1948) compared 6-, 8-, 10-, and 12-week-old birds and found a direct correlation between age and band return with the oldest group showing the best recovery. Moreland (1948) made a similar study in the State of Washington. Six hundred pheasants, made up of equal numbers of 6-, 8-, and 10-week-old birds, were released simultaneously in Spokane County in 1946. Hunters in the release area were checked during the entire season, and results showed an 11 percent return of 6-week-old birds, 26 percent of 8-week-old birds, and 29 percent in the 10-week age group. The State of Oregon made releases of various ages in 1948 and also found that older birds survived better (Table 4). Beyond the 10- to 12-week age group there seems to be little improvement in survival with increased age, as shown by Mc-Namara and Kozicky (1949), in New Jersey, and by Pushee (1948) in Massachusetts.

TABLE 4. Age-class comparison of young-bird releases.

Area	Age	Date	Number Released	Percent Harvested
Oregon, Summer Lake				
	6 wks.	August, 1947	200	21.0
	7 wks.	August, 1949	500	19.0
	8 wks.	August, 1946,47	586	41.0
	12 wks.	August, 1950	600	21.0
	16 wks.	August, 1946	176	57.0
Washington, Spokane Co.				
	6 wks.	August, 1948	791	11.6
	8 wks.	August, 1948	597	21.1
	10 wks.	August, 1948	597	28.4

It is not uncommon to find a considerable loss of pheasants shortly after they are transplanted from the game farms. Some of this loss has been shown to be a result of injury from handling, but some has no evident cause. This is assumed to be a shock loss resulting from handling and transfer of semi-domesticated birds to a strange habitat. Information on this subject was secured by Wadkins (1948) when a number of pheasants were transferred from a Washington game farm to holding pens at Pullman, Washington, for a feeding experiment. The birds were weighed immediately upon arrival, and although the same game-farm feeds were continued, they lost weight for a week before starting to recover from the shock of transfer.

The loss of weight was approximately at the starvation rate. This undoubtedly was an extreme case, since the transfer was made during winter months; but it does support the theory that transplanting results in a shock of varying degree.

To get away from this problem of liberation shock, and at the same time expand their propagation program, Oregon started what is known as field-rearing projects in 1946. In a project of this kind, about 100 field coops with 2,000 pheasant chicks are installed on about 5 acres of leased land in the area where pheasants are to be liberated. A man is assigned to water, feed, and protect them from predators until they are about 8 weeks of age, when they can care for themselves, after which the hens and coops are removed. Thus, the birds are established on the planting site without the necessity of being trapped, handled, or transferred. The projects have proved quite successful, and Oregon and Washington both have operated a few each year for several years. There are advantages and disadvantages to this type of propagation.

Under this system the cost per bird evidently is reduced in that there is little capital outlay involved and less feed is used, since the birds can pick up natural food. The projects also eliminate the shock of transplanting, but it still has not been shown that a proportionately higher percentage survive and reach the hunter's bag. Studies conducted by the State of Oregon at Summer Lake where field-reared and farm-planted birds were hunted on the same site resulted in a 29 percent kill of each group. The result was the same in a similar experiment in Washington (Table 5).

Field-rearing projects also have the disadvantage of concentrating a large number of birds in a relatively small area. Some banded birds have been recovered as much as 4 to 5 miles from the project site, but most of them remain within a 3-mile radius. If there are any farm crops on which pheasants can feed near to the rearing site, the damage problem may become severe. Such projects, generally, are best suited for areas owned and operated by the state for public hunting where heavy annual stocking is a necessity.

TABLE 5. Kill of banded pheasants.

Field rearing projects[1] compared with planted game-farm birds

Area	Year	Source of Birds	No. Banded	Percent Harvested
Oregon, Summer Lake				
	1948-1950	Field Project	5,745	29.0
	1946-1950	Game Farm	2,062	29.2
Washington, Spokane Area				
	1948	Field Project	491	27.7
	1948	Game Farm	597	28.4

[1] Field rearing projects are game-farm operations moved to the site where birds are to be liberated. They are raised without confinement and are allowed to disperse naturally.

Pheasants from game farms are liberated at various times during the year. The largest release occurs in August and consists of 8- to 10-week-old birds. In more recent years, the practice of planting cocks just before or during the hunting season has gained favor. This is planting merely for "gun fodder," but it undoubtedly is the best way to utilize cock birds. Before the straight cock limit was adopted, several states held hens and planted them when the hunting season closed in November, but since hens are protected, this liberation has been discontinued as undesirable. Instead, these birds are released with the August liberation when weather and feed conditions are more conducive to survival.

Another distribution period is in March or April preceding the nesting season, the hens for the most part being held to this period. Although the cost of holding and feeding these hens all winter on farms is quite large, it is justified on the assumption that winter carrying capacities are the principal "bottleneck" to increased production. The wintering of hens on game farms should be one method of by-passing the weakest link in the habitat chain and make possible a larger population for the fall hunting season.

The last planting in early June consists of the broodstock which was used on the game farms. It has been shown that some of the hens still can raise a small brood in the wild. Although it is known that their production is low, they are liberated to facilitate operation of the game farm during the rearing period.

Widespread banding of liberated pheasants, with hunters expected to return the bands voluntarily, always has resulted in a low recovery (Table 6), usually ranging from one to 3 percent. These voluntary return figures appear to be unreliable when compared with returns secured where all or most of the hunters were checked for banded birds during the open season. Table 7 gives a summary of banding recoveries where all hunters were contacted through field checks or by the operation of checking stations. It cannot be shown that these were all representative hunting areas, indicating an average for the entire region, but they do show a fairly high recovery of planted birds compared to previously secured voluntary data. The table also confirms the already established fact that direct recoveries of pheasants are inversely proportional to the length of time between liberations and the hunting season. Cocks planted in the open season gave returns of from 45 to 60 percent, while spring release broodstock recoveries were only 3 percent.

TABLE 6. Voluntary band returns—typical recoveries.[1]

Area	Age	Year	Release Season	Number Released	Percent Recovered
Washington	8 wks.	1934	August	18,307	2.8
Idaho	10 wks.	1947	Aug., Sept.	2,754	5.3
Oregon	1 year	1941	April	2,337	1.4
	4 mos.	1941	November	1,607	1.6
	4 mos.	1941	November	2,759	0.4
	4 mos.	1940	November	1,810	1.7
	8 wks.	1940	August	2,327	0.6
	8 wks.	1941	August	24,841	0.6

[1] No attempt was made to gather bands or check hunters in the field.

Birds raised on Oregon game farms in 1950 cost an average of $1.76 each, while Washington reported $2.25 expended per bird liberated. The difference between the two states is accounted for largely by the number of birds held through the winter for release in the spring. These costs include all yearly expenditures, but they do not include interest on investments or depreciation on farm facilities. Oregon has broken down costs by age groups showing that 8-week-old, summer-released birds cost $1.66 each, cocks liberated at the hunting season cost $2.33, and hens planted in March involved an investment of $3.13 each. It is relatively easy to determine the cost of a bird in the hunter's bag as a direct result of game-farm liberations, but an adequate evaluation of indirect returns through reproduction of planted birds never has been made.

TABLE 7. Banded pheasants—game-farm birds.

		Recoveries from hunter-checked releases			
Area	Age	Release Season	Year	Number Released	Percent Harvested
Oregon					
Summer Lake	Juv.	August	1946,1950	2,062	29.2
	9 mos.	April	1947,1950	562	5.0
	5 mos.	December	1945	501	3.6
	Adults	Hunt. Sea.	1950	296	47.6
Washington					
Spokane County	10 wks.	August	1948	597	28.4
Sammamish Valley	4 mos.	Hunt. Sea.	1948	600	49.0
Whitman County	10 mos.	March	1940	115	7.8
	1 yr.	May	1940	98	16.3
	8 wks.	August	1940	60	36.7
British Columbia					
Ladner Area	18 wks.	Sept.	1949	200	20.5
	1 yr.	March	1949	154	10.3
Idaho					
Owyhee County	12 wks.	Sept.	1947	350	17.1
	Adults	May	1947	111	9.1

Hens planted in the late summer or fall into already stocked habitat might be marked off as a total loss, as they go directly into the winter limiting period. The ones that do survive to spring may be merely replacing wild birds that would have survived. However, spring-released hens do not face this same limitation and it is known that many do survive and raise broods. Yet their productivity is difficult to measure. The best data available is that secured by Einarson on Eliza Island where the capabilities of spring-released hens were tested.[1] In those

---

[1] Oregon State Game Comm., Ann. Rept. 1951, pp. 43-78.

studies, March-released birds showed a 60 percent loss to October and averaged two young produced per hen liberated. From those studies, and other survival studies conducted at Summer Lake, the Oregon Game Department has estimated that with a March release of hens the cost is $8.94 per cock harvested. From the August release of 8-week-old mixed sexes, the cost is $18.44 per cock killed, while cocks planted during the hunting season cost only $4.50 per kill. However, the latter figure includes none of the cost of hens also raised. The Washington Game Department estimates that cock birds liberated in August cost about $8.00 per bird bagged, while the same birds held until the hunting season can produce a kill for about $6.50. The Washington figures likewise do not include hen costs, which would almost double these amounts if the hens were fall planted. However, holding as many as possible until spring appears to be much more profitable.

Studies conducted by the Oregon Game Department at Summer Lake, and by Einarsen on Eliza Island, tend to show that good game-farm birds survived almost as well as wild trapped pheasants (Table 8), when both groups were transferred to new habitat. The samples are small and the conditions were not all identically controlled, but they are the only comparisons made between field-reared and wild-trapped birds. It also should be noted that all of the wild pheasants in North America today can have their ancestry traced back a relatively few generations to some game-farm stock. This is interpreted to indicate that there is nothing basically inferior about a propagated pheasant or that it is possible to propagate a bird that is nearly the equal of wild stock. The difficulty has been with the use of these birds in that they are employed largely to "over-stuff" an already saturated habitat.

Pheasants and the Farm

The pheasant, perhaps more than any other northwestern species, is dependent upon the farmer and his methods of operation. Here is a game crop that is truly a by-product of domestic agriculture. The game manager must seek the assistance of the private landowner in his efforts to retain or increase the basic habitat which limits the game supply.

As pointed out previously, a shift in farming practices in many instances has resulted in a downward trend of bird populations, or, again, an upward sweep has been gained through the transformation of semi-arid cattle ranges into farmstead units through irrigation.

TABLE 8.   Young bird releases.

Area	Year	Wild compared to farm birds Release Season	Wild or Farm Birds	Number Released	Percent Harvested
Oregon					
Summer Lake	1950	Feb., March	Trap. wild	139	11.5
	1950	April	Farm adults	87	10.3
Washington					
Eliza Island [1]	1948	December	Farm birds	16	31.0
	1948	December	Trap. wild	16	62.0
	1949	December	Farm birds	16	87.0
		December	Trap. wild	16	94.0

[1] Eliza Island studies by Einarsen of the Oregon Cooperative Wildlife Research Unit. All of these birds were harvested in March following release, and predator control was practiced in 1949.

There is a definite correlation between farming practices, farm production, pheasant production, and the inherent fertility of the soil. Generally, the pheasant production potential of a piece of private farmland is in direct relation to its productive capacity for agricultural use.

It is difficult indeed to envision a piece of farmland in the Northwest that does not contain many factors essential to the livelihood of pheasants. Too often, however, one or more of the other essential factors are missing and the farmstead carries either a low seasonal population of birds or none at all. The states of Idaho, Oregon, and Washington each are carrying on pheasant habitat development projects which are similar basically in that they are aimed at supplying the limiting factors on privately owned lands. Hence, through cooperation with the landowner, it is possible to make the over-all farmstead unit more productive of birds. Recognizing the fact that an adequate supply of birds would be of little value to the public unless they were available for hunting, these programs also provide for hunter entry onto at least portions of the private lands to harvest the crop that is being produced.

Because of the extreme diversity of pheasant range in the area under consideration, no single program can be formulated to apply to the over-all area.

Wheat-land pheasant range is the least complex. Farming practices there are extensive, and the use of mobile combine harvesters leaves considerable crop residue in the fields as a basic food supply. In some regions, the landscape is wheat fields predominately and perennial-grass side hills and gullies with a definite lack of woody cover. In others, permanent water is the limiting factor.

The approach to pheasant habitat development in these regions is to place a trained game manager in the district and have him survey each farmstead to determine the areas that are of value to upland birds and what factors would increase utilization of the over-all farm. An agreement then is reached with the landowner, securing the use of certain land areas free of charge where the necessary shrubs or grass are planted or permanent water is supplied through the development of springs or the construction of self-filling water devices.

The method of operation is varied to fit conditions in the particular work area. In some instances, the district technician works through a county on a township basis contacting each landowner within the township before moving on to the next township. This type of operation is well suited to the Palouse-type pheasant range where, because of rolling topography and higher rainfall, the development possibilities are more varied and scattered.

In the more level wheat-land type, the district manager normally works from farm to farm along the dry swales or run-off waterways through the area. These coulees contain the only existing cover and, in many cases, are bordered by shallow soil and rock outcrops. Farming areas between the coulees are truly a wheat desert of level, tilled land, normally containing no perennial cover of any value to upland birds.

There are advantages in entering into a general agreement of cooperation and understanding with landowners comprising soil conservation districts. In meeting with groups of farmers in the district, the mechanics of the program can be explained thoroughly. Particular emphasis is placed on the fact that the work is carried on from farm to farm, as it has been found that each development interacts with the next if the program is handled in that manner. Nevertheless, there may be certain landowners within the general project area who are interested enough in the work to want to proceed on their own, even though the district manager may not be working on the farms in that segment of the project area until two or three years later. In such cases, a one-day joint inspection of the ownership made by the management technician and the landowner usually will bring out certain important steps in land use that can be effected to the advantage of the farmer and game. The interested farmer thus can be stimulated to carry out these changes on his own, and the work progresses with little or no disturbance to the coordinated farm-to-farm planning by the district manager.

In many instances, the farmstead maps prepared by Soil Conservation Service personnel are adequate. It is still essential, however, that the game management representative survey the farmstead unit thoroughly. His interest is not in increasing the agricultural value of the farm alone, plus the occasional designation of the wildlife area; rather it is to determine how best, through a minimum of effort, to increase the usability of over-all wildlife potentials so that the development work on the farm will be of maximum value to the landowner.

Once the determination has been made as to wildlife development needs, a formal agreement is entered into between the Game Department and the landowner. This agreement stipulates that the designated areas on the farm will be set aside for wildlife development for a period of ten years without charge. It further defines what materials will be furnished by the Department and what labors will be performed by

PLATE XII.—Habitat development—before and after the establishment of grass nesting cover on a critical slope in Washington's Palouse wheat country (Washington Dept. of Game).

each party. In addition, it provides that areas of the farm (normally not less than three-fourths) will be opened to public hunting, and provides that the Department of Game shall furnish appropriately worded signs which will designate safety zones closed to hunting and ask the cooperation of the hunter while on the remainder of the farm.

Selling points to the landowner are the combined values of game and soil management and erosion control. In one instance, the landowner may be interested in fencing and planting a watershed with permanent cover which will enhance the value of his farm pond, lessen silt deposition in it, and eliminate gullying. In another, it may be that the owner and his boys will receive recreational benefits through development of a permanent water supply to assure the utilization of existing cover by birds. The possibility of retaining existing cover and increasing its use by upland birds is an important phase of the program. Often the landowner has read or been told that removal of brush along a temporary waterway will aid in stream bank erosion control, if the banks are sloped and seeded to perennial grasses. Without realizing that this technique may apply to one area, but be harmful to another, the landowner may assume that what is good for Pat is good for Mike; it is the job of the district manager to correct such an impression.

Too often woody or grassy vegetation potentially beneficial for holding soil has been impaired for either soil erosion control or wildlife through indiscriminate pasturing. Such situations can be corrected and valuable benefits derived with little or no expenditure of development moneys.

Actual planning depends upon the work necessary to improve existing habitat on the farm and therefore will vary with each land ownership. Certain general principles are adhered to; the first being that development of unrelated or isolated units is avoided. For example, a patch of good brushy winter cover complete with permanent water and surrounded to the very edge of the brush with wheatland would provide all the requirements of a pheasant population except for nesting. In such instances, nesting attempts would be made in the adjacent stubble, where nest destruction from farming activities is severe, and the work would be of little gain. Examples could be pointed out using almost any single factor. In the illustration above, the game manager would attempt to supply a strip of perennial grass cover immediately adjacent to the area in order to place the entire unit in production. The species planted, either shrub or grass, would depend upon soil and climatic conditions. However, shrubs should provide compact, low-growing cover and furnish either food supplement or a grit substitute in their fruits. The planting should be planned to prevent its being filled completely with drifted snow. Grass species should be those in which dried vegetation remains erect throughout winter and into the nesting season. Although not recommended for planting in agricultural areas, but cited only as an illustrative example, a patch of common quack grass would remain erect and furnish both roosting and nesting cover throughout the year; whereas, a patch of Kentucky bluegrass would be left flat and of no value with the first snowfall following the growing season. County agricultural authorities can advise whether or not the species under consideration will in any way constitute a menace to domestic agriculture in the district. If so, a suitable substitute should be selected.

Correlated with this program is the stimulation of independent development work by interested landowners through cooperation with soil conservation districts and dissemination of informational bulletins. The State furnishes technical planning assistance and planting stock for woody coverts.

This work was started in Washington on an experimental basis in 1941, and was established as a full-scale program in the wheat-producing regions of the State in 1947. Since that date, 300,825 acres of privately owned land has been placed under agreement, and the free use of slightly over 3,000 acres of this land has been secured for the purpose of development to improve game habitat and make the farms more productive. The basic aim of these farmer-cooperative, habitat-development programs is not necessarily to develop high carrying-capacity units of isolated pheasant range, but rather to increase the use of the entire pheasant range by supplying missing factors.

As a result of increasing public awareness of the value of permanent cover both for wildlife and for soil erosion control, modifications have been made in the Production and Marketing Administration's Agricultural Conservation Program, which should result both in an increased production of pheasants and better land use.

The indiscriminate use of herbicides remains, however, as a threat to any program aimed at retention or increase of pheasant habitat in these or other regions.

The pheasant population response to development has been exceptional in certain parts of the wheat-land development areas. This is true particularly where lack of permanent water was the limiting factor. An example farmstead unit in Adams County, Washington, which in 1948 probably carried no permanent pheasant population, but was visited by a few birds during the fall and winter period, was carrying a post-hunting season population of over 100 pheasants in 1951. In that case, the addition of water through the construction of two self-filling cisterns made the over-all farmstead attractive to a permanent pheasant population. Perhaps the second most rapid population increases have been achieved in those areas lacking any permanent erect cover. Here, sweet clover plantings have been made to provide cover until the woody plantings have had sufficient time to attain usable growth. In one instance in Spokane County, the permanent population of pheasants on a 160-acre wheat farm was increased from zero to 17 in one year.

Farming practices in the irrigated pheasant ranges are much more intensive, farmstead units being much smaller in size, and as a result it is more difficult to have certain portions of the farm set aside exclusively for game-bird use. It likewise is true that those areas, because of the diversity of land use, are the most productive of birds now and the most congested hunting areas in the region. In those areas little effort is being devoted to increasing bird production, inasmuch as populations now are good, and it would be more desirable to continue development in the wheat-land type to put that area into production and spread hunting intensity.

Here the major phase of habitat work is that of furnishing technical assistance and planting stock, primarily multiflora rose, to interested landowners. Undoubtedly, as the various states progress in habitat work, additional effort will be applied to the fringe areas of this type to increase over-all productivity.

The population riddle still is so far from being solved in the humid coastal ranges that the game manager is at a loss to lay out a sound habitat-development program.

The only significant results which have been produced through experimental habitat-management practices in the humid coastal areas have been through supplying release areas complete with food for the release of adult hens which have been held through the winter on game farms.

The Prospect

The Northwest region appears to be a favorable climatic zone for ringneck pheasants, since they have increased and maintained populations for over 70 years. The most recent intensive studies indicate that breeding populations in good habitat are quite consistent from year to year. What fluctuations there are in hunting kill seem to be attributable primarily to variations in the success of reproduction. A favorable nesting season is followed by a good hunting season as surely as a poor reproductive season is followed by poor hunting. Spring populations remain relatively constant, supporting the belief that winter is the principal limiting factor, and that wintering habitat has a definite carrying capacity.

Some areas that in the past produced many pheasants now yield sparingly. General habitat deterioration due to more intensive farm management is one of the chief causes.

It can be shown that complete closure on hens benefitted the pheasant population to some degree but not as much as would be expected if hunting kill were an important limiting factor. This limited general increase in response to the hen closure is interpreted to show that most populations were at or near habitat carrying capacity.

Widespread liberations of game-farm pheasants undoubtedly have wasted large sums of money and are continuing to do so. Some benefit is received, but it is not in proportion to cost. Recent improvements in propagation methods and techniques of stocking have resulted in better returns to hunters, but still the cost of pheasants bagged as a result of these liberations will average well in excess of $10.00 each. In most instances, stocked pheasants are employed in futile attempts to overload capacities of already populated habitat or they are placed in barren ranges which, by their lack of birds, have proved already that they will not support pheasants.

Unquestionably propagation has been tremendously overemphasized, and it is done at the expense of other types of management. There is a common tendency to oversell any new program in order to get it adopted, and, as was done with pheasant propagation, it may be carried far beyond the point of diminishing returns. The result may be a complete swing of the pendulum with all of the old management discarded and new techniques pushed to their limit. Such a complete change is not always best, and, in this case, there may be merit in maintaining some pheasant propagation in game programs of the future. At least, the change-over should be slow enough to test new techniques thoroughly as they are expanded. There is a chance also that greater efficiency may be secured in the utilization of a much smaller supply of propagated birds. Three possible methods of employing these birds are:

1. The stocking of hens in spring in regions where winter is the season of greatest stress. If weather is favorable, and proper nesting and brood cover are available, the young produced should survive to hunting season and justify the cost.

2. "Catastrophe Insurance" is another use for propagated birds. Such plantings seldom are needed, so their value is

largely psychological rather than actual, but they can hasten the recovery of a depleted area.

3. The stocking of cock birds directly before the guns in hunting season. This "put and take" management is not looked upon too favorably by many, but it can be made efficient from the standpoint of harvesting and it is the one sure way of having a crop available each year. It is a good means of stocking public shooting grounds and hunting areas close to large metropolitan centers.

Habitat improvement is basic and unquestionably the most important phase of any game program. However, with pheasants merely a byproduct on privately owned land, the development of a practical plan to benefit that byproduct is difficult to attain. The farmer cooperative system now used in the northwestern states is the most successful yet attempted, but it operates only in grain-producing regions where farms are large. As techniques are improved and tested, this work can be expanded and possibly extended to other types of farming areas. It always will be a slow, tedious and expensive type of management. It is unspectacular because of the long waiting period before cover plantings develop to maximum value. Actual costs of putting another pheasant in the bag through present methods of habitat improvement are unknown, but it is possible that the expenditure (interest on investment) may be as great or greater than that shown for artificial propagation.

There is no known economical method of producing more pheasants. When considered from the standpoint of expense compared to hunting license revenue, all management might be viewed as economically unsound and the only alternative would be to do nothing. However, such conclusions do not satisfy the hunting public, which continually demands more birds. They expect administrators to do the best they can with the present knowledge and money available.

Unknowns with regard to the ringneck are many. The conundrum of what causes poor reproductive seasons is most baffling. Until it is solved, managers will be unable to predict the crop that can be harvested. However, knowledge that has been gained generally points to weather or low temperatures and heavy precipitation during the nesting season as being in some way responsible for low yields. At least this seems to be true in most northern regions. This suggests that these cycles of pheasant abundance never will be brought under control. Since weather is uncontrollable, it is inevitable that there will be periods of both abundance and scarcity. Management can only hope to make the highs go a little higher and keep the lows from going so low. Nature will continue to carry the bulk of the production load.

One undoubted fact is the importance of habitat. The production of pheasants in good habitat may fluctuate from year to year, but poor habitat will have few birds regardless of highs or lows. This is the logical management approach, and hence the important need at the present time is an answer to the problem of how, practically and economically, to improve farm land for pheasants. The farmer cooperative program is believed to be part of the answer, but better techniques and other methods must be developed before it can be applied universally.

One bright spot in the Northwest's pheasant picture is the continued expansion of irrigation projects, which create some of the best-quality bird range. Washington's Columbia Basin Project alone will add over a million acres of habitat from lands that are barren now. These new wildlife areas will help to replace habitat losses in other parts of the region.

It is difficult to predict the future of ringnecks in the Northwest. The fact that they have been here for over 70 years, however, and have proved their great adaptability and hardiness, makes it doubtful that they ever will be eliminated. To maintain them in huntable numbers probably will require continuous efforts and emphasis on management research. The greatest hope lies in the fact that conservation practices which must be adopted to preserve for future generations the soil and water resources of the land also should be of benefit to the pheasant.

CHAPTER 3

THE PHEASANT IN CALIFORNIA

By

CHESTER M. HART, BEN GLADING AND HAROLD T. HARPER

IN LESS than thirty years the ringneck pheasant has advanced from the position of an obscure alien to become one of California's best known and most highly prized game birds. The gaudy immigrant from the Orient fulfills a real need in replacing the native quail which has been reduced materially in recent years by intensive farming in the state's main agricultural areas.

So successful has been this transition that more California hunters now go afield in quest of the ringneck cock than any other kind of feathered game; and a long-tailed rooster is second only to the vaunted Canadian honker as a game-bird prize.

As shown by the distribution map (Fig. 3), California pheasant lands are isolated from other ringneck ranges of the country and offer extremes of conditions found almost nowhere else. Birds living in the oven-like Imperial Valley and the extension of this range into Baja California, represent the southernmost productive pheasant population on the North American Continent. The bulk of the state's shooting is furnished by the fertile irrigated lands of the Central Valley—much of which was a vast extent of tule marshes, aswarm with waterfowl, in 1826 when Jedediah Smith led the first band of fur trappers across the Sierras to take an appraising look at the land of the Spanish Padres.

How this region was converted into an environment suitable for pheasants is a story of man-made hunting. It involved a radical program of "habitat improvement" and the importation of an exotic species to fit it. To both sportsman and scientist the results are significant.

How Pheasants Came to California

The earliest attempts to establish the ringneck in California were private releases in coastal areas near San Francisco Bay during the late 1870's or 1880's. Despite the usual optimistic reports, those English birds disappeared, and it became evident that the trials had failed.[1]

Success with pheasants in Oregon stimulated further interest in this state, and from 1889 to 1898 the State Board of Fish Commissioners purchased some 850 birds which were stocked in various localities in northern and central California. Most of these came from Oregon, but at least one importation was made direct from Hong Kong.

Evidently some of those liberations succeeded in establishing breeding populations. The Biennial Report of the Board of Fish Commissioners for 1899-1900 stated that "nides of young birds have been seen in Humboldt, Santa Clara, and Fresno Counties." The next two reports were optimistic. Santa Clara County had the most pheasants, with about a thousand on the Morrow Ranch near San Jose. There were favorable records also from Fresno, Humboldt, Santa Cruz, and Kern Counties.

Thus, stocking prior to 1900 may have been responsible for getting this species started in many areas where it is found today, although extensive liberations since 1908 have obscured the effects of earlier work.

In 1905, the Commission decided to discontinue importations because of high costs. No further state liberations were made until a state game farm was authorized in 1908. This was established near Hayward, Alameda County, and breeding stock was secured from various sources, including Oregon and Pennsylvania.

---

[1] Information in this section is taken largely from Hjersman (1947).

During the next ten years, 4,183 pheasants were reared and released in at least 31 counties. By 1918, it was believed that sufficient stocking had been done, and the game farm was abandoned. Strange as it may seem to some sportsmen, this may have been a sound outlook. It is possible that the distribution of breeding stock up to that time would have been sufficient to produce present populations.

By 1916, it was estimated that there were between 7,000 and 8,000 pheasants in the state. Santa Clara County still led with about 2,000, and Humboldt, Inyo, Siskiyou, Santa Cruz, Tulare, Lake, and Napa Counties claimed from a few hundred to a thousand.

It is noteworthy that the only ringnecks then reported in the Sacramento Valley were 200 to 300 near Williams, in Colusa County. It was in this locality that J. S. Hunter, former Chief of the Bureau of Game Conservation, reported seeing two broods and several adults in 1916 (Grinnell, Bryant, and Storer 1918). These were the first published records of pheasant establishment in what later became the most important pheasant shooting area in the state.

In the next few years there were indications of increasing local populations. Ranchers in Santa Clara Valley reported destroying numerous nests with mowers. Claims of crop damage by pheasants came from Owens Valley, Inyo County, culminating in the declaration of an open season there in 1925. In the early 1920's, flocks of these birds were seen in the Delta area of the Sacramento and San Joaquin rivers, and boys were said to be selling sacks of them to restaurants. By this time it was evident that the ringneck had come to stay, and pressure to plant more birds was generated.

Demands for more stocking became so great that the Fish and Game Commission started building another game farm in 1925. Meanwhile 5,000 ringnecks were purchased from a private breeder. Most of these were stocked in Owens and Round Valleys, Inyo County, with some liberated in San Diego County and near Modesto, Stanislaus County.

The following year (1926), the Yountville State Game Farm

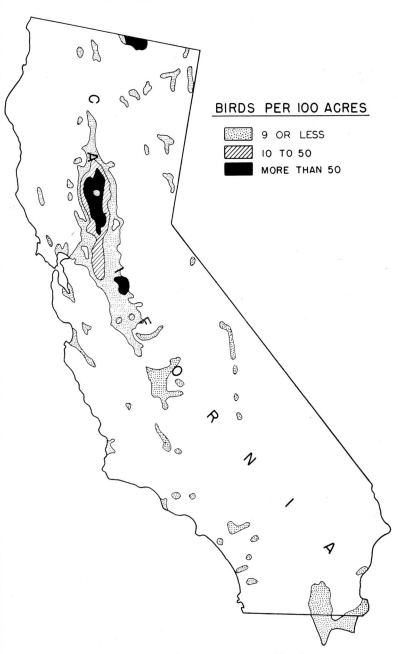

BIRDS PER 100 ACRES

9 OR LESS
10 TO 50
MORE THAN 50

FIGURE 3.—Pheasant distribution in California.

was in production and liberated more than 3,000 pheasants. In ensuing years, until 1952, there was a steady trend toward more and larger plants and greater production. Pheasants were released in increasing numbers until the peak of approximately 107,000 birds was reached in 1951. A total of more than a million pheasants have been stocked through 1955.

It is of particular interest that until 1933, when pheasant hunting started generally in California, the area producing the most pheasants, Sacramento Valley, had received comparatively little stocking.

The first legalized hunting of pheasants was in 1925 in Inyo and Mono Counties. The season was December 1-7, with possession and season limits of six birds, evidently of either sex. Pheasants were reported to be numerous and were hunted heavily. The season was not reopened the following year.

The first general open season was declared in 1933 from November 15 to 20, with daily and possession limits of two male birds. Shooting hours were from a half-hour before sunrise to a half-hour after sunset. These hunting regulations were continued annually until 1941, when the season limit was reduced from 10 to 8 male birds.

The next four years saw various hunting regulations in force. The season was 10 days in 1942, 15 days in 1943 and 1944, and was cut back to 6 days in 1945. Bag limits remained 2 per day and 10 per season, except that in 1943 and 1944 four cocks could be taken on opening day alone.

In recent years regulations have stabilized on a 10-day season, a permitted bag of 2 cocks per day and 10 per season, and shooting hours from 8 a.m. to 4:30 p.m. The open season is set to coincide with the usual short period in late November between completion of the rice harvest and the advent of heavy rains. This insures hunter access to the state's heaviest pheasant populations in the rice growing area of the Sacramento Valley.

Regulations since 1951 permit taking one hen per day, but not more than five per season, in lieu of the same number of cocks throughout roughly the southern half of the state. Reproduction of pheasants is generally poor in most of this area and the bag has been increased to allow the harvest of stocked game-farm hens that have little chance of surviving and reproducing.

CALIFORNIA'S PHEASANT HABITATS

Distribution of the ringneck in California illustrates at once the wide tolerance of this bird for extremes of climate and altitude and its relatively strict requirements for favorable farming practices. Breeding populations exist in the Imperial Valley, along the Mexican border, where even incubators at the game farm must be maintained at temperatures below those of the outside air in summer, and at elevations of 200 feet below sea level. In contrast, Great Basin areas of northeastern California, lying at elevations above 4,000 feet, and experiencing winter temperatures below zero, support high local populations where sagebrush gives way to favorable farm habitat.

Within this wide variety of conditions, three natural subdivisions can be differentiated: (1) the warm, irrigated Central and Imperial valleys, (2) the upland Great Basin area, and (3) the coastal valleys along the Pacific (Fig. 3). These regions are dissimilar both in conditions and in relative importance for pheasant production.

Pheasant Areas of the Central and Imperial Valleys

The Central Valley occupies the heart of California, stretching approximately 45 miles from the Coast Range to the Sierras and extending from the vicinity of Redding about 380 miles south to the Tehachapi Mountains. It consists of the Sacramento and San Joaquin Valleys, whose rivers meander from the north and south, join in the Delta area, and flow into San Francisco Bay. These rivers and their tributaries are the life of the valley, furnishing irrigation water for a tremendously wealthy and diversified agriculture supported by the rich alluvial soils they have deposited in the valley floor.

Main crops include both irrigated and dry-farmed cereal grains, a variety of vegetables and melons, orchards, vineyards, permanent irrigated pastures, and field crops such as alfalfa and other hay, sugar beets, beans, and cotton.

The climate is characterized by hot, dry summers and mild winters. Summer heat is tempered in the Delta area by ocean breezes and the proximity of San Francisco Bay. Temperatures increase gradually north or south from this locality, with

Plate XIII.—Ha! (California Dept. of Fish and Game).

maximum summer temperatures ranging between 100° F. and 120° F. common throughout most of the valley. Relative humidities are high in winter and low in summer but are affected locally by heavy irrigation in summer. Rainfall is concentrated in winter and early spring and increases from an average of approximately 6 inches in the South to 25 inches in the North. Winters are mild, as evidenced by the growing of citrus fruits in the central part of the San Joaquin Valley and the northern part of the Sacramento Valley. Light frosts occur, but temperatures seldom fall below 25° F., and snow is rare.

This large valley contains California's best pheasant habitat and a high percentage of its total pheasant population. The Sacramento Valley presents the most widespread area of high-quality habitat and, according to postcard surveys, furnishes approximately 50 to 60 percent of the total state kill. Habitat predominantly of medium quality is found throughout the smaller Delta area, which provides 15 to 20 percent of the bag. The San Joaquin Valley yields about 15 percent of the kill, with habitat generally poor and more spotty.

TABLE 9. Relative importance of the main pheasant producing regions in California by percentages of the total state kill reported, 1948-1952.

Region	1948	1949	1950	1951	1952	Ave.
Sacramento Valley	59.2	54.2	51.2	49.7	51.2	53.1
Delta Area	15.5	18.6	17.3	22.4	17.8	18.3
San Joaquin Valley ..	14.6	15.6	16.1	14.0	13.7	14.8
Imperial Valley	1.8*	1.2*	0.4	1.6*	0.8	1.1*
Central and Imperial Valleys	91.1	89.6	85.0	87.7	83.5	87.3
Great Basin	3.2	4.6	8.7	5.2	9.1	6.2
Coastal Valleys	5.7	5.8	6.3	7.1	7.4	6.5

* Believed to be high due to small area and small sample.

Imperial Valley, although far removed from the Central Valley, is similar basically to southern sections of the San Joaquin Valley. Its pheasant population is of particular interest because of its existence in this southern latitude and sub-tropical climate; but it is of little importance in the over-all picture, furnishing only about 1 percent of the total California bag.

Sacramento Valley rice belt

In the rice-growing section on each side of the Sacramento River in Butte, Glenn, Colusa, Sutter, Yolo, and Sacramento counties is found California's largest and best area of pheasant habitat. The flat terrain presents a pattern of rice fields interspersed with barley and wheat, fallow stubble, and weedy, dry pasture and wasteland. The whole is dissected by irrigation canals, drain ditches, swales, and sinks having a heavy growth of cattails, tules and bulrushes, and other aquatic plants and weeds. Watercourses are bordered by cottonwoods and willows, accompanied, in many areas, by jungle-like growths of berry vines and wild grapes. Here, ringnecks thrive, and eager hunters converge when the long-awaited opening day in November arrives.

Although correlation of heavy pheasant populations with rice growing is novel in the United States, habitat conditions in this region undoubtedly correspond more closely to the Chinese ringneck's ancestral home than do those of any other locality in North America. Beebe (1926) listed three general types of country inhabited by these birds in China: (1) dense reed beds along river banks, (2) low hills covered with grass and trees, and (3) flat paddy fields. Pheasants took cover in the beds of annual reeds and fed about paddies of rice, wheat, or millet bordering the reeds. The paddy flats included level country where wheat and rape were grown in addition to the actual rice beds. This brief description of the reed bed and paddy flat habitat indicates conditions remarkably comparable to the rice-growing area of the Sacramento Valley. Here, dense beds of cattails and tules substitute for the reed beds, and the main crops of rice, barley, and wheat are nearly the same as those mentioned by Beebe.

Rice farming was introduced to the Sacramento Valley in 1912 and proved to be ideal for the heavy clay and clay-adobe soils, hot summer weather, and plentiful irrigation water in this region. Dry farming of wheat and barley prevalent throughout the area was augmented increasingly by rice culture. The acreage in rice reached 100,000 by 1918, exceeded 200,000 in 1942, and has neared 300,000 acres in recent years.

This combination of agricultural practices created conditions much to the liking of the ringneck, and its numbers increased with the rice. Thus, as a result of large-scale "habitat improvement," an area at one time not worthy of mention as a producer of pheasants was, in 20 years, furnishing the bulk of California's pheasant shooting.

The plentiful supply of water evidently required by pheasants during periods of hot weather and low humidity is provided by the network of canals, drains, and rice fields flooded from late spring until September.

This abundance of water promotes a luxuriant growth of cover throughout the rice-growing area. Heavy cover, mainly cattails and tules in low areas and ditches, is utilized as resting and escape cover in midday, and as a place of refuge when the hunting season begins.

The principal crops associated with rice are wheat and barley. Interspersion of these, and the abundance of weeds and grasses in fallow fields and along canals and contour levees, furnishes a rich food supply. Studies have shown that waste rice makes up nearly 40 percent of the total volume of food consumed (Ferrel, Twining, and Herkenham 1949). The methods employed in harvesting rice leave waste grain available practically year-round in fallow fields of rice stubble. Also, in the spring, pheasants glean a great deal of waste seed, which falls on dry ground when airplanes are sowing rice in the flooded fields.

Another excellent source of food is provided by barnyard grass *(Echinochloa crusgalli),* commonly called watergrass in this region. It is the common invading plant in rice, growing abundantly in shallow water or moist sites, and its seeds form approximately 10 percent of the pheasant's annual diet.

Barley and wheat furnish an important food supply during periods when rice is not readily available. These grains pro-

vide more than half the total volume of food in July and
about 16 percent of the yearly diet. They are utilized nearly
every month.

Stubble fields that are plowed and leveled for another
crop, or worked up to summer fallow, are used to a surprising
degree by pheasants in this region. Morning and evenings,
large numbers of birds feed across these bare fields, picking
up grain and possibly insects. Frequently, they roost on bare
ground near the middles of large fields.

Of the several systems of crop rotation followed, the common
three-year plan probably is most favorable for pheasants. This
consists of rice, followed by a year of fallow, then dry-farmed
barley or wheat. Brood observations in this area indicate a
fairly direct relationship between high production and the
interspersion of crops under this system.

Repeated cropping of the same ground with rice is becoming more common and is less beneficial to pheasants. Good
rice yields are maintained by growing a winter cover crop
of vetch. This forms attractive nesting cover, and there is
considerable nest destruction and some mortality of nesting
birds when this cover crop is disked under in late spring.
In addition, this practice results in larger blocks of land being
devoted entirely to rice culture, so that there is less interspersion of crops providing safe nesting grounds.

After a normally wet fall and winter, fields of fall-planted
grains provide good nesting sites that are not subject to
spring flooding. Nesting studies, in sample areas totaling
about 60 acres, indicated a density of at least one nest per
five acres in dry-farmed grain near rice fields. Thus, the 500,-
000 to 800,000 acres of wheat and barley produced annually
in the rice-growing area assumes considerable significance in
providing nesting places.

Crops associated with high nest mortality, such as alfalfa,
have not been important here. Although nesting densities usually are higher in alfalfa than in grain fields, it is believed that
the greater security and larger acreages of grain fields make
these areas more important in the production of pheasants.

Clean farming has not been general in the Sacramento Valley rice-growing area in the past. Many holdings vary from a few hundred to several thousand acres in size, and there seems to be a tendency for such large tracts to be less intensively farmed than smaller ones. However, the general trend at present is toward cleaner and more intensive farming, which gradually is reducing the permanent cover and thus lowering the quality of the pheasant habitat.

In many places, where fields remain fallow after the rice crop is harvested, contour levees are permitted to grow to a good stand of weeds and grasses. Where these are not burned or grazed, they contribute to favorable nesting conditions. Also, seeds or foliage of the following grasses and weeds growing in these waste areas make important or persistent contributions to the pheasant's diet: rye grasses *(Lolium* spp.), wild oats *(Avena* spp.), chickweed *(Stellaria media),* prickly lettuce *(Lactuca scariola),* milk thistle *(Silybum marianum),* bull thistle *(Cirsium lanceolatum),* ground cherry *(Physalis* spp.), and miscellaneous flower buds and flowers.

Dry ditchbanks, pastures, and waste areas throughout this region are invaded by a heavy growth of yellow star thistle *(Centaurea solstitialis).* This weed is an agricultural pest, and considerable effort is made to eradicate it in some localities. In terms of pheasant requirements, this is unfortunate because it furnishes valuable cover and some food. Its thorny growth is selected for roosting in some localities, and dry growth from previous years provides the preferred type of non-cultivated nesting cover. Studies in 1950 indicated that nest density in waste areas where star thistle predominated was approximately three per acre.

The rice belt carries a large proportion of California's pheasant hunting load. Hunters from all over the state cram into this section during the open season, but the majority are from the thickly populated San Francisco Bay area or local communities including the City of Sacramento. Hunting pressure and harvest are high where public access is permitted. Recent years have seen maximum seasonal gun pressure usually reaching 200-300 man-hours per 100 acres on controlled hunting areas in this region, where access was free but where hunters were limited to not more than one per 5-12 acres at a given time. Censuses indicated that this hunting pressure harvested approximately 75-85 percent of the cock population during a 10-day season. Lower hunting pressures and poorer harvests are the rule when bad weather occurs during the short open season.

Observed fall sex ratios in this region in recent years usually have varied from about 1.5 to 3 hens per cock on intensively hunted areas. Pre-hunting sex ratios approaching 1:1 have been recorded only in 1948, a year of exceptionally high breeding success, or on refuges or lightly hunted areas. This high ratio of hens in the fall probably is the combined result of a high harvest of cocks the previous season, good survival of hens, and fair or poor reproduction for the year.

Sex ratios after the hunting season generally range from 3 to 4 hens per remaining cock where hunting has been light and 6 to 10 hens per cock where the roosters have been hunted intensively. However, both hiking censuses and cock-hen counts from airplanes in 1946 and 1947 indicated that the male pheasant population after the hunting season on the Sartain Ranch had been reduced so that there were approximately 27 and 19 hens, respectively, per cock. Such heavy harvests are local only, and counts on the Sartain Ranch in the breeding season of 1947 showed the ratio had changed to five hens per cock. Many areas in the rice belt are harvested lightly or not at all, and movements of one or both sexes prior to the breeding season seem to even out locally unbalanced sex ratios.

Although the rice belt has been noted for heavy production of pheasants since the hunting of these birds was permitted in California, accurate information on pheasant reproduction and kill per unit area are not available for the years prior to 1947. This is unfortunate, since game wardens and other people familiar with the rice-growing region believe that peak pheasant populations in this area occurred before that time. Thus, maximum populations that have existed, or even what should be termed average, are a matter of conjecture.

Annual harvests of cock pheasants in the rice belt have varied greatly in recent years as evidenced by complete bag checks made on large sample areas in this region. From 1947 to 1952, the average annual kill of wild cocks per 100 acres, on checked areas, varied from a low of 10 to a high of 38, with average hunting pressures ranging from 110 to 236 gun-hours per 100 acres (Table 10). Although hunting pressure is of considerable importance up to a certain level in influencing kill per unit area, the available crop of birds is the prime factor. That the population has fluctuated greatly is evident from these kill figures.

TABLE 10. Kill and hunting pressure on controlled hunting areas in the rice belt of Sacramento Valley, 1947-1952.

Year	Number of Areas	Acres Hunted	Wild Cocks Bagged per 100 Acres			Seasonal Gun-hours per 100 Acres		
			Highest Area	Lowest Area	Weighted Average	Highest Area	Lowest Area	Weighted Average
1947	2	14,720	13	13	13	120	100	110
1948	2	14,720	43	34	38	295	185	236
1949	6	58,680	18	9	16	308	172	225
1950[1]	5	83,623	13	7	10	186	57	120
1951	5	83,544	12	5	10	190	42	138
1952[1]	6	83,293	16	6	11	251	71	148

[1] Bad weather preceding and/or during hunting season.

Both detailed information and general observations indicate that from 1945 to 1952 the pheasant crop could be termed fair or comparatively poor for the Sacramento Valley, except for the year 1948. Bag checks on controlled hunting areas in 1947, and 1949 to 1952 showed average harvests of 10 to 16 cocks per 100 acres with heavy hunting pressure. Censuses in 1947 and 1949 indicated fall population densities of 80 to 113 birds per 100 acres. General observations and less complete hunting checks made in 1945 and 1946 indicate that probably these years, too, were only fair for pheasants.

Suddenly, following several mediocre years, a banner crop of pheasants was produced in 1948. Approximately 43 wild cocks per 100 acres were bagged that year on the Sartain Ranch west of Gridley. Although this may have been a local concentration not typical of the entire area, checks of hunter's bags on a total of nearly 15,000 acres in this region showed the harvest to be at least 38 wild cocks per 100 acres. Census results on the same areas indicated fall population densities varying from 125 to 150 birds per 100 acres.

TABLE 11. Pheasant productivity and spring rainfall for Sacramento Valley, 1947-1950 [1]

	1947	1948	1949	1950
Average clutch size	10.7	12.9	12.3	11.9
Average eggs hatched	9.0	10.8	9.0	8.5
Percent hatch	84	84	73	71
Average brood size (6 weeks of age)	5	7	5	5
Young:adult ratio in bag	6:1	10:1	4:1	3:1
Rainfall, in inches (April 1—June 30)	2.06	7.87	1.90	2.60

[1] Data from Federal Aid in Wildlife Restoration Project California 22-R quarterly reports as follows: Clutch size and hatch from nesting studies involving 90 to 422 nests annually on Gray Lodge Refuge, Gridley; brood size from complete counts of 272 to 953 broods made annually in area between Chico, Woodland, and Sacramento; young:adult ratio from bag checks on Sartain and McManus experimental areas; and rainfall from Biggs rice field station, Biggs, California.

Nest and brood studies in the Sacramento Valley during this period showed some correlation of hunting season success with clutch size, percent of hatch, and brood size (Table 11).

Increased clutch size, and slightly better survival of chicks in 1948, resulted in a corresponding increase in brood size over the previous year. Furthermore, it appears that more hens must have been successful in rearing broods in 1948 than in other years of the study, although the actual percentage of success was not computed for that year.

Counts made in 1949 showed that about 50 percent of the

hens reared young, and studies in 1950 indicated that approximately 65-70 percent were successful.

In recent years there has been practically no correlation between the amount of breeding stock present in spring and success of the next hunting season. Here, weather is mild and food is plentiful, so that there is no great drop in hen numbers because of heavy winter mortality. The breeding population appears to be adequate consistently for the production of a heavy crop of pheasants when a favorable nesting season occurs. Large breeding populations do not yield a good crop when nesting conditions are poor. This is illustrated by the considerable fluctuations in kill from year to year instead of a gradual build-up or decline.

All available evidence on pheasant populations and reproduction for this area points to the fact that success hinges upon weather conditions during spring and early summer.

PLATE XIV.—Aerial view of typical fall pheasant habitat in the Sacramento Valley, south of Chico, showing the interspersion of sloughs with heavy cover, standing rice stubble (marked by contour levees), and land prepared for planting (California Dept. of Fish and Game).

Plate XV.—Seasonal aspects of California's best pheasant range in the Sacramento Valley rice fields. *Upper,* worked up for planting—good cover remains along irrigation ditches, levees, and fencerows; *center,* flooded—waste areas still are available as bird retreats; *lower,* at harvest time, all that a bird could want (Chester M. Hart, California Dept. of Fish and Game).

The spring of 1948 was late and wet for this region (Table 11). Nesting and brood survival data show that the effects this increased moisture and humidity had upon improving clutch size, hatch, and survival of chicks was not sufficient to explain the magnitude of the pheasant crop that year. More broods must have been produced than during 1947, 1949, or 1950. Evidently this was made possible by heavy rainfall late in spring which effectively delayed burning, plowing, and mowing so that pheasants were allowed to nest unmolested. It is believed that this indirect effect of spring rainfall upon nesting by influencing farming practices is more important than the direct effect upon clutch size, hatch, or chick survival.

The dense pheasant populations in the Sacramento Valley are found where heavy soils, plentiful irrigation water, and adequate drainage make rice growing practicable. Surrounding and dividing these areas are regions having lighter-textured soils and other basic agricultural conditions better adapted to different corps, which almost invariably support lower numbers of birds. In some such places, the habitat is favorable enough over extensive areas to produce moderate numbers of pheasants, but frequently the transition is abrupt from concentrated ringneck populations in heavily irrigated rice areas to low numbers of birds in poor habitat.

Other Sacramento Valley habitats

The Sacramento Valley, outside the rice belt, presents, as a whole, an extremely varied agricultural picture. Depending upon locality, farming may be diversified or highly specialized. Various kinds of orchards and row crops are grown. Considerable acreages are planted to dry-farmed cereal grains and grain hay, and occasional rice fields are found. Alfalfa, irrigated pasture, and dry pasture are other main crop types.

The inclusion of a sizable proportion of row crops and orchards in the habitat results in cleaner and more intensive farming without the profusion of water, good cover, and high quality grain food available to pheasants in the main rice belt. Also, the growing of hay and many other crops almost invariably has a sequel of interference with nesting and high pheasant mortality from mowing. The over-all effect of these factors usually is a pheasant population level considerably below that supported by the rice areas.

However, much of this area is moderately good pheasant habitat. Where land-use and farming practices provide plentiful irrigation water during the dry season, fair supplies of grain food, suitable nesting sites in waste areas and dry-farmed grain or other crops, and some cover throughout the year, ringnecks are plentiful. Their numbers usually vary directly with the balance among these vegetation types.

The only kill figures available for this type of habitat in the Sacramento Valley are from the cooperative hunting area near Meridian, Sutter County. Beans are the principal crop there, but some rice and dry-farmed grain are produced. Hunting pressures of 85-105 gun-hours per 100 acres produced bags of 6-10 wild cocks per 100 acres from 1950 to 1952. Lower pheasant populations in such regions result in less hunting pressure than in the main rice areas. In the Sacramento Valley, hunting pressure usually is proportional directly to the acreage of rice stubble open to hunting.

Adjoining regions of heavy-to-medium populations, the numbers of pheasants taper off to nothing through a wide variety of marginal habitat conditions. Irrigated areas that are cleanly and intensively farmed to row crops, orchards, and alfalfa rarely support appreciable numbers of birds. However, at least a few are found in almost any place where surface water is present throughout the summer on the floor of the Sacramento Valley. Similar light populations parallel watercourses back through dry-farming and pasture areas along the edges of the valley and into surrounding foothills.

Pheasants of the Delta

Medium quality pheasant habitat is found in the area forming a rough triangle between Sacramento, Stockton, and the northeastern tip of San Francisco Bay. The population there is, in reality, a southward extension from the rice belt, which terminates west of Sacramento.

Formerly this was an extensive marsh area surrounding the lower stretches and combined deltas of the San Joaquin and Sacramento Rivers. The marsh has been reclaimed, and now much of the region consists of islands bordered by high levees and separated by river channels and sloughs. Heavy growths of willows, cattails, and tules border the waterways or occur on small islands in the larger sloughs. Rainfall of about 15 inches is sufficient to produce good cover on the levees.

The islands vary from a few hundred to 10 or 15 thousand acres in size. Their muck and peat or clay and clay-loam soils are productive, and most of the islands are farmed intensively. Some vegetable farming is done, with asparagus, tomatoes, potatoes, and celery the principal truck crops. Larger acreages also are devoted to alfalfa, barley, beans, field corn, milo, and sugar beets.

These agricultural conditions, in conjunction with plentiful permanent cover and water, furnished by river channels and sloughs, support moderate numbers of pheasants, and in favorable years, produce high local concentrations. Barley, corn, and milo furnish a fair supply of grain feed. Dry-farmed barley augments favorable nesting cover on ditchbanks and levees. Weedy cornfields also supply excellent cover, as do fields of perennial asparagus following the early summer harvest.

It is difficult to obtain a high pheasant harvest in this region because of heavy cover along waterways, and the ease with which birds move from one island to another to escape hunters. Many entire islands, or portions thereof, are closed to the general public, and trespass is minimized by moat-like channels with few bridges or ferries.

Hunting pressures on open lands in the Delta usually are heavy, averaging approximately the same as in the Sacramento Valley rice belt, due to the nearby population centers of Sacramento, Stockton, and the San Francisco Bay area (Table 12).

Harvests of cocks on cooperative hunting areas in this region, reflected in Table 12, have averaged from 7 to 11 per 100 acres from 1949 to 1952, or approximately 70 to 80 percent of the bag taken per unit of area in the rice belt. In 1952, four of the five cooperatives in the Delta produced kills of 9 to 15 wild cocks per 100 acres, which were equal to rice belt pheasant harvests in that year.

TABLE 12. Kill and hunting pressure on controlled hunting areas in the Delta Area, 1949-1952.

Year	Number of Areas	Acres Hunted	Wild Cocks Bagged per 100 Acres			Season Gun-hours per 100 Acres		
			Highest Area	Lowest Area	Weighted Average	Highest Area	Lowest Area	Weighted Average
1949	1	7,500	11	11	11	232	232	232
1950	2	19,402	8	6	7	165	162	164
1951	3	27,268	8	5	7	205	112	142
1952	5	45,036	15	2	9	197	103	136

To the east of the Delta is an extensive area supporting lower numbers of pheasants. Agricultural and habitat conditions are similar basically to the poorer ranges of the Sacramento Valley where orchards, row crops, alfalfa, and dry-farmed grain predominate. Scanty distribution of permanent water in summer, as a result of irrigation from wells instead of canal systems, is believed to limit pheasant numbers where the habitat appears favorable otherwise.

San Joaquin Valley habitats

South of the Delta, pheasant populations decline abruptly to the light category. Distribution of ringnecks becomes spotty, and breeding populations of wild birds disappear before the lower end of the valley is reached.

Detailed studies of limiting factors have not been made in this region, but low rainfall and unfavorable agricultural conditions generally are believed to be basic.

The agricultural economy of most of the San Joaquin Valley is based on orchards, vineyards, barley, wheat, cotton, alfalfa, truck crops, and, in some localities, dairying and livestock. Farming is more intensive and cleaner than in the major pheasant producing areas of the Central Valley.

Rainfall is low, about 6-10 inches annually in most of that region, so that natural cover on non-cultivated areas is poorer, and dry-farming of grain entails risk of crop failure. Barley and wheat usually are flood-irrigated when grown on leveled land where water is available. Normal water-use includes pre-watering in the fall and one or two irrigations in the spring, during March and April. Thus, early pheasant nests in grain or hay crops in the irrigated areas are subject to flooding.

With few exceptions, water is less available to pheasants throughout the summer than in better habitat, being limited mainly to small acreages in rice, main irrigation canals, and the few natural water-courses that do not dry up in summer. Much irrigation is by pumping from wells, and supplies available to the birds over large areas may be intermittent or shifting constantly. There are local conditions in central and northern San Joaquin Valley, however, where heavy irrigation and more favorable farming practices support somewhat larger numbers of ringnecks. Low-to-medium populations occur in small areas near Merced and between Mendota and Gustine.

Some rice is grown where soils and water permit in this region, but not on the scale or under the conditions found in Sacramento Valley. Fields usually are leveled and have regular boundaries, so that there is little interspersion of tule-filled swales and sloughs with rice or other grain fields. Also, lower rainfall permits early-fall farming activities. Rice fields there are burned and worked up soon after the harvest and do not provide good winter habitat.

Bag checks on controlled hunting areas operated by the Department of Fish and Game have given indications of productivity in the region between Mendota and Gustine. The Firebaugh cooperative hunting area is located near the rice-growing center of the San Joaquin Valley, where main crops are irrigated barley and wheat, rice, and cotton. The checked kill in 1950 and 1951 was approximately two wild cocks per 100 acres under hunting pressures of 136 and 161

gun-hours per 100 acres. During these same years, the Los
Banos cooperative hunting area, where main crops were cotton, barley, alfalfa, dry-pasture, and sugar beets yielded three
wild cocks per 100 acres with gun pressures of 97 and 151
gun-hours per 100 acres.

Oakdale area

Some heavy pheasant populations comparable to those
found in the rice belt of the Sacramento Valley occur in the
northeastern San Joaquin Valley, in or near the undulating
terrain approaching the western base of the Sierras. Approximately 5 percent of the pheasants bagged in the state, and
about half of the total for this valley, are produced in parts
of Stanislaus and San Joaquin counties within about 15 miles
of Oakdale. The climate there is slightly cooler with a little
more rainfall than is found farther south. Maximum summer
temperatures reach 110° F. Some freezing weather occurs in
winter, but January temperatures average about 45°. Average
annual rainfall is approximately 11 to 14 inches.

Soils are predominantly alluvial and older loams formed
from ancient sedimentary deposits. A fairly shallow hardpan
prevents deep percolation of moisture and causes irrigation
water to drain and collect in low spots.

Principal land use throughout this region is irrigated pasture
for cattle and sheep, although there is a scattering of barley,
rice, alfalfa, corn (ensilage), dry pasture, orchards, and vineyards. The general aspect is one of low rolling hills or gently
undulating terrain covered with perennially green vegetation.
The small valley bottoms or swales typically have drain ditches
or poorly drained spots supporting beds or stringers of cattails,
Dallis grass, watergrass, and other aquatics that provide heavy
cover and some food.

Most pastures are planted to a mixture of ladino clover,
annual ryegrass, perennial ryegrass, orchard grass, and alta
fescue. Spots and fields in clover appear almost lawnlike, but
grasses attain waist height in particularly favorable sites and
furnish excellent bunchy or massed cover.

Some pastures temporarily offer good cover conditions resulting from weed invasion. This leads to spring mowing, however, usually twice, and causes some mortality and destruction of nests. A dense growth of foxtail *(Hordeum murinum)*, soft chess *(Bromus mollis)*, rip-gut grass *(Bromus rigidus)*, and other annuals provides good nesting cover on low hills, risers between fields terraced by leveling, some fencerows, roadsides, dry pastures, and other non-irrigated places. Occasional dry spots and dry border tops supporting this type of vegetation occur throughout the irrigated pastures as a result of imperfect control of irrigation water on rounded knolls and slopes and provide additional nesting sites with optimum moisture conditions.

Grain and grain hay in this irrigated region usually are prepared for irrigation in case it is necessary, but they are dry-farmed when there is sufficient rainfall to produce a good crop.

Water is plentiful and well-distributed throughout the year. Pastures are irrigated at 7-10 day intervals from early spring until late fall. Drain ditches carrying tail water, and low, poorly drained spots have surface water present throughout the year from irrigation or rainfall.

The food supply supporting dense pheasant populations in some localities of this general region is of interest. Crop examinations of 101 pheasants collected in an area almost entirely in irrigated pasture near Oakdale showed that ladino clover was the staple food (Leach *et al.* 1953). Leafage and flowers of this plant occurred in 85 percent of the crops, and comprised by volume from 8 to 49 percent of the food taken during different seasons of the year.

Other plants making up more than 5 percent of the food during any one season of the year were mannagrass *(Glyceria fluitans)*, ryegrass *(Lolium* spp.), chickweed *(Stellaria media)*, dotted smartweed *(Polygonum acre)*, annual bluegrass *(Poa annua)*, bristlegrass *(Setaria* spp.), barley *(Hordeum vulgare)*, barnyard grass *(Echinochloa crusgalli)*, and knotweed *(Polygonum* spp.).

Insects did not constitute an appreciable volume of food but were found in 49 percent of the crops. Insect life is abundant in the moist pastures and provides a plentiful supply of high-protein food necessary in the diet of pheasant chicks.

It is noteworthy that barley is the only grain in the above list. It made up about 17 percent of the diet in summer, when it ranked third behind ryegrass and mannagrass florets in the volume of food ingested. Grain evidently is not a highly important item of food there, although it undoubtedly is taken when available.

Thus, the dense pheasant population in this irrigated pasture area is an exception to the general rule that pheasants are abundant only where grain is available to provide the staple diet throughout much of the year. It is evident that the proper combination of clover, grasses, and weeds will provide a food supply adequate to support a heavy pheasant population, provided that winters are mild and other habitat conditions are favorable.

This type habitat is stable, which may have some bearing on the success of pheasants. One or two mowings of some pastures in spring, movement of livestock, and occasional ditch cleaning are about the only agricultural disturbances in irrigated pastures, other than occasional rotation to barley or some other crop. Birds can use adjoining grain or hay fields and still have cover when the grain fields are worked.

Hunting pressure in this area is light. The presence of large numbers of livestock and the network of fences cause property to be posted and patrolled, limiting hunting to landowners and their friends. It is evident that many more birds could be taken, but there seems to be little possibility that an area of this type can be opened to the intensity of hunting pressure that would result in an adequate harvest.

It appears that the extent of land leveling has considerable influence on pheasant habitat conditions. Steeper hills are not well adapted to irrigation, resulting in poor distribution of water and cover and less productive agriculture. On the other hand, well-leveled land frequently does not provide balanced habitat because of the lack of both high ground where nests are secure from flooding and poorly drained low spots that

PLATE XVI.—Irrigated pasture habitat near Oakdale, California. Nesting areas on dry knolls and levees *above and center*, and the heavy cover and open water of drainage ditches *below*, create favorable conditions for the ringneck (Chester M. Hart, California Dept. of Fish and Game).

provide heavy cover. Other extensive irrigated pasture areas on flat, well-leveled land in the San Joaquin Valley do not approach this region in production of pheasants.

Light and medium pheasant populations occur where those rather circumscribed areas merge with surrounding orchards, dry-farmed grain, dry pasture, or other agricultural conditions, with the decrease in pheasant numbers corresponding to the transition from good to marginal habitat. In some places the transition zone of medium-quality habitat is rather extensive, but frequently, as in the rice belt, there is an abrupt change from good to non-productive areas.

The irrigated pasture in this region, which has been developed during a recent pronounced trend in California agriculture, may be the forerunner of an ultimately large acreage in similar habitat. It appears that much of the rolling topography around the borders of the Central Valley eventually may be brought under irrigation as units of the great Central Valley Project irrigation system are completed.

Imperial Valley pheasants

A rich agricultural area surrounded by desert straddles the International Boundary between the United States and Mexico approximately 50 miles west of the Colorado River. Slightly more than half of this area, lying in California north to Salton Sea, forms the Imperial Valley. The southern extension in Baja California, Mexico, is the Mexicali Valley. Practically all cultivated land lies between sea level and 230 feet below. Small numbers of pheasants are scattered over most of this irrigated section, which is roughly 800,000 acres in extent.

The pheasant population there is of interest despite its low density because it probably is the southernmost establishment of these birds in North America.

Farming in the Imperial Valley is undoubtedly the most intensive to be found over any large area within the state. Mild winters permit production of crops throughout the year, with much of the economy of the valley based on winter vegetables. These and similar crops occupy only a small part of the total acreage, however. Most of the land is planted to alfalfa, flax, barley, wheat, sugar beets, milo, and sesbania. Fairly large acreages have been planted to cotton since 1951, but cotton growing probably will go out of the picture again with declining prices.

The varied, highly productive soils are of recent origin, geologically speaking, being derived mainly from alluvial or sedimentary deposits laid down by the Colorado River.

Abundant irrigation water is brought in from the river by canals and is distributed to cultivated land by a network of secondary canals. Crews employed by irrigation districts are at work continuously burning or spraying with oil and chemicals to keep these canals and drain ditches free of vegetation that might inhibit movement of water.

The first known liberations of pheasants in the Imperial Valley were by the Division of Fish and Game, in 1926. In 1926-1928, a total of 450 birds were planted. Stocking has been heavier in recent years, especially since 1948 when a new state game farm went into production in Imperial County.

The general failure of pheasants to become established in the southern part of the United States usually is attributed to climatic factors. Comparatively higher temperatures during the nesting season usually are associated with more southern latitudes, and recent experiments of Yeatter (1950) in Illinois show that hatchability of pheasant eggs decreases with temperature increase during the laying period. For these reasons, climatic conditions in this southern point of pheasant establishment are of more than usual interest.

The climate is decidedly hot and arid; summers are long and sunlight intense. Relative humidities are low but are increased locally by heavy irrigation. Warm, drying winds sweep in from the surrounding desert, especially in the spring. Rainfall is unpredictable and almost negligible, averaging about 3 inches annually (Table 13). Of course, Weather Bureau climatological data may not be representative of micro climates in which successful pheasant nesting may occur. This is true particularly in an irrigated area where there may be numerous spots with relative humidities adequate for nesting.

Difficulties encountered at the Brawley Game Farm are indicative to some extent of problems faced by pheasants in the wild. In 1949, standard game farm practices resulted in a hatch of about 25 percent, as compared to the usual statewide average of approximately 60 to 65 percent. During the storage and incubation of eggs, indoor temperatures reached 108° F., and incubator temperatures as high as 106° F. were noted.

TABLE 13. Ranges of climatic factors during and shortly preceding nesting season in Imperial Valley, California, 1945-1950 [1].

	Temperature Degrees F.		Relative Humidity [2] Average	Precipitation Total
	Average	Maximum	Percent	Inches
February	55-70	82-86	37-47	0.00-0.12
March	60-68	81-95	33-44	0.00-0.12
April	70-76	100-104	31-35	0.00-T
May	74-79	102-115	25-33	0.00-T
June	85-90	110-119	28-31	0.00-0.52

[1] From El Centro Naval Air Station near Seeley, California.
[2] Years of 1945, 1949, and 1950 only. These relative humidities were taken at a site not typical of locations where successful nesting may occur.

In 1950, the laying season was advanced artifically about five weeks into weather 10-15 degrees cooler. Starting in early February, the brood stock was forced with lights. Eggs were gathered three or four times a day to reduce exposure to daytime heat. Air conditioning was installed, and this maintained egg-storage temperatures at 67° F. and the incubator room near 74° F. The combined result of those measures was to increase the hatch to 59 percent. This leaves little doubt but that hot weather during the normal nesting season had been reducing the productivity of pheasants raised under artificial conditions.

Limited nest and brood studies in the Imperial Valley in 1950 provided little evidence that climatic conditions were hampering the reproduction of wild birds. Enough broods ranging in size from 6-10 were reported by reliable observers to indicate that many nests were fairly successful. It is evident from field investigations that the two main factors limiting pheasants to their present low numbers are (1) lack of suitable nesting areas, and (2) mortality due to alfalfa mowing.

Low rainfall is the basic reason for poor nesting conditions. The short, dense, herbaceous growth preferred by pheasants for nesting cover does not grow in this arid region without irrigation. Cover on ditchbanks and other waste areas consists mainly of a sparse growth of shrubby, drouth-resistant, desert-type plants. Thus, pheasants selecting cover for nesting almost always turn to cultivated crops. These, of necessity, are irrigated, mostly by flooding, so that many nests are destroyed or abandoned.

Most nest locations not likely to be flooded are vulnerable to other farming operations. The harvest of field crops is in progress throughout the nesting period, mainly April through June. All available evidence indicates that this harvest, and other farming practices, cause the destruction of approximately 80 percent of the pheasant nests. Because of the unusual conditions, there appears to be little possibility of changing this situation materially.

Some years, nearly 40 percent of the farmed acreage in the Imperial Valley has been in alfalfa. This is mowed for hay in spring and early summer and for dehydration into alfalfa meal from fall until early summer. The harvest for alfalfa meal continues 24 hours a day from October through May, and all clipping is by highspeed mowers, usually at 7-10 miles per hour. Many pheasants and other wildlife are killed. Night mowing is especially destructive, and losses throughout the year undoubtedly constitute a severe drain on the light population of pheasants.

Despite unfavorable conditions, the wild stock of birds in the Imperial Valley evidently has furnished from about 40 to 60 percent of the bag in recent years. Sample checks indicated that game-farm cocks made up 45 percent of the bag in 1949 and 58 percent in 1950. About 2,600 cocks were planted in 1949, while heavy botulism losses cut stocking to nearly 1,000 cocks in 1950. The total pheasant bag taken was estimated to be less than 1,500 in 1949, and not more than 1,100 in 1950.

The kill was believed to be greater in the Imperial Valley in 1951 and 1952, due mainly to heavier stocking and permitting hens to be taken. More than 7,500 pheasants were liberated in 1951, and nearly 9,000 in 1952. Hunters checked leaving the valley at the end of the second day of the 1951 season averaged slightly more than half a bird per hunter. The bag composition was: wild cocks, 28 percent; wild hens, 14 percent; banded cocks, 38 percent; and banded hens, 20 percent. After the hunting season, local sportsmen reported averaging 3.6 birds per hunter for the season, with a somewhat higher percentage of both banded and wild cocks in the bag. The actual bag check data indicated that hen shooting had increased the bag about 54 percent, while the probably less-accurate reports indicated the hen kill had made the bag 26 percent greater.

Comparison between pheasant habitats on the two sides of the Mexican border brings out the fact that highly efficient agriculture is not always good game management. In the Mexicali Valley, associated with less intensive and more primitive farming methods, pheasants have been moderately successful despite long open seasons, high bag limits, and market hunting.

Correlated with different economic conditions, the agricultural pattern of the Mexicali Valley differs strikingly from that on the American side. Crops are generally non-perishables grown for export. Cotton is the most important, with some winter barley, wheat, field corn, and milo as grain crops. Alfalfa is of minor importance.

South of the border, alfalfa is cut by horse-drawn mowers in many localities. There often is a growth of weeds, grasses, and volunteer grains in cotton fields. Waterways are not kept free from weeds and brush, and waste water is spread over waste and fallow fields, or collected by gullies, washes, and rivers. Fields are smaller and less regular in shape than on the California side, and frequent waste areas and fallow fields provide a more stable cover with greater interspersion of types.

Ringnecks have been established in this Mexican area for a long time, evidently much longer than in the Imperial Valley. Private individuals are known to have stocked pheasants, believed to have been imported from China, south of Mexicali in 1912. Residents state that the birds were established in the valley prior to 1922, and that market hunting for pheasants was in progress by 1929.

Pheasant hunting regulations in that part of Mexico have been lenient and poorly enforced. The open season has extended from December 1 to March 31, and either sex could be taken. There was no bag limit prior to the 1949-50 season, when a daily limit of 15 was established. The season was declared closed after the first 16 days of the 1949-50 season, but hunting continued.

The long seasons and generous bag limits south of the border attract American hunters to that region, but mainly for doves, quail, and waterfowl. Several hundred hunters declaring pheasants at the Customs Port in Calexico during the 1948-49 and 1949-50 hunting seasons averaged nearly two birds apiece, but many of the ringnecks were bagged while other game was being hunted. Hunters familiar with the area and who concentrate on pheasants frequently make sizable kills.

Several Mexican market hunters kill pheasants and other game here mainly for local restaurant trade. The prohibition against market hunting evidently is not enforced.

An accurate appraisal of the total pheasant kill in Mexicali Valley is difficult to obtain. A rough estimate of approximately 1,000 pheasants bagged per season was arrived at for the 1948-49 and 1949-50 seasons, based mainly on the number of pheasants declared by American hunters at the Calexico Custom Ports, and by what are considered to be fairly reliable reports on the activities of market hunters. No person contacted in the course of the investigation could remember ever killing or seeing a banded pheasant in this area, so there is no doubt that practically all of the pheasants bagged are wild birds produced locally. This kill has been from areas totalling not more than half the size of the Imperial Valley.

Thus, available evidence indicates that the production of pheasants in this nearby section of Mexico is greater per unit of area than in the Imperial Valley, under the conditions of hen shooting, practically no protection, and no stocking. This seems rather conclusive evidence that the numbers of Imperial-Valley pheasants are not limited solely by climatic conditions. The hot, dry climate possibly would determine a moderately low ultimate population level, but it is evident that this level has not been reached in the Imperial Valley and probably not in the Mexican area. There is little question that unfavorable farming practices and habitat conditions hold the birds to their present low level on the California side. It is surprising indeed, that pheasants can persist under these adverse conditions, rather than a puzzle as to why they do not increase.

Great Basin Pheasant Areas

California has two general sections which are related climatically and, to a certain extent, geographically with the Great Basin. These are (1) northeastern California, comprising the eastern portion of Siskiyou County, Modoc and Lassen Counties; and (2) the Owens Valley area, in Mono and Inyo Counties. In these two broad areas, habitats resemble similar valleys in eastern Oregon, Idaho, and Nevada. Elevations are above 4,000 feet mostly.

The valleys are surrounded by semi-arid, sagebrush-covered, mountainous lands and are subject to severe winter weather. Thus they differ markedly from other major pheasant habitats in California. Subzero winter temperatures are encountered yearly, and high winds are to be expected at all seasons. Precipitation is relatively light, with annual averages varying from 6 to 20 inches, which falls mainly as medium to light snows from October through March. Generally, in the part of the area occupied by pheasants, deep snows do not remain long. Occasional summer thunderstorms are to be expected, but they seldom supply much moisture or affect plant growth to any extent, since they almost always are followed by long periods of clear weather with low humidities.

The agricultural economy of these regions is based primarily on livestock in some areas, livestock and grain in others, and to a limited degree, diversified farming in such areas as

Tule Lake. Farming is less intensive than in the Sacramento and San Joaquin Valleys, and shrubby and annual cover is much more plentiful.

The relationships of pheasants to habitat conditions in these Great Basin areas have not been studied intensively, since the focus of recent pheasant investigations has been in the Sacramento and San Joaquin Valleys.

Highest populations tend to be in the areas having the greatest diversification of crops, with grain predominating. Such conditions are found primarily around Tule Lake near the Oregon border, and in part of Honey Lake Valley in Lassen County. Tule Lake is one of the important pheasant hunting areas of the state. Although it is relatively small, and is 8 to 10 hours travel distance by car from important metropolitan areas, it furnishes about 5 percent of the annual statewide kill.

As crops become less diverse and the local economy becomes dependent on livestock and grain, ringneck numbers trail off through medium to sparse. Light populations are found in livestock areas that grow hay for over-wintering, but where little or no grain is produced. Except for Tule Lake and parts of Honey Lake Valley, the northeastern part of this Great Basin complex supports only local hunting.

Owens Valley presents a special case worthy of summary treatment. That area, a long, narrow valley at about 4,000 feet elevation lying just east of the Sierra Nevada in Inyo County, was one of the first in the state to be stocked and had the first open season on pheasants. At present, however, its populations are of slight significance and the area is of interest chiefly for what is to be learned of the adjustments of its pheasant population to land use.

Prior to the mid-twenties, Owens Valley was an area of small ranches existing largely on a self-contained economy. Farming was diversified, with emphasis on grain and livestock. Even though precipitation is low, averaging about 6 inches annually in the valley itself, adequate water for all sorts of crops was available from streams and springs that arose in the high Sierra immediately to the west.

During the twenties, the City of Los Angeles acquired rights to nearly all water in the valley and diverted it through their aqueduct system for municipal use hundreds of miles away. This resulted in making a virtual desert of the major portion of Owens Valley, displacing both ranchers and pheasants. Significant pheasant populations have remained only in isolated spots, such as the vicinity of Bishop, and in other small farming areas that persist by virtue of adjudicated water rights or water that is not at present usable in the aqueduct system.

At present, there are no more than 17,000 acres of land in Owens Valley that is producing pheasants in the wild. Field checks made in 1949 showed that 500 hunters had bagged 176 pheasants, consisting of 65 percent wild and 35 percent game-farm birds. The total kill for the valley that year was estimated to be 650-700 pheasants.

In a similar check confined to the northern half of Owens Valley in 1952, 435 hunters checked had taken 315 pheasants, made up of 57 percent wild and 43 percent stocked birds. Heavier planting for the gun and increased rainfall, which had bettered habitat conditions, contributed to the higher success in 1952.

More complete hunting checks were made of an isolated area of 2,600 acres at Fort Independence in 1950 and 1951. The bag taken by 371 hunters in 1950 was 106 cocks, of which 77 were game-farm birds and 29 were wild. The same number of 106 birds, made up of 59 banded and 47 wild pheasants, was checked again in 1951, taken by 413 hunters. Plants of 300 and 310 cocks, respectively, were made before the two hunting seasons. The higher kill of wild birds in 1951 probably was a reflection of the break in drought conditions which had persisted in this area during the latter 1940's.

A study of crop contents collected in the Fort Independence area in 1950 revealed that the principal foods used during the fall were seeds of Johnson grass, wild millet, wild sunflower, and thistle. Little grain is grown in that locality.

Owens Valley has a great potential for sportsmen, and it and the surrounding mountains provide recreation to hordes of

PLATE XVII.—*Upper.* A few pheasants are found in meadowlands of this type, where some grain is grown, in mountain valleys of northeastern California (Chester M. Hart, California Dept. of Fish and Game). *Lower.* In Owens Valley near Bishop, where pheasants were first hunted in California. Both agriculture and the ringneck now are disappearing from the area (Chester M. Hart, California Dept. of Fish and Game).

trout fishermen and deer and quail hunters from the Los Angeles area. A tradition exists among the die-hards of those metropolitan Nimrods that Owens Valley still has good pheasant hunting, but few ever return to Los Angeles with the roosters in hand to prove it.

Of minor importance, but worthy of mention, are isolated occurrences of pheasants in some of the more level valleys of the Sierra Nevada. Those valleys are related to the Great Basin type but they generally are higher and have surrounding vegetation tending toward Canadian or upper transition life-zone types rather than to sagebrush. Precipitation is higher and winter snows deeper. However, generalities with respect to local crop conditions and their relation to pheasants remain the same; wherever weather is not too extreme, and grain is a part of the economy, there is a chance for a light pheasant population.

Coastal Pheasant Areas

Coastal habitats that support pheasants naturally are the least important of the three major classifications and furnish local hunting mostly. Pheasant populations are light and disappear gradually as one proceeds from the Oregon line to the Mexican border. The most important populations are in the vicinity of Eureka, Humboldt County—an area somewhat similar to pheasant habitats farther north in Oregon.

Weather of the Coast Ranges is characterized by wet, rainy winters and dry summers. Annual rainfall, most of which comes from October to March, varies from 40 to 50 inches near the Oregon line to about 10 inches near the Mexican border. Daytime humidities are low during late spring, summer, and early fall, except immediately adjacent to the Pacific Ocean.

The major factors influencing coastal pheasant populations evidently are (1) some type of grain economy, and (2) spring moisture from rainfall, unusual fog conditions, or irrigation. The drop in pheasant populations from north to south seems to be related to a corresponding decrease in rainfall.

Throughout much of the South Coast area, a great deal of

dry-farmed grain, both wheat and barley, is grown, but even though pheasants were planted widely, they have been largely unsuccessful.

Perhaps the best populations of ringnecks that ever existed in the Coastal types were in the Salinas and Santa Clara valleys, when those areas were primarily in grain production. Santa Clara County was one of the first to show any degree of success, but crops in the valley have changed from grain to orchards. Crops of the Salinas Valley to the south have been turned from irrigated or sub-irrigated grain to truck crops, or as one disgruntled pheasant hunter put it, "all salad and no solid."

Light numbers of ringnecks are found in remnants of old diversified grain farming types in these two valleys, and other similar areas in Coast Ranges, as shown on the distribution map. They are of little statewide importance, however. Those localities commonly have some kinds of grain crops, and higher than ordinary spring humidities.

Recent Trends in Pheasant Numbers

The question often arises as to how population trends in California fitted the national picture of pheasant depression in the middle 1940's. Unfortunately, the intensive pheasant research program in the state did not get under way until the end of World War II, hence there are only sketchy figures and impressions on which to base conclusions. Nevertheless, it appears that the widespread depression of the forties was not evidenced in California.

Within the three major habitat types, each of which extends nearly the length of the state, there are climatic differences which appear to preclude action as a unit by the various pheasant populations. In recent years, with more accurate observations on populations, important differences have been observed between areas; and those differences may be reversed in succeeding years.

The only evidence that might indicate a pheasant decline in the early forties was a general hunter dissatisfaction with the seasons of 1943 and 1944. Prior to those years, the daily bag limit on pheasants had been two birds. During '43 and '44, however, the limit for the opening day only was four birds and two birds for succeeding days. It is possible that much of the dissatisfaction stemmed from inability to fill the opening day's bag of four, which task was at least twice that of filling the previous year's opening-day limit of two. Aside from that rather doubtful evidence, there seems to be no reason to believe that California shared in the general pheasant decline. On the other hand, there are indications that fairly wide variations occur in the populations of California's major pheasant area, the Sacramento Valley, and that those fluctuations are independent of midwestern pheasant conditions—even independent of conditions in other pheasant habitats of California.

Information from checking stations, and state-wide hunter postcard questionnaires, indicated an extremely good pheasant harvest in 1948. The succeeding years of '49 and '50 saw a harvest of a third to half that of 1948 in the Sacramento Valley. This does not fit the pattern of the East and Midwest, nor does it fit conditions shown in California's second-best pheasant habitat in northeastern California, which produced a better crop in 1950 than in either of the two preceding years.

We believe that pheasant numbers in this state have no relation to the general rise and fall of pheasants in the North Central and Middle Western states. The populations appear to be an expression of local weather effects on agricultural practices, and on the nesting and hatching of the birds themselves.

MANAGEMENT

Until recently, California's pheasant management program has been limited to the stocking of birds. In 1949, a program was undertaken to improve farmer-sportsmen relations, and to increase the kill of pheasants being produced in the wild but not being adequately harvested. Problems within the state are magnified by the combination of roughly 200,000 pheasant hunters and only about 3,500 square miles of good-to-excellent pheasant habitat. Nearly all this area consists of highly productive, intensively farmed land, where large-scale habitat management generally is not practicable. Furthermore, the concentration of large numbers of hunters into the limited area of good pheasant hunting resulted in much of it being closed to the public because of trespass abuses and property damage. Improvement of that situation has been the main pheasant management problem in California, and excellent progress has been made.

Stocking Program

In terms of money expended and personnel employed, stocking game-farm pheasants has been and continues to be the main pheasant-management practice in California. Until recently, there was a steady trend to increase facilities and output, although, as in many other states, much of this expansion was not initiated by the Fish and Game Commission or the Department of Fish and Game. However, the facilities and production probably reached their ultimate peak in 1951. Since then, there has been a marked decline in the number of pheasants produced as well as some decline in the number of game-farm units producing them.

Game farm system

Present propagation facilities were started in 1925, with the construction of the parent plant at Yountville, a short distance north of San Francisco Bay. Over succeeding years, the system was expanded to a total of 14 plants (now 12), scattered from near the Mexican border to the northern end of Sacramento Valley. Table 14 presents pertinent data on the present status of state-operated game farms.

During nearly all the period from 1925 to 1946, game farms were administered by a separate bureau of the Division of Fish and Game. Placement of game farms under the Bureau of Game Conservation, and later under regional management, and the ensuing integration of facilities and personnel with

TABLE 14. California's state game farms in 1952 [1].

Unit [2]	Year Established	Area	Estimated Capital Investment	Regular Employees	Rated Capacity	Group Game Bird Capacity
YOUNTVILLE	1925	72 A	$100,000	14[3]	25,800	
Willows [4]	1938	5 A	18,000	2	6,000	
Sacramento	1938	3 A	16,000	2	6,000	43,800
Marysville	1948	11 A	25,000	2	6,000	
LOS SERRANOS	1929	29 A	57,000	6	8,000	
Castaic	1938	6 A	14,000	1	4,600	15,200
Valley Center	1938	8 A	14,000	1	2,600	
FRESNO	1938	20 A	40,000	6	8,000	
Bakersfield	1938	3 A	15,000	1	3,000	
Los Banos	1948	5 A	16,000	2	6,000	23,000
Porterville	1947	10 A	25,000	2	6,000	
CHICO	1948	12 A	44,000	5	6,000	
Redding	1938	14 A	38,000	2	6,000	12,000
BRAWLEY	1947	14 A	40,000	4	6,000	6,000
Totals		212 A	$462,000	50		100,000

[1] Revised from Gordon (1950).
[2] Names in capitals indicate base plants.
[3] Exclusive of 83 man-months of seasonal aid, equal to seven full-time employees.
[4] Willows and Bakersfield units discontinued in 1954.

other game management work, have been an important step toward combining and solving pheasant management problems.

Sums of money budgeted to operate game farms up to 1951 were larger than for any other game-conservation function, exclusive of law enforcement, and have aggregated from about 12 to 20 percent of the total fund (Table 15). Although game-farm employees assist in other management work, and some other game birds are produced, most of the propagation budget can be charged directly to rearing and liberating pheasants.

TABLE 15. California state game farm expenditures in recent years.

Year	Expenditures [1]
1945	$ 97,433
1946	135,248
1947	177,278
1948	224,900
1949	225,395
1950	218,451
1951	250,560
1952	250,355

[1] In addition the Wildlife Conservation Board spent $105,644 for game farm expansion from 1947 to 1950.

Annual production of pheasants has paralleled expansion of the game farms, except for the decreased production during World War II, and the erratic output prior to 1938 (Table 16). Annual output now is more than twice as great as the previous peak in 1942.

In recent years, about 20 percent of the birds have been reared from the age of 6 to 12 weeks in pen units of cooperators. These usually are operated by sportsmen's groups, which then may liberate 50 percent of the birds at sites of their own choosing. The remaining 50 percent are stocked at locations selected or approved by a representative of the regional fish and game manager. This program increased from its inception in 1931 to more than 1,400 pens in 1940, and recently there has been a movement to re-activate old pens abandoned during the war.

The exact cost per pheasant liberated has not been determined. The average cost from 1947 to 1951 varied from $2.25 to $2.33, based on direct operating costs with amortization of capital investments not included. This cost includes other game birds, but a high percentage of all birds propagated were Chinese or Mongolian ringnecks. The expense per bird planted went up to $2.60 in 1952, caused mainly by holding more pheasants until near the season to stock for the gun.

TABLE 16. Liberations of pheasants from California game farm system, 1926-1952.

Year	Number Liberated	Year	Number Liberated
1926	3,023	1940	25,370
1927	6,362	1941	35,919[1]
1928	6,697	1942	43,740
1929	6,648	1943	22,468
1930	7,211	1944	20,336
1931	11,434	1945	29,821
1932	6,651	1946	49,885
1933	7,246	1947	52,348
1934	10,646	1948	75,787
1935	4,456	1949	96,430
1936	9,314	1950	92,929
1937	3,700[1]	1951	107,697
1938	24,300	1952	94,868
1939	24,086		
		TOTAL	879,312

[1] Minimum numbers; records incomplete. All records prior to 1945 are subject to possible upward revision due to inconclusive records of releases from co-operating sportsmen's pens. Unless there was definite evidence of a planting release, birds given to sportsmen's pens are not considered as "liberated" in this table. (Figures before 1945 from Hjersman; from 1945 to 1952 from Bureau of Game Conservation Records.)

In recent years, the benefits and advisability of continued game-farm stocking have been questioned and investigated in most pheasant states. Action taken has varied, but leveling or decreasing trends of production are reported from the majority of states (Wandell 1949). Various sources of public opinion have given California's game administrators little discretion to adjust game-farm production to the economic or numerical level justifiable according to conditions here. Also, until recently there was little information positively applicable to California conditions upon which such adjustments could be based.

The purpose of a survey started in 1946, and completed early in 1951, was to determine the success of previous stocking by mapping pheasant distribution and relative density. The results showed that, in numerous areas, there should be no further attempts to establish breeding populations, unless there is a change for the better in habitat conditions. Although numerous highly productive liberations have been made, it is evident that the selection of many stocking sites resulted from wishful thinking or a misconception of what conditions constituted favorable pheasant habitat. By the time pheasants became well established in California, more birds had been stocked in areas that supported few or no pheasants than in the areas that afforded good hunting.

Intensive studies on the results of stocking reared birds were carried out from 1946 through 1949 on the Sartain and Mc-Manus experimental areas, in the rice belt between Colusa and Chico (Harper, Hart, and Shaffer 1951). Complete bag checks and collection of bands from large numbers of pheasants liberated and subsequently killed on these large areas gave positive results that had not been attainable by previous methods.

The results of all phases of this study emphasized the same conclusion: The most profitable stocking was that done immediately before the gun. Heavy stocking of hens for two years had no appreciable effect on the population or the kill on the Sartain Ranch. Also, stocking males for breeders was found to be unnecessary because adequate numbers of cocks remained in the field after intensive hunting. However, about 45 to 85 percent of the cocks liberated in this excellent habitat two months or less before the season were bagged by hunters.

Since most areas of suitable habitat in California had been stocked repeatedly for 25 years to establish or supplement breeding populations, it became evident that if game farms are to be continued, emphasis should be shifted now to stocking for the gun. This is expensive gunning, admittedly. It costs a lot of money to increase the total kill of pheasants in the state by even a small percentage. Where hens and cocks are liberated in equal numbers, and only cocks are taken by hunters, under the best conditions in California it costs a minimum of $8.50 to $10.00 to put one game-farm cock in the hunter's bag. Sexing to dispose of hen chicks may reduce the expense to around $5.00 per game-farm bird bagged. However, stocking in this manner probably is reducing this cost to a half or quarter of what it was in previous years. In addition, no cheaper method of increasing pheasant populations is known that will increase hunter success or the bag correspondingly on intensively hunted areas in California.

The information gained has been put into practice to utilize the large game-farm production to the greatest advantage for the hunters. The Fish and Game Commission has adopted policies to guide pheasant production and planting, first in 1948, and again in 1952, based on the previously mentioned fact-finding and evaluation of the game-farm program.

The 1952 policy emphasized stocking for the gun. Breeding stock was to be planted only where breeding populations appeared to be below the carrying capacity of suitable habitat, with not more than 2 percent of the game farm production for this purpose. State game farms were to concentrate on producing high-quality pheasants for shooting purposes and to stock them as near as possible to the opening of pheasant season. Public hunting areas open free to the general public were to have the highest priority for birds produced.

To forestall excessive demands for planting for the gun, and to keep such a program on a reasonable basis, a limit of 50,000 pheasants per year was placed on the future state game farm production. The number of birds to be furnished cooperating sportsmen's pens was not limited, so that total pheasant production probably will be around 75,000 annually. This will be a reduction of approximately 30 percent from the peak year of 1951, when 107,000 pheasants were planted.

The first-year results after starting to put the 1952 policy into effect appear significant. The over-all band return for cock birds increased from 25.6 percent in 1951 to 34.8 in 1952, while hen band returns went up from 11.6 to 14.1 percent. The actual take of stocked birds undoubtedly was much greater. Only about a third of the birds were stocked on controlled hunting areas where bands were collected, and voluntary band returns are notably incomplete. Although other factors, such as operating more cooperative hunting areas, contributed to this increased band return, planting more pheasants for the gun unquestionably put more birds in the hunter's bag.

Planting in this manner for the gun, on cooperative hunting areas where there is intensive hunting pressure, has yielded good returns and effectively bolstered the kill, as shown in Table 17. The smaller portion of the kill, 30 percent, made up by game-farm birds in 1949 was due partially to only 77 percent of the pheasants being stocked before the gun in November of that year. From 91 to 95 percent of the birds were planted in November in 1950 to 1952, which resulted in reared birds making up 39 to 50 percent of the bag on cooperative areas.

TABLE 17. Game-farm pheasant planting and contribution to the bag on cooperative hunting areas in California, 1949-1952.

Year	Acres Hunted	Pheasants Stocked		Percent of Bag Made Up of Game Farm Birds
		Total Number	Acres Per Bird	
1949	66,180	7,797	8.5	30
1950	119,902	13,021	9.2	47
1951	135,746	15,267	8.9	50
1952	154,000	19,688	7.8	39

Average returns by period of release on cooperative hunting areas, and on the Sartain experimental area, are given in Fig. 4. Actual practice for several years with large numbers of pheasants has shown that stocking shortly before or during the pheasant season will put 55 to 70 percent of the planted birds in the bag. Survival to the hunting season decreases as progressively earlier plants are made.

In continuation of the trend toward stocking for the gun, both hen shooting and sexing out hen chicks have been started to put a higher percentage of birds in the hunter's bag. Hen shooting has been permitted in the southern part of the state since 1951 to utilize these hens where their survival and reproduction are virtually nil. In northern California, where cocks only were taken prior to 1955, a sexing program was started to sell or dispose of day-old hen chicks. This eliminated

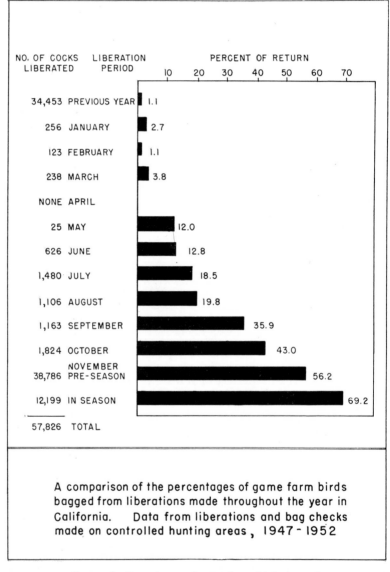

NO. OF COCKS LIBERATED	LIBERATION PERIOD	PERCENT OF RETURN
34,453	PREVIOUS YEAR	1.1
256	JANUARY	2.7
123	FEBRUARY	1.1
238	MARCH	3.8
NONE	APRIL	
25	MAY	12.0
626	JUNE	12.8
1,480	JULY	18.5
1,106	AUGUST	19.8
1,163	SEPTEMBER	35.9
1,824	OCTOBER	43.0
38,786	NOVEMBER PRE-SEASON	56.2
12,199	IN SEASON	69.2
57,826	TOTAL	

A comparison of the percentages of game farm birds bagged from liberations made throughout the year in California.   Data from liberations and bag checks made on controlled hunting areas , 1947 - 1952

FIGURE 4.—Percentages of game-farm birds bagged.

unnecessary and wasteful planting of hens where adequate breeding stock already was present in the wild, and made pen space available for holding additional cock birds.

As another step toward better survival, propagation of Mongolian pheasants was discontinued in 1949, after repeated stocking had failed to establish this subspecies anywhere in the state in competition with Chinese ringnecks. Also, wild breeding stock from the Sacramento Valley was introduced into local units of the game farm system. The survival of offspring from these wild birds was compared with the old game-farm stock by planting both types of birds, reared under the same conditions, on two controlled hunting areas in 1950. Results indicated that, when liberations were made in mid-summer, the wild stock would put 20-25 percent more birds in the bag. Consequently, breeders at the Chico Game Farm, and part of those at Yountville, are from this recently introduced wild strain.

Transplanting wild pheasants

Removal of surplus wild pheasants from refuges, or other areas not open to hunting, offers a source of birds for stocking that has been used experimentally in California and may be developed into a regular management program. Such a program was contingent upon first developing methods to capture sizable numbers of pheasants.

Conventional trapping methods gave poor results under the conditions of mild climate and plentiful food in the Sacramento Valley. Success was attained by the use of water and shade as lures to attract pheasants during the hot summer weather, and 467 pheasants were trapped on Gray Lodge Refuge in 1949. This was an average of approximately five pheasants per trap day, with catches at the better locations running considerably more.

Further attempts to refine trapping methods led to experimental work with the old system of "shining," or using spotlights at night, to capture pheasants. During the summer and fall of 1949 a total of 1,258 pheasants were caught in the

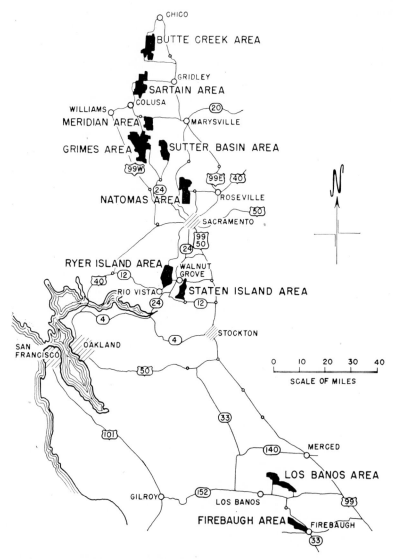

Figure 5.—California's coöperative hunting areas, 1950.

course of developing techniques and equipment for this method, and similar or greater numbers have been caught in succeeding years.

Experimental results indicated that wild pheasants caught in this manner cost less and survived better after transplanting than game-farm birds. Catching both cocks and hens by spotlighting in 1950 cost approximately $.50 per bird, while removing cocks alone from refuges cost about $1.60 per bird. Fifty-three percent of the 472 wild cocks removed from refuges and liberated on a controlled hunting area in 1949 were killed by hunters. This was nearly double the 29 percent band return from 599 game-farm cocks stocked on the same area during the same period (Harper, Hart, and Shaffer 1951).

The cost per cock bagged by the hunter from these releases was nearly $3.00 for the wild transplanted birds, compared with about $7.80 for game-farm birds, if the economic question of the equivalent number of game-farm hens raised is ignored. As long as considerable sums of money are spent for stocking, it is evident that at least part of this money will benefit hunters more if spent for transplanting wild pheasants instead of propagating birds.

Cooperative Hunting Area Program

Farmer-sportsmen relations reached a low point in the main pheasant producing areas of California shortly after World War II. Hunter numbers were nearly double those of prewar periods. Property damage increased, and the task of attempting to regulate hunting on large holdings was so great that it became a time-consuming nuisance to many landowners, in addition to expenses for posting and patrol. More and more land was closed to the general public, and each piece of property so closed made the hunting load carried on land still open that much greater. A vicious cycle was in operation.

In 1947 and 1948, a system of controlled hunting was used experimentally on a ranch west of Gridley. Checking stations operated by Division of Fish and Game personnel were established on roads leading out of the study area. In 1948, the Division was asked to issue written permits for hunting on

PLATE XVIII.—Above. Such an end awaits many a game-farm bird. Feral house cats killed most of these pheasants stocked in the rice belt (California Dept. of Fish and Game). *Below.* The best returns have been on birds held to the hunting season and stocked on heavily hunted cooperatives (California Dept. of Fish and Game).

the area to help relieve the landowner of the task of being host to thousands of hunters. The system worked well. Hunters were glad to gain access to excellent hunting, and property damage was negligible.

It was believed that such a system would be welcomed by other landowners, and would solve hunting problems facing farmers, hunters, and game managers. As a result, a bill was introduced and passed in the State Legislature in 1949 authorizing the Fish and Game Commission to establish cooperative hunting areas for upland game birds.

Provisions in the bill, and additional regulations, stipulated that minimum size would be 5,000 acres. The Division of Fish and Game was responsible for posting and patrolling to enforce the trespass provisions of the Penal Code and provisions of the Fish and Game Code. Zones closed to all hunting could be established to prevent property damage. Provision was made to restrict limited hunting areas for the landowners and their guests, or, in lieu of that, to reserve a number of hunting permits for the landowner. The balance of the area was open to hunting by the general public, under written permits, with a limited number of hunters allowed at one time. By mutual agreement, landowners or lessees could make a charge for hunting not to exceed $2.00 per hunter per day, with 25 percent of all money collected to be devoted to habitat improvement and maintenance. If a fee was charged, it was necessary that all landowners in the area agree upon this policy, appoint a single agent to act for them, and be responsible for issuing permits and collecting fees. The Division of Fish and Game was to issue permits where no fee was charged. As it turned out, a charge was made on only one of the areas.

In 1949, six hunting areas totalling more than 72,000 acres, with nearly 58,500 acres open to the general public, were operated in the Sacramento Valley and Delta region. The areas furnished more than 41,000 man-days of hunting, and nearly 13,500 pheasants were taken. A survey showed that 95 percent of the hunters, and all of the participating landowners, liked the plan (Harper, Metcalf, and Davis 1950).

PLATE XIX.—The spotlight crew catching pheasants (California Dept. of Fish and Game).

In the ensuing years, the program expanded steadily (Hart, Jones, and Shaffer 1951). Fifteen pheasant hunting units, comprising nearly 175,000 acres, were regulated by the Department in 1952. Nearly 66,000 man-days of hunting were expended on the areas, and a bag of 26,000 pheasants was taken. Approximately 20 percent of the state's pheasant hunters used the cooperative areas during the 1951 and 1952 seasons (Hart, Davis, and Myers; Metcalf 1953).

The cooperative hunting areas have been a marked success. Landowners have been relieved of the expense and trouble of posting and patrolling, and of the nuisance of being bothered at all hours of day and night. Property damage has been reduced materially. Hunter's have been permitted access to areas of good pheasant hunting, much of which was closed formerly, and they know ahead of time where they can go and be welcome to hunt. Operation of the plan by the Department of Fish and Game has improved farmer-sportsmen relations and, to a great degree, has solved California's most pressing management problem—that of obtaining hunter access to heavy but under-harvested pheasant populations.

Miscellaneous Practices

Other phases of pheasant management work in California are of relatively minor importance. Some have no place in this treatise, but recent predator control work, and methods used to obtain population and kill figures basic to management, are of sufficient interest to warrant brief discussions.

Predator control

Results of nesting studies in the rice belt of the Sacramento Valley indicate that certain types of predator control are beneficial in that area. From 1947 to 1950, when pheasant nesting studies were made on Gray Lodge Refuge, nest losses due to predation decreased as predator control work was intensified shortly before the nesting season (Table 18). The percentage of total predation caused by the principal species trapped also declined. Comparable studies were not made on similar areas where there was no predator control, but it is doubtful that

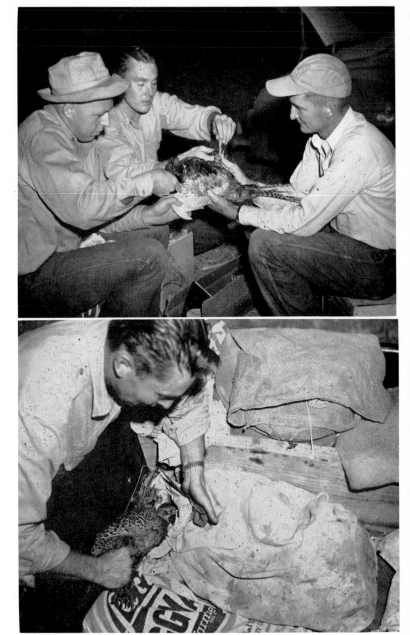

Plate XX.—Handling, wing-marking, and banding pheasants caught by spotlighting (California Dept. of Fish and Game).

nest predation would have decreased to that extent on such areas. Comparable studies were made in 1950 on the nearby Sartain Ranch, where some predator control is practised, and nest predation losses there were greater than on Gray Lodge Refuge.

In the rice belt, the combined density of skunk, raccoon, and feral house cat populations is high. The excellent pheasant habitat there also is to the liking of those important predators on pheasants and pheasant nests. Feral house cats alone may average more than one per 20 acres; one cat per 21 acres has been removed over a large area in the Sacramento Valley in the course of a year.

A food-habits study of cats in this region showed that about a fifth of the stomachs collected year-round contained pheasant remains (Hubbs 1951).

TABLE 18. Apparent effect of intensive predator control on pheasant nesting success, Gray Lodge Refuge, California.

| | | Gray Lodge Refuge | | | Sartain Ranch |
	1947	1948	1949	1950	1950
Total nests found	90	204	422	271	120
Nests destroyed	40%	30%	14%	28%	47%
Nest destruction due to skunks, raccoons, and house cats	97%	84%	47%	54%	63%
Predators taken					
House cat	Light trapping;	49	82	31	..
Raccoon	number unknown	17	25	23	..
Skunk		15	9	26	..
Total		81	116	80	

In this region, the carrying capacity of pheasant habitat during summer and fall evidently is approached only, if ever, during years of exceptionally good nesting success and brood survival. Thus, any increase in the nesting success, or survival of pheasants, that can be attained by local, intensive predator control, will mean that many more birds to hunt.

For that reason, intensive predator control programs are

PLATE XXI—The pre-dawn line-up *above*, and issuing hunting permits *below*, at the checking station, Sutter Basin Cooperative Hunting area (California Dept. of Fish and Game).

being conducted on the Department of Fish and Game refuges and waterfowl management areas shortly before the nesting season, and some cooperative hunting areas are being trapped and hunted in a similar manner.

It is doubtful that the expenditure of large sums of money specifically for this purpose would be economical. However, the Department of Fish and Game maintains a staff of about 35 hunter-trappers whose principal duties are controlling predators and trapping and transplanting beaver. This probably is the most beneficial work these trappers can do during late winter and early spring when snow inhibits work at high elevations. Private trappers have provided practically no check on skunk and raccoon numbers in the main pheasant areas of California in recent years because of the low price of long-haired furs.

The annual accounting

Attempts to estimate the population level of pheasants in California have been limited to studies on sample areas, or to estimating the total kill through hunter interviews and questionnaires. The present system of setting hunting seasons and bag limits in January precludes obtaining an index to pheasant numbers after the breeding season and then recommending appropriate annual hunting regulations.

The main census method used in investigation work has been the calculation of pheasant numbers by sex ratio and kill data in formulas presented by Kelker (1940, 1944) and similar to those of Allen (1942), Riordan (1948), and Petrides (1949). This method has been applicable especially to the type of study made, since determination of sex ratios before and after hunting season, and the complete bag taken on limited areas, already were objectives of the study. Results have agreed closely with population totals calculated by use of band returns from wild pheasants marked shortly before the hunting season.

These census methods do not give results until after the hunting season. Recent pre-season estimates on limited areas have been obtained by capturing and marking a sample of the

PLATE XXII.—Successful hunters, Sutter Basin Cooperative Hunting Area, 1949 (California Dept. of Fish and Game).

wild pheasant population with conspicious markers of the type originated by Taber (1949). Ratios of marked to unmarked birds counted then are used in the simple proportion of the Lincoln index to obtain population estimates.

The main use of crowing counts has been to convince sportsmen and farmers that all cocks have not been killed in certain areas during the hunting season and that adequate numbers remain for breeding stock. This is a perennial task, even though roosters still are plentiful, after hunters have had a difficult time bagging the wary cocks and see plenty of hens, or the large winter flocks of hens are seen by sportsmen or farmers. One farmer of Italian ancestry, evidently familiar with turkeys, quaintly expressed this viewpoint when he insisted that the cause of low pheasant numbers in his locality was "Not enuf a da gobble."

The results of counts to determine the average brood size, and the percentage of hens successful in rearing broods, have been used to predict general hunting season success, but such studies have been made mainly to obtain basic production data and life-history information.

Other methods of obtaining pre- and post-hunting sex ratios have been discarded in favor of flush counts made by working through heavy cover in midday. Early-morning and late-evening airplane counts of pheasants feeding in open fields have given accurate sex ratios and a general index to pheasant abundance. However, successful use of this method is limited to periods of good weather in late winter and early spring when cover is at a minimum.

Estimates of the total kill of pheasants in the state have been obtained by the questionnaire and interview methods for a period in the 1930's, and since 1948 (Table 19).

TABLE 19. Calculated total pheasant kill in California for 1935 to 1938 and 1948 to 1952[1].

Year	Reported Kill	Corrected Kill	Source
1935	......	66,000	Game kill questionnaires filled out with application for license
1936	......	80,000	
1937	......	80,000	
1938	......	125,000	
1948	559,100	232,000	Opinion Research Center interview survey
	586,100	234,000	Regular game take postcard survey
1949	381,390	153,000	Special pheasant take postcard survey
	388,700	155,000	Regular game take postcard survey
1950	416,000	166,000	Regular game take postcard survey
1951	533,700	213,000	Regular game take postcard survey
1952	573,000	229,000	Regular game take postcard survey

[1] Kill figures for the two periods were obtained by different methods and, therefore, may not be comparable. Data are from Hunter and Fry (1941) and Hjersman (1951).

The checks that could be made on the validity of these reports indicated that in recent years they all were exaggerated from approximately 141 to 164 percent (Hjersman 1951). Hence, reported kills have been corrected by factors obtained from comparing known figures with the corresponding figures calculated from the reports of hunters.

The corrected figures may represent a fairly accurate estimate of the total bag for the state, and either the corrected

PLATE XXIII.—*Above*. The bait in this California pheasant trap was—water. The principal losses were caused by the clawing of jackrabbits (California Dept. of Fish and Game). *Below*. Visible plastic markers enable research workers to recognize and follow movements of individual pheasants in the field (California Department of Fish and Game).

or original figures are useful in showing the trend of kill. They indicate recent peaks of kill in 1948, and 1952, and that the bag since 1947 may have averaged about double that in the years 1935 to 1938. This gain in kill probably has been due more to a growth of hunting pressure than to an increase in pheasant numbers, but presumably it has resulted from both factors.

The reported kill by counties has helped to establish the relative importance of the various areas of pheasant habitat and has substantiated other evidence that the Sacramento Valley rice belt is by far the most important pheasant producing region of California (Table 9).

Private Pheasant Management

In recent years there has been a considerable increase in pheasant management activities by private individuals or organizations. Chief among these has been the operation of various types of hunting areas.

Licensed shooting preserves

An act authorizing private "game management areas" was passed by the State Legislature in 1939, and became part of the Fish and Game Code. The motive behind this legislation was to increase pheasant and quail populations on private lands by encouraging the improvement of habitat conditions and private stocking of game-farm birds. Special provisions were made for longer seasons and larger bag limits on licensed, regulated areas to enable hunters to harvest part of the increased supply of game, with the landowner permitted to charge for the privilege of shooting pheasants or quail in his improved coverts. Basically, the plan was similar to the shooting-preserve system operated previously in the eastern part of the United States and Europe. Proponents of this measure believed that the additional income realized from the game crop would be an incentive to the farmer to manage his land to produce more game.

During the ensuing years, operation of this system for pheasant hunting has been essentially as follows: Private lands approved as suitable pheasant habitat by the Department of Fish and Game could be licensed for a fee which has varied from $10.00 to $50.00. Subject to a 6-bird daily bag limit, and a 50- to 108-day season, hunters on these areas were permitted to shoot pheasants until the total bag was equivalent to 70 or 80 percent of the number of game-farm birds stocked privately. Any pheasant on the area, cock or hen, wild or domestically reared, was legal game. Special shooting credit, equivalent to 225 percent of that allowed for summer and fall-stocked birds, was given for pheasants liberated in the spring as potential breeders. Various minor regulations, such as standards for quantity and quality of birds stocked, mandatory use of trained retrievers, maintenance of records and sub-mission of reports, etc., were established as conservation meas-ures or to insure the prescribed operation of the areas.

Soon after its inception, the plan was opposed strongly by many sportsmen, mainly on the ground of special privilege. Proponents of the plan countered with supporting arguments, and the controversy was continued through the years. The Legislature has reviewed and amended the original law many times. Between sessions of the State Legislature, the Fish and Game Commission has controlled the program within the limits established by the law. Although the general trend of regulation has been restrictive, the basic concepts of the orig-inal law have remained unchanged.

An early change in the law required that all areas be open to any licensed hunter, for a limited charge, as long as the authorized take for the area had not been reached. This pro-vision made control of hunting on the areas virtually im-possible, and practically did away with private areas and profitable regulated shooting areas. The trend that followed is shown by the data for 1940-43 in Table 20, although part of this decline was due to various difficulties of operation during the war years.

In 1947, the Legislature revised the law to approve non-com-mercial areas where no charge was made for shooting. Since that time there has been a steady increase in stocking, kill, and hunting on the non-commercial shooting preserves (Table 20), and commercial shooting areas, open to all hunters, have faded out of the picture.

Areas which actually are semi-commercial or commercial operate freely under the non-commercial regulation. The non-charge provision is evaded by forming clubs and selling season memberships which entitle the members to hunt on a licensed preserve and bag a prescribed number of birds. The membership fee usually is dependent upon the number of birds that may be killed, averaging $6.00 to $7.50 per bird for most clubs in recent years. There has been a considerable increase in such operations by private game-bird breeders to insure a market for their pheasants.

TABLE 20.   Private game management area trends in California.

Year	Number of Areas	Total Acreage	Birds Stocked	Total Kill	Man-Days Hunted
1940[1]	18	70,318	7,008	2,369	1,052
1941[1]	21	53,447	8,750	4,480	1,617
1942	15	37,311	5,713	3,797	2,055
1943	11	32,946	3,927	2,124	887
1947	25	32,828	7,337	3,896	1,919
1948	47	61,954	13,761	10,080	3,897
1949	43	44,556	20,720	11,539	5,446
1950	57	46,613	27,354	13,939	5,748
1951	63	53,403	32,127	19,855	9,069
1952	67	58,541	38,441	25,648	11,250

[1] Some quail and combination quail and pheasant areas are included for these years.

The long season and large bag limit of either sex permit an efficient harvest of the pheasants. In 1950, the ten preserves leading in kill per unit of area, totalling nearly 8,000 acres, reported taking an average of approximately 70, and as many as 120 birds, per 100 acres. The kill of wild pheasants alone on those areas averaged nearly 50 per 100 acres, with a maximum of 86. On the whole, wild birds have provided 50 to 75 percent of the kill in recent years. Hen pheasants usually have made up 50-60 percent of the bag.

Analyses of their kill records, and band returns, show that the privately stocked pheasants have given low returns and have constituted only a minor percentage of the total bag. From 1948 to 1950, about 12 to 18 percent of the pheasants stocked were re-taken on the game management areas, and volunteer band returns from surrounding lands added about 1 percent to the total. These birds comprised up to 35 percent of the total bag taken on the preserves. The net contribution made by privately stocked pheasants to the hunting in surrounding areas seems to have been a little significance.

A review of the operation of the game-management-area plan over an 11-year period reveals little similarity between the original intent of the law and what it has accomplished. The incentive for a farmer to produce game as a crop has been lacking. The high-quality pheasant habitat, where most of the game management areas are located, usually cannot be improved measurably without interfering with farming practices. In most cases, the landowners are comparatively wealthy, and the money that they could derive from such game management activities would represent only an insignificant addition to their incomes. Frequently, their participation in the program, either by managing private areas, or allowing others to operate on their property, is solely for the additional hunting privileges that they and their friends may enjoy. In the few cases where actual cash payments are made for pheasant shooting rights, the landowners usually receive one dollar or less per acre. The control of hunting trespass, which becomes the responsibility of the area operator, obviously has been the outstanding value of this plan to the landowners.

A few private game-bird breeders and licensed shooting preserve operators have benefited financially by this system of hunting. Those Nimrods who are able to foot the bill have had the privilege of enjoying high bag limits and long seasons in which to hunt and work their dogs. The actual number of hunters using these areas is small.

The various inspections and administrative work connected with the regulation of the private game management areas have caused this to become no small management problem. Considerable unwarranted criticism of the plan has been directed toward the Fish and Game Commission by poorly informed sportsmen, much of it stemming from the unfortunate misnomer of those private or commercial shooting preserves as "game management areas."

The law was enacted before present knowledge of the poor survival of game-farm pheasants in California became known, and before the high cost of the benefits derived from continued stocking was realized. The Act was based on the premise that all game-farm pheasants liberated in good condition in suitable habitat would survive and reproduce, a conception now known to be incorrect. In the past few years, good information has been obtained that is pertinent to California conditions, but as yet acceptance of those data by all factions involved has not been complete enough to use it as a basis for devising biologically sound regulations.

Compromise regulations for this plan, agreed upon by all interested parties, were put into law by the 1951 session of the State Legislature. A minimum season of 75 days was allowed, and some of the objectionable features were improved. The credit given for spring stocking was eliminated. Instead, higher shooting quotas were given for pheasants liberated during or shortly before the hunting season, with the requirement that at least half of the birds be planted during that period. License fees were increased, regulations were revised to permit the successful operation of commercial areas, and the name was changed to "licensed game-bird clubs." Also, in order to obtain more information for use in formulating future regulations, a special study was initiated.

In part as a result of these studies, the Legislature made an even greater modification of this basic law in 1955. The new provisions zone the state according to habitat conditions. In areas of non-pheasant habitat the preserves can be no liability to wild birds and hence may be largely unrestricted. In areas of good pheasant range, restrictions on the clubs have been increased.

Community and club hunting areas

In addition to the licensed game-bird clubs specifically provided for in the Fish and Game Code, sportsmen's clubs and communities have operated charge areas for hunting pheasants. Those organizations have obtained exclusive pheasant-hunting rights on large tracts of land, which have been used as inducements in the selling of memberships.

Controlled shooting areas operated by communities in California were started in 1949. The little town of Maxwell led off in this venture, to obtain money to build a community swimming pool. The financial success enjoyed by that association led to its continuation, and prompted other communities to follow suit. The movement has grown until it has developed into the largest controlled shooting program in California. Eleven areas of this type, totalling 225,000 acres, were operated in the Sacramento Valley rice belt in 1952.

The purpose of the controlled shooting areas has been comparable to similar plans in operation 20 years ago in Ohio, and at times in various other states. Non-profit organizations are created and landowners are requested to donate pheasant-hunting rights on their lands. Memberships with hunting privileges are sold, usually at the rate of $7.50 for the season, with $1.00 fees for wives or children of members, and the profits are spent on some community project.

The plan opens large blocks of land to controlled shooting that could not be included in state-operated areas. Part of the land probably would not be available for public hunting under any other system. Property damage and nuisances to landowners have been reduced and farmer-sportsmen relations improved. Hunting is made available to many sportsmen who are willing to pay a low fee, and who want less crowded hunting conditions than they find elsewhere.

A less desirable feature of this system of controlled shooting is that comparatively few hunters can be accommodated for the large acreage tied up. Hunters won't pay for crowded hunting and low success, so the continuing, profitable operation of those areas is contingent upon limiting the season membership to a number considerably less than could be handled safely on non-charge areas of similar size.

The Pheasant Management Potential

California's pheasant management program for the foreseeable future probably will continue with emphasis on cooperative hunting areas and stocking to supplement the bag. However, there are good possibilities for exploration and development of the phase of management which remains practically untouched in the state—improving habitat.

This can be accomplished most effectively on state-owned lands where game management is of primary consideration. The greatest immediate opportunity in this field is offered on multiple-purpose waterfowl public-shooting grounds, the problem being to harvest the maximum number of pheasants consistent with the waterfowl program. The Honey Lake Waterfowl Management Area in Lassen County has been making an important contribution to pheasant hunting in that region, and other similar areas can help carry the pheasant-hunting load.

It may be possible also to improve or stabilize cover conditions on privately owned lands. There is a trend toward cleaner and more intensive farming in much of California's better pheasant habitat. Leveling land and filling sloughs and swales inevitably results in reduction of permanent cover and edge. Coupled with the normal farming practices of burning and plowing, the loss of these stringers and islands of waste land often causes temporary but important deficiencies of cover over widespread areas. A cover management program on levees and ditch banks owned by the state or reclamation and irrigation districts would help to remedy this situation in many places. Also, it may be feasible to purchase or lease key areas of privately owned waste land to stabilize cover in pheasant habitat where farming practices make cover conditions critical.

Accompanying or following the general trend toward controlled shooting areas undoubtedly will come a desire to improve the hunting in those places. The interest of landowners and other persons in community-welfare projects probably will cause those individuals to become more receptive to suggestions about slight changes in farming practices that will benefit pheasants. This indirect method of habitat management by informing landowners and other interested individuals or organizations possibly will become much more practical and important in coming years.

There are other possibilities for habitat management in the Great Basin type of northeastern California, where winters are severe and raising livestock is the major agricultural activity. Correcting deficiencies in winter cover, nesting cover, or high-quality food may increase pheasant populations substantially in many parts of this region.

Portions of the central and northern San Joaquin Valley appear to offer potentialities of being made better pheasant habitat by developing permanent water supplies, and by improving cover for nesting. The creation of summer shade may pay dividends in some localities.

In summary, pheasant management in California may develop in the future along the following lines: the trend toward controlled shooting areas undoubtedly will continue in the better pheasant habitat of the Central Valley, until much of this area has regulated pheasant hunting of some type. The pheasant cooperative hunting areas operated by the Department of Fish and Game will be increased somewhat, but that program seems to be nearing physical limitations that will prevent much additional expansion.

There probably will be an increase in the management work aimed at increasing or maintaining the yield of wild pheasants, mainly on public shooting grounds or other controlled hunting areas where harvest of the pheasant crop is assured. As habitat management and other phases of management work become more practicable there may be a gradual shift in the channeling of funds from game farms into more promising management practices that will give the hunter greater benefits for the funds expended.

CHAPTER 4

PHEASANTS IN THE ARID SOUTHWEST

By LEE E. YEAGER, JESSOP B. LOW AND HARRY J. FIGGE

EXCEPT on cultivated land along some of the watercourses, the Southwest, and indeed much of the West, was not pheasant country until the advent of irrigation. Consequently, ringneck production in this region is considered best in terms of the ecology and economics of some 6,000,000 acres of artificially watered land. The remaining 358,000,000 acres, except for a limited area of dry-farmed wheat, seem destined to remain without pheasants.

In the Beginning

The story of the ringneck in the arid Southwest is one of high success or deep disappointment, depending upon locality. In Utah and Colorado, the species is well established; in Nevada, New Mexico, Arizona, Oklahoma, and Texas, the going has been uphill and discouraging to game men and sportsmen alike.

Unofficial records indicate that pheasants first were introduced into New Mexico in 1872, and into Colorado in 1875. Both plantings were unsuccessful. The 1875 plant in Colorado seems to illustrate the appeal of this gaudy bird to hunters; of the two hens and one cock released, the male and one hen were "poached" on the day liberated. These birds, therefore, were not the ancestors of present-day pheasants in that state.

The earliest authentic records of pheasant introductions in the Southwest relate to Colorado in 1885, Utah in 1898. Other states soon followed. Oklahoma began to stock pheasants in 1909; Arizona started its program in 1912; New Mexico in 1916. Citizens of Nevada became interested in this species and made a few releases prior to 1917. The last state in the arid Southwest to initiate pheasant stocking was Texas, in 1939.

In the first releases, the number of birds usually was small, due to the difficulties and expense involved. Utah's first release was 50 ringnecks from a Mr. Walker's personal game farm in Cottonwood Canyon near Salt Lake City. Other people raised pheasants as a hobby and turned out the surpluses. Colorado stocked 24 cocks and hens on four separate sites in the first successful introduction. Most states, however, have no record of the numbers involved in early releases.

After initial introductions, there was a rapid spread of the idea of artificially propagating pheasants. Shortly after the turn of the century, pheasant success in Utah created such enthusiasm that the Fish and Game Commission asked the Legislature for an appropriation for a game-bird farm. Repeated requests were denied until 1922, when authority and funds were provided for the Springville Farm. Continued demand led to its enlargement and, in 1944, to the building of a second farm at Price. From those establishments, and temporary facilities, the rearing of birds increased from a yearly production of about 8,000 in 1940 to a maximum of 28,000 in 1948.

Studies from 1943 to 1946 showed the relatively low return of such birds in hunters' bags (Low 1948). This, coupled with a demand for the use of farms for other game birds, is expected to result in a decrease in pheasant rearing in the state. In 1951, only one of the two hatcheries produced pheasants.

Nevada started raising pheasants artificially as early as 1922 and, since 1945, has maintained a state game farm. Colorado, New Mexico, and Arizona also have game farms producing this species.

Early pheasant stocking met with success in some states and failures in others. Utah and Colorado were among the former. By 1914, 16 years after the first introduction in Utah, pheasants were causing crop damage. Even before that, birds were trapped from concentration areas and released where they could not damage crops. The first known releases in Nevada, Arizona, New Mexico and Oklahoma were reported as unsuccessful, and despite repeated liberations, population increase has been slow. The suitability of certain local areas for the pheasant is manifest, however, in the rapid build-up of shootable populations.

In regard to recent trends, there was little evidence of a general pheasant depression in this region during the 1940's. Colorado experienced a decline in 1949 and a recovery in 1950, with no changes noted earlier. In Utah, the highest population generally was conceded to be in 1942, after which a decline occurred. This was in line with trends in the eastern half of the country. Similar, also, is the recovery that appears to have been made in the last 3 or 4 seasons. It must be emphasized, however, that local conditions appear to be highly important in determining pheasant numbers in the arid Southwest.

Distribution and Numbers

Introduced into the Southwest a little more than half a century ago, the ringneck has experienced some notable ups and downs. Its heyday here, as in other regions, was during the early forties. It still is the number-one species among feathered game in Colorado and Utah, and of varying interest elsewhere in the region.

Pheasant distribution in the Southwest, and a rough indication of density, are given in Fig. 6. The most striking feature of this pattern is the close association of inhabited areas with stream courses and, therefore, irrigated land. This association is so characteristic that, for practical purposes, land under irrigation (Table 21) can be considered to be the productive pheasant range.

Of course, some irrigated land in the Southwest is not entirely inhabited by pheasants, the most noticeable instances being in Arizona, New Mexico, and Texas. There, evidently due to environmental shortcomings, pheasants fade out in an irregular pattern. Moisture-temperature relationships and land-use practices that severely reduce cover and food seem to explain the lack of success of the ringneck in the south and south-east portions of the region.

An appreciable acreage of dry-farmed wheat land in eastern Colorado carries a well-established pheasant population. That area is somewhat larger than the total of irrigated land in that state. The ringneck, likewise, is becoming important in some dry-farmed sections of Utah, notably Box Elder County. This is not true generally, however, and the statement holds that occupied pheasant range in the Southwest roughly is equal to the irrigated area. Table 22, based on present and potential irrigated land, together with Fig. 6, indicate the small proportion of the various southwestern states constituting actual or potential pheasant habitat.

TABLE 21. Irrigated land area in the Southwest, present and potential.

State	Area, square miles		Percent	
	1945[1]	Potential[2]	1945	Potential
Arizona	1,150.0	2,465.6	11.4	13.0
Colorado	4,216.5	7,869.2	42.0	41.4
Nevada	1.8	99.5	....	0.5
New Mexico	1,053.4	1,665.0	10.5	8.8
Oklahoma [3]	835.4	1,704.4	8.3	9.0
Texas [3]	1,031.4	1,802.7	10.3	9.5
Utah	1,756.4	3,382.7	17.5	17.8
Total	10,044.9	18,989.1	100.0	100.0

[1] Census of Agriculture, 1945, as given in U. S. Dept. Agr. Misc. Publ. 670 (1948), p. 9.
[2] National Resources Board, Land Available for Agriculture Through Reclamation, 1936, as given in U. S. Dept. Agr. Misc. Publ. 670 (1948), p. 9.
[3] Panhandle region only as determined by pheasant distribution.

The limited extent of such habitat is in contrast to conditions in such states as South Dakota and Nebraska, where two-thirds or three-fourths or more of the land area is pheasant-occupied range. In the over-all hunting picture, therefore, the pheasant does not, and never will, represent more than a small portion of the game harvested in the Southwest.

In the Southwest, continuous pheasant populations are found only in eastern Colorado, the principal concentration being along the South Platte River from Denver to the Nebraska line. This area may be regarded as the western-most extension of the grain-belt pheasants, for there, as in Kansas, Nebraska, and the Dakotas, wheat, barley, corn and oats are the main crops. The pheasant population in this grain-growing section of Colorado is of long standing, vigorous, and firmly established. The birds are doing well, even in the presence of a gradual reduction of cover resulting from increasingly intensive agriculture, a circumstance now almost universally characteristic of pheasant range.

TABLE 22. Present and potential pheasant range in the arid Southwest.

State	Area square miles	Pheasant range			
		Area, square miles		Percent	
		1945	Potential	1945	Potential
Arizona	113,909	1,150.0	2,465.6	1.0	2.2
Colorado	104,247	4,216.5	7,869.2	4.0	7.5
Nevada	110,540	1.8	99.5	....	0.1
New Mexico	121,666	1,053.4	1,665.0	0.9	1.4
Oklahoma	6,250[1]	835.4	1,704.4	13.5	27.3
Texas	27,100[1]	1,031.4	1,802.7	3.8	6.7
Utah	84,916	1,756.4	3,382.7	2.1	4.0
Total	568,628	10,044.9	18,989.1	1.8	3.3

[1] Estimate of over-all pheasant-inhabited area; occurrence of birds on area not continuous. Percentage figures for these two states distorted because of small area involved.

Of other southwestern states, Utah undoubtedly carries the next heaviest pheasant population. Distribution is far less continuous here than in Colorado, being confined to a few irrigated valleys. The main concentrations of birds are in the northern tier of counties, although good numbers are found in central Utah as far south as Sevier County, and in the Uintah Basin, in the northeast corner of the state. Increasing numbers were recognized in the valley around Great Salt Lake in 1914, and shooting began some years later. Other northern counties having established populations are Cache, Box Elder, Weber, Davis, Salt Lake, and Utah. In all instances, irrigation and grain agriculture provide the food and cover requirements of the birds. In other small, scattered areas throughout the state, pheasants are maintaining relatively stable numbers.

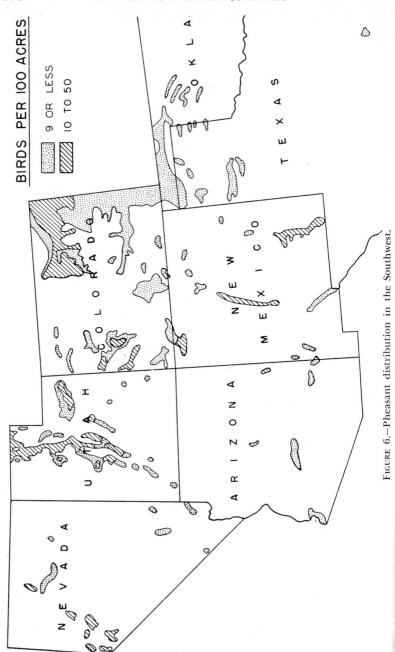

FIGURE 6.—Pheasant distribution in the Southwest.

The distribution and status of pheasants in Nevada are much the same as in Utah, but on a smaller scale. Nevada birds also are concentrated in a few irrigated valleys, by far the greatest number being centered around Reno and Carson City. Small, scattered populations occur elsewhere in the state.

Other parts of the arid Southwest are unquestionably on the fringe of the pheasant distribution. Included are Arizona, New Mexico, and the panhandles of Oklahoma and Texas. Of these states, New Mexico has had the longest experience with the ringneck, for they reached huntable numbers there in 1932, with the first season coming in 1935. Subsequently, seasons have been intermittent, and of one and one-half or two days in length. Both conditions denote limited numbers of birds.

Oklahoma has had two pheasant seasons, the first in 1948 and the last in 1950. Both were regarded as unsuccessful by the Game and Fish Department, but that was the result of extensive closed areas rather than local scarcity of birds. The Oklahoma panhandle, with 16 to 20 or more inches of precipitation, and broken by numerous eastward-running streams, offers an abundance of natural cover along watercourses. That factor, together with grain farming and the infrequency of severe winters, results in fair-to-good pheasant range. Certain crops of this region, such as grain sorghums and sudan grass, probably are less valuable for pheasants than either corn or wheat.

The Texas panhandle offers a habitat similar to that of Oklahoma, except for poorer cover resulting from less rainfall. Consequently, pheasants are less thrifty than in the former state. Water scarcity, and perhaps extremes of temperature, seem to be the principal physical factors retarding establishment of productive populations. Texas never has had a pheasant hunting season (Jones 1950).

Despite stocking, there are few pheasants in Arizona. Small, isolated colonies, apparently declining, are found in three or four irrigated regions. The reasons for this failure in establishment are not known, but high temperatures during the

PLATE XXIV.—*Above*. The quantity of insect food available to pheasants in this area near Fort Collins, Colorado, is illustrated by a flock of Franklin gulls eating grasshoppers on a newly raked hayfield. *Below*. Pheasant nest in irrigated wheat (Colorado Cooperative Wildlife Research Unit).

nesting and rearing seasons are regarded with suspicion. There has been no hunting season, and the Arizona Game and Fish Commission no longer is giving serious consideration to the pheasant as a game species.

Pheasant Homes on Arid Lands

The over-all character of southwestern ranges has been indicated, but that tells little of pheasant adjustments to the highly variable conditions in the region. Agricultural practices, and dry-farmed and irrigated crops, differ widely from one state to another. The fact that the bird is successful on so broad a front implies that racially it is tough and adaptable.

Alfalfa is the most important crop, acreage-wise, produced on irrigated land in the Southwest. This early-growing cover furnishes broody pheasant hens with enticing nesting sites on a scale exceeding that of grassland and weed patches in most watered regions; and its proximity to grain fields and bottom-land weeds and brush (when burning and overgrazing do not occur) adds to the attraction. The consequences of alfalfa-field nesting will be discussed later.

Farm-game investigators in Colorado have given attention to the relationship of irrigated and dry-farmed crops to pheasant habitats, and their findings are summarized for a typical township in Table 23, which lists the crops by percentage of land area (Yeager, Sandfort, and Lyon 1951).

TABLE 23. Irrigated and dry-farmed crops for a township in Larimer County, Colorado, 1948-50.

Crop	Irrigated		Dry-farmed	
	Acres	Percent	Acres	Percent
Alfalfa	4,761	41.0	00	0.0
Corn	2,334	20.1	00	0.0
Wheat	1,185	10.2	2,090	23.2
Pasture	1,173	10.1	2,189	24.3
Barley	976	8.4	774	8.6
Oats	650	5.6	00	0.0
Sugar beets	499	4.3	00	0.0
Gardens, fruits	29	0.25	00	0.0
Cucumbers	6	0.25	00	0.0
Fallow	00	0.0	3,954	43.9
Total	11,613	100.0	9,008	100.0

This agricultural pattern is typical for Colorado, either on the eastern plains or in the man-watered valleys of the Western Slope, and, on a much larger scale, it also characterizes the Utah pheasant habitats. Little or no corn is planted west of the Arkansas and South Platte Valleys in eastern Colorado. Sugar beets and small grains are of importance in both Colorado and Utah, but of little significance elsewhere in the Southwest, except in the panhandle areas where wheat is a staple crop.

In Nevada, alfalfa is the main irrigated crop; water and irrigable land are too scarce for extensive grain production. On a decreasing scale, the alfalfa-without-grain pattern holds for Arizona and New Mexico, although Keiffer and milo maize are of some importance in the latter state. Head grain crops are not of major significance until extreme southeastern Colorado and the panhandles of Oklahoma and Texas are reached, where they become the chief crop, grown largely on non-irrigated land.

The land pattern characteristic of irrigated regions, wherein ditches, streams, roads, and railroad rights-of-way are interspersed with cultivated fields, supplies the physical basis of a fair-to-excellent pheasant range. This interspersion of types in the Larimer County area is indicated in Table 24.

Included in the non-cultivated acreage are several permanent cover types represented by ditches, fencerows, wooded bottomlands, roads, railroads, old gravel pits, and others, most of which are associated with irrigated land. These cultural and natural land features are of paramount importance to pheasants. The permanent water surface is large. Farmsteads, feed lots, and miscellaneous developments make up the relatively small remainder of non-cultivated acreage. A total of 2,419 acres (10.5 percent of the township) is thus non-cultivated, and about half of the acreage is in more or less permanent cover, subject to burning, grazing, and feed-lot use.

Table 24 suggests that the extent of non-cultivated land should be ample for pheasant production. The acreage potentially available is 10 times greater than that stated by Kimball

(1948) as essential under conditions of excellent food and cover. Involved are 153 linear miles of various cultural features, and about 300 linear miles of small feeder ditches and narrow fencerows (not indicated in Table 24). The degree of interspersion attained by natural waterways, the main ditches, roads, railroad rights-of-way, and impoundments is shown in a general manner in Fig. 7. The general characteristics of cover are indicated in the photographs.

TABLE 24. Acreage and linear miles of non-cultivated land, by types (T7N, R68W, 6th PM, Larimer County Colorado).

Cover or cultural type	Area, acres	Linear miles	Percent of non-cultivated land	Percent of township
Streams, Cache la Poudre River ..	88	7.7	3.6	0.4
Ditches, primary, all-year	64	24.5	2.6	0.3
Ditches, secondary, intermittent..	38	32.2	1.6	0.2
Marshes and wet lands	192	...	7.9	0.9
Open water (Reservoirs, Ave. Lvl.)	610	...	25.3	2.4
Woods and shrub pasture	459	...	19.0	2.0
Roads, public	724	70.6	29.9	3.2
Railroad rights-of-way	212	18.0	8.8	1.0
Misc., gravel pits, feed lots trench silos, etc.)	32	...	1.3	0.1
Total	2,419	153.0	100.0	10.5

For present purposes, predation pressure and weather can be considered as a part of the environmental complex to which the pheasant is exposed.

Rasmussen and McKean (1945) regarded predators as of relatively minor importance to Utah pheasants. Predation by striped skunks was observed only during the nesting season; the species destroyed 12 of 22 nests on which records were obtained. Coyotes and magpies were abundant on the tract in question, but there was no evidence that either was responsible for low pheasant numbers. The magpie, with strong competition from the California gull, avidly consumed all eggs uncovered by mowers and, in addition, broke up 5 of 22 unexposed nests under observation. No other loss of significance was attributable to predation.

In Colorado, the comparative insignificance of predation is indicated by an observed nest loss of 16.5 percent from this cause over a 3-year period, or slightly less than half of that incurred in crop harvesting, and a fourth of the total recorded for all nest-destroying agents.

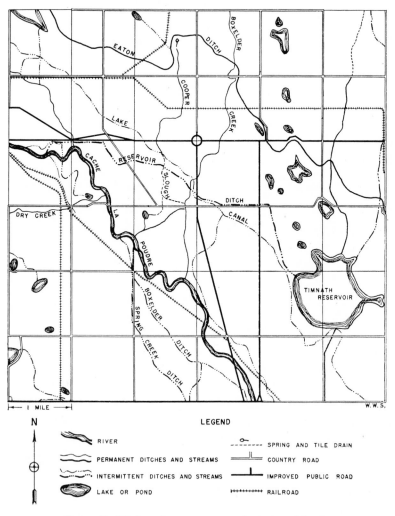

Figure 7.—Ditch and stream pattern in irrigated land.

In both the Colorado and Utah studies, it was evident that predation was associated closely with poor nesting cover. In Colorado, magpies were most destructive to nests; skunks were second. So little predation of chicks and adult birds was observed that no single important source could be singled out.

The only other instance where predation becomes serious is during blizzards, when hundreds, even thousands, of pheasants may be driven to the insecure shelter of small wooded areas. Under such conditions, losses may be severe.

In the arid Southwest, the elements are believed to play a significant, but as yet unmeasured, role in the production and maintenance of pheasant numbers. South and east of Colorado, the weather generally is regarded as being too hot and dry, but it probably is true that aridity affects ringnecks more or less adversely throughout the region, and especially on dry-farmed land. Elsewhere, irrigation seems to meet their moisture requirements. Temperatures apparently tolerable to this bird are found in Colorado, Nevada, and Utah, no doubt a dividend of altitude. Precise information on these points is not available yet.

It is well known that the Southwest offers a wide range of weather extremes. Colorado, Nevada, and Utah are subject to blizzards, which may cause heavy pheasant losses similar to those in the Dakotas (Kirsch 1951, Miller 1948). In such instances, loss seems to result from the combination of low temperatures, heavy snow, and high wind; and death actually is caused by suffocation rather than freezing. The greatest mortality always occurs in cover-deficient areas, where birds roosting in stubble, or in other thin cover, receive the full force of the wind.

Despite the frequency of storms, however, snow and ice are not the controlling factor in pheasant ups and downs in the Southwest. Snow in this arid region usually is fluffy and does not crust with the regularity characteristic of the Midwest and other more humid regions. Snow thus is penetrable easily by birds seeking food in stubble or on other grounds. Unusually heavy, wet snow in May or early June, may destroy many nests, however, forcing extensive renesting and late hatching peaks. This condition is encountered commonly in Colorado, Utah, and Nevada, and occasionally in other parts of the arid

PLATE XXV.—A view of irrigated land in Cache la Poudre Valley near Fort Collins, Colorado. Foreground shows typical distribution ditch, heavily grazed, leaving little cover suitable for nesting or winter use by pheasants. Cropland in background has been fall plowed eliminating all food and cover (Colorado Cooperative Wildlife Research Unit).

PLATE XXVI.—Grassed waterway dividing fall-plowed and wheat-stubble areas on an irrigated tract near Fort Collins. Grass and weed cover along this ditch is valuable for pheasant nesting and roosting (Colorado Cooperative Wildlife Research Unit).

region. The obvious approach to meeting the contingencies of winter extremes is the creation of more and better cover.

How Many?

Pheasant breeding populations have been inventoried in at least two southwestern states, although on small areas in each instance. The studies also gave information on breeding sex ratios and pre-hunting numbers. These data provide the best available indications of seasonal populations (Table 25).

In this appraisal, the Colorado investigation disclosed pre-hunting numbers closely approximating those in Utah. The actual difference, however, is greater than shown, for the Colorado figures were obtained about September 1, whereas those for Utah were taken in November.

Table 25. Pheasant populations on sample areas, Colorado[1] and Utah.

State and authority	Size of area	Breeding population Cocks	Hens	Sex ratio Cocks per 100 hens	Hens per 100 acres (spring)	Pre-hunting population, birds per 100 acres
Utah: Rasmussen and McKean ...	640	26.0	104	25.0	16.3	29.7 (November)
Colorado: Yeager, Sandfort & Lyon	960	28.0	70.7	39.6	7.4	28.9 (September)

[1] Figures are 3-year averages.

A glance at Table 25 indicates that a mere statement of population density in birds per hundred acres might be misleading. Actual densities were similar, but in terms of breeding productivity, the Colorado population was slightly more than half that found in Utah because of the smaller proportion of hens to cocks. Spring sex ratios for the two areas were approximately 1 to 2.5 and 1 to 4, respectively.

The removal of an appreciable portion of the cock birds by hunting does not affect breeding potential. We have no basis upon which to appraise the effect of illegal hen shooting. In the work on a section of land in Box Elder County, Utah, Rasmussen and McKean (1945) obtained the following figures on population changes as a result of hunting during and after the 1940 open season: Pre-hunting population, 190 pheasants; post-hunting population, 105; legal kill, 55 cocks; crippling loss, 9 known (18 estimated); and illegal kill, 6 known (12 estimated). Ten birds were calculated to have been driven off the area by the hunting, but this loss probably was compensated by returns and influx from other areas.

No comparable data are available from Colorado or other southwestern states. It is known, however, that the legal kill

PLATE XXVII.—*Upper left.* Typical main ditch on irrigated land in eastern Colorado. Sloping banks grown to clover and weeds supply highly valuable winter cover (Colorado Cooperative Wildlife Research Unit). *Lower right.* Secondary ditch used for carrying water only during growing season. Bank cover makes excellent nesting area (Colorado Cooperative Wildlife Research Unit).

on the Colorado study area was somewhat less than the 8.6 cocks per hundred acres recorded in Utah. It therefore appears that one-third to one-fourth of the fall population is removed by hunting.

No accurate inventory of state-wide pheasant populations is available at this time. On the basis of the data presented, pro-

PLATE XXVIII.—Cover conditions on ungrazed and unburned section of the Cache la Poudre River bottom near Fort Collins. This tract held at least 150 pheasants during a week of extreme cold in February, 1951 (Colorado Cooperative Wildlife Research Unit).

jections, reduced by one-third to compensate for the above-average quality of samples, indicate a breeding population in Colorado of some 185,000 birds, and a pre-hunting population of perhaps a half-million. Comparable figures for Utah are 152,000 and 380,000 birds, respectively. It appears, therefore, that the total pre-hunting population in the arid Southwest does not exceed 1,000,000 pheasants—less by far, than any of several of the important pheasant states.

Where the Crop Begins

Pheasant productivity during the breeding period has been studied in both Colorado and Utah. Similarity of the results is striking and indicates that certain factors probably are common to southwestern ranges. The comparison is given in Table 26.

TABLE 26. Comparison of breeding productivity, Colorado and Utah.

Factor	Utah[1]	Colorado[2]
Size of area, acres	640	960
Number of nests	154	104.3
Nests per 100 acres	24	10.8
Average clutch	9.1	9.9
Percent of nests successful	36.4	31.0
Percent of nests destroyed by harvest	42.9	34.8
Percent of nests destroyed by predators	38.5	16.5
Percent of nests destroyed by flooding	3.5	7.0
Average number of chicks per nest	7.6	8.8
Average brood size, mid-summer	5.1	6.4

[1]From Rasmussen and McKean (1945). Percentage of nests destroyed by predators calculated from data given; percentage probably low.
[2]From Yeager, Sandfort, and Lyon (1951). Figures are 3-year averages.

In both Colorado and Utah, mortality factors other than those listed in Table 26 were disclosed. Grazing and burning took a toll in both states. Destruction by burning, especially, is much greater than the findings in either state indicate, and probably has its most serious effects on nesting pheasants when large weed patches are consumed during late April and May. Such sites were not sampled during the two studies referred to, but unpublished records obtained by both the Colorado and Utah Cooperative Wildlife Research units show that burning accounts for high nesting losses in some situations.

PLATE XXIX.—*Upper left.* Heavy snow discloses pheasant use of small cover island surrounded by corn and weed fields, Larimer County, Colorado. About 40 pheasants concentrated here on the third day after a 12-inch snow in February, 1951 (Colorado Cooperative Wildlife Research Unit). *Lower right.* Hen killed by a cat during conditions of deep snow. Severe weather brings increased predation when birds concentrate in small areas (Colorado Cooperative Wildlife Research Unit).

The loss of pheasant hens during mowing operations was severe; and such losses involve far more than nest destruction alone, since they eliminate also the possibility of renesting. On the Colorado area, 16.6 percent of all nesting birds were killed or crippled, while "high mortality" was observed in Utah. Under Utah conditions, the degree of mortality to hens nesting in alfalfa often is the key to success or failure of the year's pheasant crop. Smith pointed out that high reproductive success can be expected in a year when the peak hatch occurs before alfalfa is cut. When the peak comes after mowing, however, a poor crop of young birds follows. Hen mortality was 36 percent when hay was cut before the hatching peak; nest success increased to 68 percent when hay cutting came later than the peak hatching date (Smith 1948).

During a year when hay mowing was early (low nesting success and high hen mortality), increase over the original breeding population was only 16.6 percent. Conversely, when mowing followed peak hatching (high nesting success and low hen mortality), the increase over the original breeding stock was 310 percent (Table 27).

Further studies by Zorb (1951), in Utah, showed that the prediction of reproductive success, based on the dates of alfalfa mowing and peak hatch, gave a more reliable estimation of the fall population than did the application of intensive census methods.

The foregoing data, similar to findings in many other parts of the country, emphasize the ringneck's great productive powers, and explain its ability to hold up in the face of egg, juvenile, and adult mortality that would eliminate a less resilient species.

In Nevada, production seems to be good, on a local basis, during favorable years. In the biennial report of the Nevada Fish and Game Commission for 1917-1919, the State Game Warden reported: "The ringneck pheasants are doing remarkably well in all parts of the State where propagated and are increasing at a wonderful rate. I am convinced that this elegant game bird would do well in many other parts of the

State, particularly in the southern counties, and have made an effort to arrange for trapping and shipping a number into other counties for propagation, but without satisfactory results."

Since Nevada has had regular seasons since the late 1920's it is apparent that annual crops have been produced; and such production was almost entirely by wild birds because the state game farm was not established until 1945. In the western agricultural region hunting is considered generally good. The pheasant population a decade or more ago probably was not much higher than at the present time (H. Shirl Coleman, letter, 16 Apr., 1951).

TABLE 27. Role of alfalfa hay cutting in pheasant nesting success and population levels in Utah.

Hay mowing finished	Year	Date	Nest success (percent)	Hen mortality (percent)	Young per adult hen [1]	Percent increase over original	breeding population
Before peak hatch:		June					
(Smith 1948)	1947	6-17	9	36.3	...		16.6
After peak hatch:		June					
(Smith 1948)	1947	23-27	68	10.6	...		310.0
After peak hatch:							
(Zorb 1951)	1949	...	...	...	2.5		...
Before peak hatch:							
(Zorb 1951)	1950	...	...	...	1.7		...

[1] Based on spring sex ratio and age data from kill.

General information on reproduction in Oklahoma indicates that fair pheasant crops may be expected during some years. Thus, the increase was encouraging in 1946, 1947, and 1948, but poor in 1949 and 1950. The over-all picture indicates ". . . slight production in the wild" (Lawrence Temple, letter, 6 Apr., 1951).

Pheasant production in Arizona, New Mexico, and Texas has been sporadic, and far from satisfactory. Arizona reported (Phil Cosper, letter, 10 Apr., 1951): "The only place we have found that a population can even maintain itself is in the Springerville area, an agricultural district which compares

PLATE XXX—*Upper left.* Winter aspect of irrigated pheasant range in Colorado (Colorado Cooperative Wildlife Research Unit). *Lower right.* Water and grain farming make these Colorado bottoms favorable in spring and summer, but deep snow and a dearth of cover are important limitations in winter (Colorado Cooperative Wildlife Research Unit)

PLATE XXXI.—Fire is the agent most destructive of cover in irrigated regions. In fall it does even more damage than in spring, since the utility of winter roosting areas may be lost (Colorado Cooperative Wildlife Research Unit).

quite closely with that found around Fort Collins [Colorado]. As far as the rest of the State's agricultural area goes, about all we can say for the pheasant is that we tried." Production in New Mexico has been sufficient to allow, some years, a season of 1½ or 2 days, always restricted to a few local areas. Texas never has had a pheasant season.

The Pheasant Pay-off

Despite its restricted distribution in western Colorado and Utah, the pheasant is the most important game bird in these two states; in Nevada it has a strong competitor in the chukar; in New Mexico, the bandtail pigeon and wild turkey surpass it in importance; and in Oklahoma, the bobwhite quail, of course, is the predominant game species. As stated previously, pheasants are not hunted in Arizona and Texas. In the five states where pheasant hunting is permitted, the season is one of the major field events for perhaps 300,000 hunters.

Pheasant hunting in the arid Southwest began in Utah in 1917. In the late 1920's Nevada opened hunting on ringnecks, and Colorado, New Mexico, and Oklahoma followed in order. A summary of the regulations in force in 1950 in the five pheasant-hunting states is given in Table 28. The fact that no seasons have been statewide emphasizes the localized nature of

PLATE XXXII.—Instruments check the weather in a willow thicket. It's one of the methods used by game biologists to study the effectiveness of cover types (Colorado Cooperative Wildlife Research Unit).

PLATE XXXIII.—*Above*. Complete absence of cover on the high plains. There is abundant food at harvest time, but few pheasants can winter in such range (Colorado Cooperative Wildlife Research Unit). *Below*. Good pheasant habitat along the Weber River, Utah. Winter feeding areas are surrounded by heavy cover (Utah Cooperative Wildlife Research Unit).

the pheasant range and distribution. Colorado, with a season applying to most of the eastern slope, has the largest and most continuous open area by far.

TABLE 28. Pheasant hunting regulations in the Southwest, 1950.

State	First season, year	Month of season	Length, days	Bag limit Cocks	Bag limit Hens	Remarks
Colorado	1933	Nov..	3 [1]	3	0	Season cut about two-thirds since 1947.
Nevada	Late 1920's	Oct.	3	3	0	Low pressure; fair to good hunting.
New Mexico [2]	1935	Oct.	1½	2	1	Season later than formerly.
Oklahoma ...	1948	Sept.	2	2	0	Two seasons, both "unsuccessful."
Utah	1947	Nov.	3 [3]	3	0	12-bird limit for season; 6-bird possession limit.

[1] Half-days (12:00 noon—5:00 p. m.) only.
[2] Seasons not annual.
[3] Two week-ends 1½ days each.

In most states there has been a reduction in the length of season during the last few years. Colorado, for example, permitted hunting for 14 days in the northeastern part of the state, and 7 days in the north-central part, in 1947. In 1945, the season was 30 half-days.

The 1950 season was in marked contrast, which did not exceed three days in any southwestern state except in one damage area in western Colorado. This region-wide reduction in seasons is one indication of decreasing pheasant populations, although it must be recognized that the effect of increased hunting pressure also has been toward shorter shooting periods.

On a basis of the best estimate available, it appears that 300,000 or more pheasants are killed in the arid Southwest each year. It is apparent that the kill has declined materially from that of 1945, or a few years earlier, and that the present take is characterized by considerable fluctuation from year to year. Trends in hunting pressure, and ringnecks brought to bag in recent years, are indicated in Table 29.

Since 1947, the Colorado Game and Fish Department has operated check stations on the opening days of the pheasant season. The stations are located strategically so as to intercept a large number of hunters returning from important pheasant-producing areas. The figures obtained are shown in Table 30.

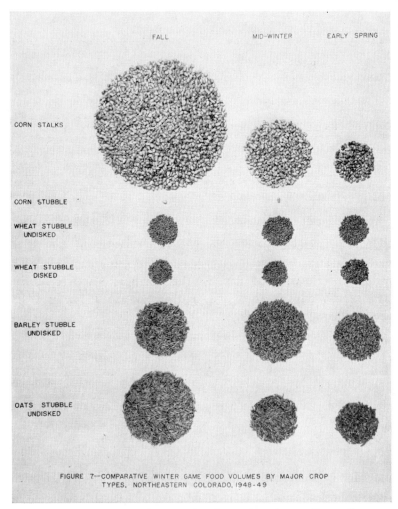

FIGURE 7—COMPARATIVE WINTER GAME FOOD VOLUMES BY MAJOR CROP TYPES, NORTHEASTERN COLORADO, 1948-49

PLATE XXXIV.—Crop residues are the pheasant's mainstay. Shown above are the comparative winter game food volumes by major crop types, northeastern Colorado, 1948-49 (Colorado Cooperative Wildlife Research Unit).

TABLE 29. Number of pheasant hunters and estimated kill, arid Southwest, 1940, 1945, and 1950[1]

State	Number of pheasant hunters			Estimated kill		
	1940	1945	1950	1940	1945	1950
Colorado	59,600	83,000	117,800	178,700	251,100	151,700
Nevada	No estimate available. Small percent of license buyers hunt pheasants.					
New Mexico[2] ..	......	......	11,600	......	......	13,900
Oklahoma[3]	......	......	8,000	......	......	1,800
Utah	60,000	74,100	102,000	150,000	150,000	200,000

[1] Estimates supplied by various Game and Fish Department officials who emphasized the inadequacy of the sample or other shortcomings of data. All figures rounded to nearest 100.
[2] Figures for New Mexico are for 1949, and were calculated by authors from data supplied.
[3] Oklahoma reported for 1948 season a total of approximately 5,400 hunters who killed about 5,750 pheasants.

This summation represents stations located in the five major pheasant-producing areas of Colorado—the Northeast, North-central, Arkansas Valley, San Luis Valley, and the Western Slope. The kill per hunting hour varied considerably, as would be expected, not only from area to area, but from year to year. Thus, a low of 0.15 birds per hour was recorded for the Western Slope in 1950, while the best hunting experienced returned 0.362 birds per hour in the San Luis Valley in 1947. The decline in hunting success, 1947 to 1950, is indicated under "Birds per hour," Table 30.

TABLE 30. Colorado pheasant-kill data, opening-day check stations, 1947-1950.

Year	No. of hunters	Total hours hunted	Birds per hunter	Birds per hour	Age classes			
					Number of birds		Percent	
					Adults	Juveniles	Adults	Juveniles
1947	4,334	16,235	1.09	.281	1,434	2,979	32.5	67.5
1948	6,973	26,107	1.08	.289	2,844	4,689	37.7	62.3
1949	3,451	13,823	0.80	.198	767	1,982	27.9	72.1
1950	4,222	15,986	0.72	.191	1,092	1,955	35.8	64.2

Check-stations established at three hunting areas in Utah showed that the cock kill varied from 7.4 to 65 birds per 100 acres (Table 31). The high kill on the Warren Area may be attributed, in part, to tremendous hunting pressure, averaging two hunters per acre in the seasons from 1946 to 1950. Pressures on the other two tracts were one hunter per 12 acres and 25 acres; and the kill declined in about the same proportion as the hunter pressure.

Age ratios, even though varying in different parts of the state in the same year, did not drop below 66 percent in juvenile pheasants. Although they are not significant without accurate sex-ratio data, age ratios as high as 92 percent young birds were recorded on the Corrine Hunting Area in Box Elder County in 1949; the average was 86 percent during the 1949 and 1950 seasons. Hunting success on a state-wide basis— 0.234 birds per hour—approximated that of the four-year average in Colorado. Bird returns per hour of hunter effort dropped to 0.14 in the West Warren Hunting Area, where hunting pressures were great, and the total kill per 100 acres was 6 to 10 times as large as on more moderately shot habitats (Table 31).

Table 31. Hunter pressure and pheasant kill on three Utah posted hunting areas.

Area	Size of area, acres	Date	Acres per hunter	Average yearly kill (males)	Kill per 100 acres	Young in hunters' bag (percent)
West Warren [1]	258	1946-1950	0.58	168	65	..
Corrine Posted Hunting Area	12,000	1949-1950	12.4	1,292	10.7	86
Young Ward Posted Hunting Area	7,100	1949-1950	25.0	528	7.4	77

[1] A small irrigation project surrounded on all sides by grease-wood and salt flats.

The recorded pheasant kill on Utah lands varied from 1.6 birds per hunter in the Uintah Basin and on the Corrine study area in 1949, to 1.2 on the Corrine and 0.36 on West Warren in 1950. Hunters' return cards indicated an average season bag of 2.91 birds in 1948; 2.98 in 1949.

Banded, game-farm reared birds on four study areas during the three years, 1945 to 1947, showed a return of 10.1 percent in hunters' bags. Returns in the Uintah Basin varied from 6 to 9 percent, while those at West Warren were as high as 46 percent in one year and averaged 35.8 percent over the five-year period of 1946-1950.

In Oklahoma, an estimated 5,400 hunters killed about 5,750 pheasants in 1948, of which roughly 1,900 were hens. In 1950, approximately 8,000 hunters bagged 1,800 birds, successful hunters averaging 2.2 pheasants for the season. Sexes in the

Plate XXXV.—Despite its restricted distribution, the pheasant is the most important game bird in Colorado and Utah (Colorado Cooperative Wildlife Research Unit).

1950 kill were approximately equal (Temple 1948, and letter, 28 May, 1951).

Landowners and Pheasants

It is, perhaps, no great cause for surprise if the sport of some 300,000 pheasant hunters in the Southwest clashes to some extent with the interests of roughly one-third this number of farmers on whose land the birds are produced. The conflicts are of two general kinds—problems of game production and problems of game harvest.

It is paradoxical that factors most adverse to the pheasant's life-equation are the same as those chiefly responsible for creating a habitat best suited to its needs. Thus, various farming and grazing practices take a far greater toll of ringneck production than the aggregate of hunters, predation, and the elements; yet throughout the Southwest the ringneck depends upon successful agriculture for existence.

Irrigation

As a good example of this, the artificial delivery and spreading of water on crop land frequently results in flooding. Such inundations typically occur late in the hatching and throughout the young-rearing periods. Samples studied indicated nest destruction of from 4 to 7 percent. Some young are drowned, but mortality to these precocial chicks generally is negligible. Irrigation, except for local accidents coincident with levee breakage or other mishap, cannot be regarded as an important hindrance to production.

Crop harvest

The disastrous effects of mowing, especially of alfalfa, on pheasant nesting are well known (Feast 1948; Sandfort 1951, and others). In both Colorado and Utah, 35 to 75 percent of all pheasant nests are placed in alfalfa, and loss from mowing varies from about 35 to perhaps 50 percent, plus hen mortality varying from 10 to 40 percent or more. Sandfort (1951a) summarized the mowing problem aptly by stating, ". . . the big killer . . . the thing that destroys more pheasants than all other causes combined, *including hunters* . . . is the modern mowing machine." Delay in mowing until after the peak hatching date always is in the pheasants' favor, but that is almost entirely a matter of chance—or weather.

Farmers certainly cannot forego the use of modern machinery, or discard harvesting schedules essential to profitable operation. The problem of pheasant destruction by mowers remains, therefore, unsolved. Flushing bars and similar devices are awkward to use and involve time and expense that few farmers are willing to give. Moreover, they are not fully effective on the high-speed mowers now coming into general use.

Due to the impracticability of saving hayfield nests, the best approach appears to be that of providing "safe" nesting cover on noncultivated land. Even so, pheasants will continue to nest in alfalfa, but enough of them may be induced to use ditchbanks and fencerows, so that they, together with the survivors of hayfields, will constitute an appreciable crop. The prevention of burning, and destructive grazing of uncultivated land, thus plays an important role in the provision of "safe" nesting ground. In like manner, the development of alfalfa borders along the edge of ditches and in the crooks of cleared streams shows promise and is of interest to the farmer since the forage produced can be pastured during the winter.

Fall plowing

The practice of fall plowing buries crop residues and reduces crop land to a foodless and coverless barren. In north-central Colorado about half of the land now devoted to annual crops is fall-plowed, which represents a material increase during the last ten years. In addition, some legume stubble is turned under annually.

Fall plowing is a proven moisture conservation practice, and results in improved seed-bed conditions in the spring. In addition, it saves crop-planting time. These advantages leave the game manager with little basis for objection, except that he logically may advocate the technique of "rough plowing," accomplished by setting the disk with less angle, which breaks

PLATE XXXVI.—*Upper left.* A properly constructed canal. Banks stabilized with vegetation provide wildlife food and cover (Colorado Cooperative Wildlife Research Unit). *Lower right.* Heavy grazing of ditch banks induces washing, siltation, and destruction of cover needed by pheasants and other wildlife (Colorado Cooperative Wildlife Research Unit).

the soil deeply but leaves it only partly turned. An appreciable part of the straw and waste grain is left uncovered, and thus available to game, poultry, and hogs.

One of the principal reasons for using "rough" culture is that of reducing wind erosion. This feature, plus that of leaving some grain for domestic livestock, is appreciated readily by farmers (Yeager, Sandfort, and Lyon 1951).

Soil-mining crops

Corn is the crop generally most favorable to pheasant production. Harvest by hand or picker insures good cover for feeding and abundant winter food. During the last decade, however, increasing acreages of corn have been cut for ensilage, leaving fields nearly bare of food and cover. Cutting results in the utilization of more of the crop, but robs the soil of humus and fertility needed to keep it in productive condition.

Sugar beets are more soil depleting than ensilage corn, unless the beet tops are left in the field for winter pasture. The tops often are hauled to feedlots, however, leaving the land with no return in the way of crop residue or manure.

Since both ensilage and beets are profitable, and present harvest methods are efficient, there is little prospect of change. Fortunately for pheasants, the beet acreage is comparatively small, being about a third of that devoted to corn in eastern Colorado. In other localities, it may be much greater. About half of the irrigated corn now is cut by machinery. The heavy emphasis on cash crops is likely to be mitigated only through the possibility of wider use of legume-grain rotations for soil building.

Grazing

Rasmussen and McKean (1945) pointed out that the grazing of irrigated fields during the fall and winter was common practice in Utah. Cattle and sheep are most important in this respect, but horses also are involved. Beet tops, alfalfa and corn residue constitute the principal forage, but small-grain stubble may be utilized similarly. For the most part, such grazing is by stock summered on mountain range. In some cases grazing assumes near feed-lot intensity, the combination of feeding and trampling often resulting in serious loss of cover.

In addition to fields, uncultivated land such as bottomland woods are grazed commonly. Bottomland is the natural wintering ground of pheasants in the West, and there is a definite movement of the birds to this type with the advent of deep snow and sub-zero temperatures. Where the bottoms adjoin grain fields, excellent habitat is produced. Grazing lowers its quality in direct proportion to grazing intensity.

The economic aspects of grazing on western pheasant range were pointed out recently by Yeager, Sandfort, and Lyon (1951). Since bottomland timber in this region is almost entirely cottonwood and willow, often scrubby, the stands have little commercial value. Moreover, these woods provide summer pasture and sheltered feed-lot sites. Low commercial value and utility in livestock production leave little inducement to the landowner to protect them from grazing.

Because of its economic implications, therefore, there is no easy solution to the grazing problem. Fortunately, there is a relatively large acreage of non-cultivated land which, together with field grazing, has been sufficient so far to meet the pressure without destruction of the entire habitat. In addition, stock are excluded from some ditches because grazing would induce bank caving and silting. Such protection of waterways, including reservoirs and streams, can be encouraged from the economic standpoint.

Burning

Throughout much of the western pheasant range, dry falls and winters may see a half or more of the standing herbaceous cover destroyed by fire. The importance of burning on irrigated pheasant habitat varies, therefore, with weather conditions (Yeager 1950).

In general, fall burning is more injurious than spring burning, since the former deprives game of winter roosting cover, in addition to a shortage of nesting areas the following spring.

PLATE XXXVII.—Example of cultivation to the edge of a secondary irrigation ditch. The space between ditch and fence is used by a ditch walker,
often accompanied by a dog, which eliminates its utility for pheasant nesting (Colorado Cooperative Wildlife Research Unit).

Burning in late April and May, of course, results in nest loss.
Dead weeds and grass along ditches and bottomlands are removed easily by fire, but in addition to destroying good nesting
cover, the practice subjects sites so treated to erosion losses.

One of the main consequences of fall and winter burning is
concentration of game into any remaining cover available.

PLATE XXXVIII.—*Upper left.* Hand-harvested cornfield on irrigated land in eastern Colorado. Although grazed by cattle, this field furnished abundant food and good feeding cover for pheasants during the winter of 1950-51 (Colorado Cooperative Wildlife Research Unit). *Lower right.* Corn cutting for silage is working against the pheasant. It leaves bare earth, and soil exposed to wind erosion (Colorado Cooperative Wildlife Research Unit).

Here, pheasants suffer still greater losses from exposure, food shortage, and predation. Few game-bird situations offer greater opportunity to dogs, cats, coyotes, great-horned owls, and other predators, and to poachers, than a two-acre "timber claim" holding a few hundred starving, blizzard-herded pheasants!

The use of fire on farms is partly the result of custom. It must be admitted that fire provides a quick and economical means of clearing debris; but when the ill effects of burning are considered—weed succession, destruction of humus, erosion, injury to fences, and loss of forage in fields and pastures—it is evident that it usually is an unprofitable tool. It seems probable that education involving this direct economic approach would do much to reduce the frequency of burning. As a by-product, the pheasant would be benefited substantially.

Crop damage

Pheasant depredations to farm crops never have reached serious proportions in the Southwest, despite the complaints that are heard in some localities. Investigation frequently discloses that losses have been exaggerated.

Nevertheless, crop damage does occur, and locally it may reach serious proportions. Truck garden crops, such as melons or tomatoes, are more susceptible to injury than grain crops, because pecking renders the produce unattractive to buyers. Damage of this nature has occurred in several Colorado, Utah, and New Mexico localities. Loss to sprouting corn has not assumed serious proportions, due possibly to the small total acreage involved.

Control of pheasant damage has involved shooting birds, or permitting extended or special seasons in the damage area. Utah has given attention to repellents, with some success. In Colorado, wardens and technicians often satisfy individual complaints by killing accused birds on the spot and then investigating crops and gizzards to learn what foods have been eaten. The quantity of insects, especially cutworms, revealed in such autopsies has proved convincing to most of those whose time and interest could be gained. A small percentage of the complainants, however, were "agin' " pheasants, and thus were not amenable either to reasoning or demonstration.

In summary, it can be said that, except for specialized gardening and localized grain-farming areas, pheasant depredations represent only minor management problems in the southwestern states.

Farmer Versus Sportsman

On pheasant range, the West is no longer the land of space and low hunting pressure. This circumstance is due, of course, to the natural association of dense human populations with fertile farmland. Thus, the western pheasant country, confined largely to valleys where people live, is subjected to near midwestern shooting pressure during the brief seasons now in effect. As a result, farmer-sportsman relations are likewise assuming mid-western aspects (Feast 1948).

In a recent study of this problem in Larimer County, Colorado, Boeker (1951) found landowners concerned about hunter trespass and damage, yet surprisingly reasonable in attitude. Of 75 farmers near Fort Collins, 42 percent had posted their land, but 92 percent stated that they allowed hunting by permission. The most common complaint of these farmers was the failure of hunters to ask permission to go on their property; others were numerous, and varied from leaving gates open to shooting livestock. Nine of the 75 farmers had chickens, sheep, cattle, or horses killed by hunters. The shooting of cattle was most serious, for each animal represented a loss of $50 to $300. There has been a similar trend of events in Utah, New Mexico, and other southwestern states. In Oklahoma, the chief impediment to successful pheasant seasons in 1948 and 1950 was the large area—approximately 75 percent—closed to public hunting, a condition caused at least in part by hunters' conduct afield.

In Utah, difficulties between farmers and sportsmen were recognized as early as 1939 when, by legislative action, farmers were allowed to establish posted hunting areas. These tracts, operated with the consent and cooperation of the state Fish and Game Commission, may be not less than 1,000 acres in size. Tickets costing not more than one dollar per season are issued by lottery, or direct sale, to hunters acceptable to landowners, the number being determined jointly by the farmers and the Fish and Game Department. Further, the units are established in areas having few accessible roads where they may be checked easily by the farmer-deputy wardens.

In 1950, there were 36 of these posted hunting areas in Utah. A total of 24,325 hunting permits were issued by the Fish and Game Department, or about 675 permits for each area.

The success of farmers' posted hunting areas appears to lie in the manner in which the proceeds for the sale of tickets are used. Such money almost always goes to some church or community enterprise. Projects, such as the purchase of bleachers for ball parks, or organs for churches, are examples. Division of the money among the landowners involved has not proved to be incentive enough to justify the operation of such units. In general, farmers have been satisfied with those posted hunting areas since they remove, or reduce, the two serious objections to uncontrolled hunting: (1) that of damage from hunters to private property, and (2) too many hunters. Hunters, on the other hand, complain that (1) not enough permits are issued, and (2) the method of permit distribution is not always fair.

In certain localities, the posted hunting area idea may become disadvantageous to the hunter, and eventually to the pheasant. For example, in a recent study in Cache County (Zorb 1950), it was shown that hunting areas increased from 21,000 acres in 1945 to 91,000 acres in 1950, with an additional 140,000 acres being organized. In 1950, it was determined that 38 percent of the hunters had permits to hunt on 62 percent of the best pheasant habitat. This left the other 62 percent of the shooters to compete with one another on the remaining 38 percent of the land. To make matters worse, a substantial portion of this unorganized land was posted privately. Undershooting on the posted hunting areas, and disproportionately heavy shooting on the unposted land, thus becomes a real possibility that should be guarded against.

As in other parts of the country, meeting the farmer-sports-man problem in the Southwest appears to be largely a matter of hunters voluntarily meeting the responsibilities of good behavior that are associated with the privilege of public hunting. This will require educational work by responsible agencies, and a change in tactics and attitude on the part of the man with the gun. The alternative is the loss of public pheasant shooting over a large part of the Southwest.

Plans for the Pheasant

Two earlier writers concerned with pheasants on irrigated land, cited Beebe's work in China and pointed out that ring-necks have shown the same affinity for agricultural land in the New World as on their ancestral range (Rasmussen and McKean 1945). This association with man-made habitats creates the necessity, as well as the problem, of management.

To date, management in the Southwest has consisted of little more than stocking and protecting birds by closed seasons. In some states, stocking has involved the establishment of game farms, and in all states more or less effective warden forces have been the means of protection.

The more advanced, and undoubtedly more significant, phases of pheasant management—population studies, intelligent harvest, and habitat manipulation—are appearing now.

Colorado and Utah now have active projects concerned with woody plantings that will serve both windbreak and game-cover functions (Brown 1948, Greenhalgh 1951). The scope of habitat work in Colorado is extensive (Feast 1948). In other states, including New Mexico and Oklahoma, plantings are more experimental in nature, and none of them is old enough to yield reliable information in terms of crop or pheasant production. The windbreak offers the possibility of combining agricultural benefits with a key wildlife practice, and is a promising means of gaining the interest of farm groups.

Conditions in this region suggest that habitat improvement

PLATE XXXIX—*Upper left.* Barley stubble on irrigated land, Larimer County, Colorado, provides winter food and cover which is much used in mild weather. The ordinary kind of fall plowing destroys wildlife values and promotes wind erosion. (Colorado Cooperative Wildlife Research Unit). *Lower right.* "Rough fallow" is a practice beneficial to pheasants, since it leaves part of the grain residues unburied. It is a valuable erosion control measure (Colorado Cooperative Wildlife Research Unit).

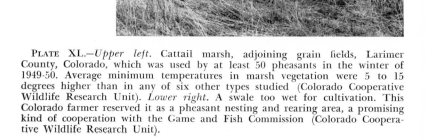

PLATE XL.—*Upper left*. Cattail marsh, adjoining grain fields, Larimer County, Colorado, which was used by at least 50 pheasants in the winter of 1949-50. Average minimum temperatures in marsh vegetation were 5 to 15 degrees higher than in any of six other types studied (Colorado Cooperative Wildlife Research Unit). *Lower right*. A swale too wet for cultivation. This Colorado farmer reserved it as a pheasant nesting and rearing area, a promising kind of cooperation with the Game and Fish Commission (Colorado Cooperative Wildlife Research Unit).

will prove to be a practical means of meeting certain short-comings in the farm-game environment. Winter cover short-ages are critical during severe weather on the extensive plains of eastern Colorado and throughout the intermountain region generally. Natural weed and grass nesting cover is short in nearly all localities, forcing birds into alfalfa fields. There, as elsewhere, predation occurs more or less in proportion to the quality of cover, whether nest, young, or adult pheasants are involved. Better habitat conditions undoubtedly are the most practical kind of "predator control."

From the over-all management standpoint, therefore, the writers regard the development of woody windbreaks, fence-rows, or shoreline plantings as the most economical, as well as the most effective, means of improving farm-game en-vironments in the Southwest without serious conflict with agricultural interests. As badly needed correlaries in habitat improvement, they recommend control of fire along ditches and on bottomlands; "rough" culture of stubble and fallow lands; and rotation of crops to insure regular occurrence of grain and legumes in the crop pattern.

CHAPTER 5

PHEASANTS OF THE PLAINS
AND PRAIRIES

By James W. Kimball, Edward L. Kozicky,

and Bernard A. Nelson[1]

PRIOR to 1905, not more than 500 pheasants were introduced into the northern prairie region. Less than 40 years later, in the period from 1940 to 1950, more than 82 million birds were harvested in North Dakota, South Dakota, Nebraska, Iowa, and Minnesota. These figures bespeak the phenomenal success of the ringneck on what formerly were the central grasslands of the continent.

Most of the early introductions failed. Dispersion of small groups, poaching, poor habitat, and unfavorable weather have been cited as causes of failure. However, good populations now are established at many sites where early stocking did not succeed, and it is possible that other, little understood, factors were involved. Among these may be the fact that introductions made during the favorable swing of a population trend or "cycle" appear to have the best chance of success.

[1] It would be impossible for the authors to thank all of the individuals who contributed to this chapter. We are especially indebted to Eldon H. Smith of South Dakota, Arnold B. Erickson of Minnesota, Levi L. Mohler of Nebraska, and Everett B. Speaker of Iowa for their efforts beyond the bounds of professional courtesy. Others who aided materially with suggestions and data from the region are Roy N. Bach, W. Arthur Benson, Floyd B. Blunt, Donald M. Christiensen, Robert F. Cooney, Richard J. Dorer, Richard B. Eggen, Lester A. Faber, George O. Hendrickson, Taylor W. Huston, David Leahy, Paul Leaverton, G. W. Malaher, Harrell F. Mosbaugh, Richard C. Nomsen, Liven Peterson, Alex J. Reeve, Melvin O. Steen, Russell W. Stuart,

State game departments of this region became interested in pheasants between 1905 and 1915, and started distributing eggs to farmers and releasing adult birds in the wild. Later, South Dakota, Iowa, Nebraska, and North Dakota trapped and transplanted pheasants from areas of high population to unstocked range. Where habitat was suitable, the program met with rapid success.

In Iowa, the pheasant probably got its initial start in the wild by accident. In 1900 or 1901, a windstorm blew down the fences on William Benton's Game Farm at Cedar Falls and liberated about 2,000 birds. About 1910 the Conservation Commission inaugurated a program of distributing eggs and pheasants, and in 1925, declared an open season (Faber 1946).

The introduction of ringnecks into Kansas met with little success until 1925; from that year through 1940, more than 18,000 birds were released and 100,000 eggs distributed to cooperating farmers. In 1940, 21 counties in northwest Kansas were open to fall hunting; in 1950 it was 47 counties.

Manitoba still is attempting to establish a shootable population. Between 1934 and 1951, the Department of Mines and Natural Resources released about 5,000 birds. At present, they are attempting to develop a strain of pheasant capable of withstanding the severe winter weather that is considered the greatest limiting factor in that province.

The first effort to introduce the ringneck into Minnesota is recorded in the 1905 biennial report of the Conservation Department. Seventy pairs were received from Wisconsin and Illinois that year, and they produced less than 100 young. In 1915, a game farm was established, which, with the exception of a period from 1943 to 1945, has continued to operate. It has released more than 691,600 pheasants and distributed 96,578 eggs to sportsmen's clubs and farmers.

The pheasant was established in Missouri by the release of game-farm birds, and by eggs furnished to cooperators. Stocking began about 1904 and was terminated in 1933.

Nebraska estimates that only 1,000 birds were purchased and released in the state. In 1926 and 1927, about 40,000

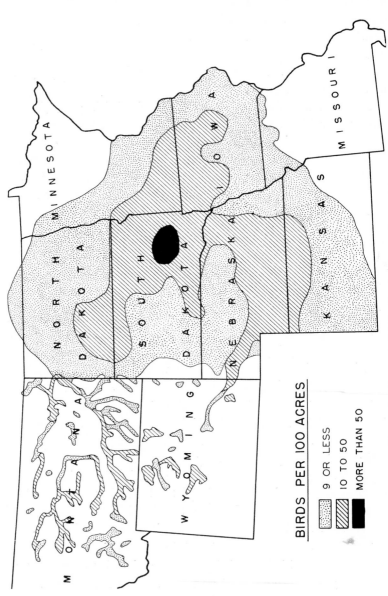

FIGURE 8.—Pheasant distribution in the northern plains.

adult birds were trapped and transplanted. A state game farm was not operated until pheasant shooting had become nearly statewide.

Attempts were made to stock pheasants in North Dakota as early as 1910, and stocking through importation was continued in a haphazard fashion until the early thirties. Stocking of pen-reared birds did not produce the desired results, and it was not until the birds moved in from South Dakota that they finally became established. Trapping and transplanting of these migrants from 1929 to 1934 formed a foundation for the high pheasant population of the early forties.

South Dakota, the greatest center of pheasant populations, never operated a game farm. As in other states, the first liberations were by private individuals. In 1911, the State Game Department started to purchase and release birds, and between 1914 and 1918, 7,000 were liberated and a large increase in wild birds was noted. In later years, more than 40,-000 pheasants were trapped in centers of abundance and released throughout the state (Anon. 1941).

In summary, the high population of the North-Central region was the result of introducing a few pheasants into suitable habitat where they multiplied rapidly. Continued artificial stocking was not necessary.

Populations

The four maps (Figs. 9, 10, 11, and 12) show pheasant population fluctuations and shifts throughout the past decade. Basic data used in constructing the maps were drawn from roadside counts, rural mail carrier surveys, and crowing cock inventories. In the case of the 1941 map, and to some extent the 1944 map, lack of survey information in some states made it necessary to review conservation officer reports, state game department publications, and to draw from the knowledge of men of long experience within each state. Detailed accuracy is not claimed for the maps, but they represent the best available information, and they should be reliable enough for many purposes.

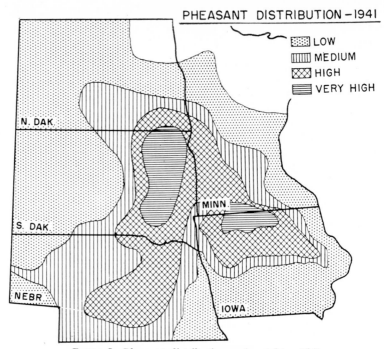

FIGURE 9.—Pheasant distribution and numbers, 1941.

The principal function of the maps is to show what major changes have taken place in pheasant populations throughout the plains and prairies, and to provide basic data for testing theories relative to population fluctuations.

Before discussing "population shifts," two points should be made clear. First, they have not been caused by actual bird movements but by increases or decreases in abundance in various portions of the range. Second, contrary to popular belief, hunting was not a consequential factor in causing pheasant declines.

In 1941, (Fig. 9), the states in the eastern and southern portions of the "pheasant island" of the plains and prairies were enjoying about the highest bird population in their history. It may be more than coincidence that this year also marked the approximate climax of a period of drouth, and low farm prices, which in turn resulted in much idle land.

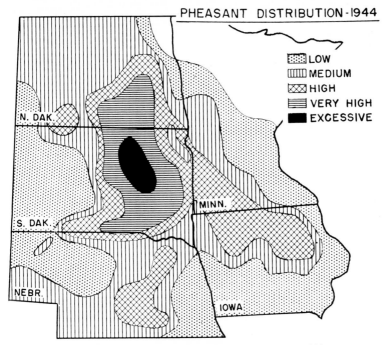

FIGURE 10.—Pheasant distribution and numbers, 1944.

Three years later, in 1944, (Fig. 10), we find a generally good regional pheasant population, but there was a definite shrinking of the better range in the east and south, with a westward shift and a population increase in the Dakotas. This general westward shift coincided with economic and climatic changes. In the east and south, higher farm prices brought about intensification of agriculture (Faber 1948), and additional rainfall converted dry sloughs and marshes, with their rank vegetative growth, into open lakes and potholes. Thus, Minnesota, Iowa, Nebraska, and the eastern quarter of the Dakotas yielded wild land to the plow and to the cloud. At the same time, pheasant range in that portion of South Dakota lying between the James and Missouri Rivers, and much of North Dakota, was improved materially. Agriculture in this region, not yet greatly intensified, but more successful due to greater rainfall, produced food in abundance.

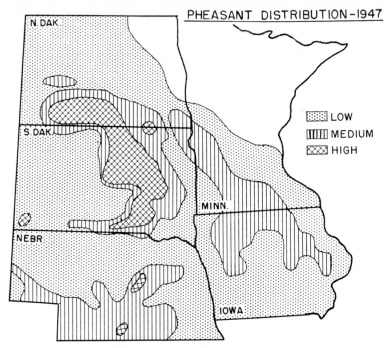

FIGURE 11.—Pheasant distribution and numbers, 1947.

The increased rainfall resulted in more abundant cover in the form of sweet clover, sunflower, and other herbaceous species.

By 1947, (Fig. 11), we find the area of highest population still farther to the west, but the general numerical level had been reduced greatly throughout the area. In South Dakota, the best range had shifted westward to the Missouri River. Except in the southern and northern extremities of the state, suitable habitat ends at the Missouri, so that the population appears to have been literally forced off the western edge of its range. At that time, due to still greater intensification of agriculture, destruction of sweet clover by weevils, and somewhat less rainfall, suitable cover and wild land reached an all-time low throughout the entire area.

The final map, (Fig. 12), depicting the 1950 pheasant population, shows a general increase and a shift back to the east but

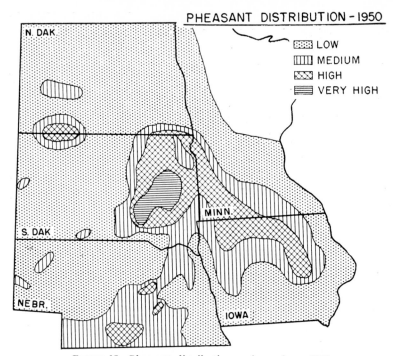

FIGURE 12.—Pheasant distribution and numbers, 1950.

a drastic reduction in the north and west. This reduction can be attributed to excessive winter mortality. Inadequate winter cover, plus severe storms during the winters of 1948-49 and 1949-50, accounted for winter losses in that area ranging from 30 to 90 percent. Not only winter cover, but all types of cover have been reduced greatly through more intensive farming, which has removed most of the idle land.

To this point, population fluctuations and shifts appear to be explainable on the basis of environmental changes. Three things, however, prevent the authors from presenting this "environmental relationship" theory without reservations. First, the one thing known with certainty about the crash decline of the early forties is that it was caused by extremely poor reproductive success, which may have included high juvenile mortality. This could have been caused by habitat deficiencies, but the relationship is neither definite nor clear,

Second, what caused the eastward population shift in 1950, in the face of continued intensive agriculture and high water in the lakes and sloughs? There had been less rainfall, but no visible improvement in habitat was detected. Third, pheasant populations on the Sand Lake and Lacreek National Wildlife Refuges have fluctuated in phase with surrounding populations, in spite of the fact that habitat changes on those areas had been slight.

In summary, environmental changes appear to have been an important factor in bringing about the pheasant population fluctuations and shifts in the plains and prairie pheasant island; but some other factor or factors also appear to have exerted an influence.

Habitat

The pheasant is one of the most adaptable game species on the continent. This becomes evident when we consider how, as an exotic, it has found suitable environment throughout much of a wide belt extending from the Mason-Dixon Line northward into southern Canada, and from the Atlantic to the Pacific Oceans.

In Missouri, pheasants and other game species have been most successful on soils of intermediate fertility. (Albrecht 1944, Denny 1944). Soils of low fertility did not prove suitable for pheasant production, while the most fertile soils were precluded from high production because of intensive agriculture. Soils throughout the plains and prairies generally are high in fertility and are a factor limiting pheasant abundance directly. This is supported by the fact that, at one time or another, much of the region has produced good pheasant populations. An exception to this may be found in the large sandhill region of northwestern Nebraska. There, we find pheasants in the marshes, stream valleys, and farmlands, but the over-all population never is high.

Pheasants also appear to be tolerant of a wide variation in rainfall. At various times and locations, they have thrived on less than 15 and more than 30 inches of precipitation.

With the knowledge at hand, the game manager, given complete control of the land, could produce good pheasant range through most of the plains and prairies. Agricultural interests are not likely, however, to turn over the bread, beef, and pork basket of the nation to game men for management. Throughout the region, whenever food, winter cover, and nesting and brood cover are found well dispersed, and in good association, pheasants usually thrive. The food may be corn, small grains, or weed seeds. Winter cover may be shelter belts, willow or plum thickets, or herbaceous cover. Nesting cover, frequently deficient and always difficult to supplement, can be almost any herbaceous growth, this year's or last, which provides concealment in April and May.

The pheasant, like all species, has definite habitat requirements, but its adaptability permits the acceptance of many substitutes.

Whether or not a cause-and-effect relationship exists, the following conditions appear to be characteristic of the best pheasant habitat of the region:

1. Fifty to 75 percent of the land under cultivation—the minimum of cultivation in a non-grass land economy.

2. Average farm sizes from a quarter section to one section.

3. A good, year-round supply of food; this frequently is corn, but small grains and weed seeds have supplied the requirements under favorable winter conditions.

4. A relatively high percentage of idle or waste land. This may be a result of economic conditions, weather, poorly drained topography, small areas of marginal agricultural soils, etc.

5. These units of non-agricultural land are characterized by one or a combination of the following: shelter belts, sweet clover, sunflower, kochia, other weeds, slough margins, plum thickets and willow thickets.

PLATE XLI.—*Above.* The pheasant range extends into the plains, where water becomes a factor for both crops and birds (South Dakota Dept. of Game, Fish and Parks). *Below.* Where there are unmowed roadsides, pheasants have weedy travel lanes and woody cover (South Dakota Dept. of Game, Fish and Parks).

6. Grazing, particularly winter grazing, moderate to light.

7. Few dairy cattle or sheep, moderate to heavy hog raising, and extensive feeding of range cattle in feed lots.

PHEASANT BIOLOGY

Reproduction

In this region, breeding activity begins in groups of birds during late winter and early spring (February and March), when winter concentrations of pheasants break up, and cocks disperse and establish crowing territories. The progress of the breeding season is marked by an increase in crowing intensity, fighting between males, and display of males before females. Nesting starts in late March and early April and attains a maximum about the last half of May. Breeding and nesting dates are affected by weather conditions, and sub-peaks in both activities may occur as a result of interruption in breeding cycle, or nesting failures.

Broods may begin to hatch as early as the latter part of April, but hatching peaks are not reached until late June or early July. Hatching peaks may vary as much as a month from year to year, depending on weather conditions. They also vary somewhat within the region because of differences in climate and varying weather conditions.

Production is dependent on nesting success, brood size, percentage of hens bringing off broods, and juvenile survival. Studies of nesting success in Minnesota, North Dakota, Iowa and South Dakota show the following success ratios:

TABLE 32.   Percent of successful nests as indicated by nesting studies.

	1939	1940	1941	1946	1947	1948	1949	1950
Minnesota	..	..	29	..	..	..	..	..
North Dakota	..	32	27	..	14	14	..	..
Iowa	36	25	23	..	..	..	37	7.7
South Dakota	..	..	..	26	12	7	41	..

The low success indicated by these studies is due partly to the fact that the nests included more than one attempt from

many of the birds; that is, hens having nest failure later produced successful nests. The end success, per hen, undoubtedly
was much higher than the success of all nests. Studies in Wisconsin have shown that it is normal for hens to lay a large
number of eggs before a clutch finally is incubated and
brought off (Kabat *et. al.* 1948). Counts of ovulated follicles
in a small sample of hens with broods, in South Dakota in
1951, showed that it was not unusual for 30 or more eggs to
be laid by each hen. A renesting study made in North Dakota
in 1951 showed hens laying 26.4 eggs apiece and averaging
2.4 nests per hen.

Unfortunately, long-term information is too incomplete for
the region to draw definite conclusions on whether nesting
success is an important factor in determining populations.
In North Dakota, the percentage of nests hatched was higher
in 1940 and 1941, years of good population, than in 1947 and
1948, years of low population. In South Dakota, 1947 and
1948 were years of low populations, and low nesting success.
In 1949, population increases were noted and nesting success
was higher. Success in 1946 was higher than in 1947 and
1948, but populations in 1946 declined and fall age ratios
of young to adults, as determined by bag checks, were low.
The Minnesota data offer no opportunity for comparison, but
success in 1941, when pheasants were plentiful, was relatively
high. Annual studies of nesting success might throw some light
on its relation to population trends (Kozicky and Hendrickson, 1951).

Brood size appears to be a logical place to look for causes
of variation in production, and hence population changes.
Many thousands of broods have been counted in this region
in the past several years. The following table shows average
brood sizes by years for several states, although figures are
not comparable between states because of the differences in
methods used.

In Iowa, during 1939-1941, comparatively large broods coincided with good population levels of pheasants; in 1949,

when pheasants had recovered partially from the recent low, nest success also was high. The low success in 1950 was not accompanied by a corresponding decrease in pheasants, but the figures were from nests in mowed hay fields, where many failures would be expected.

The data for years of high population for each state are followed by an asterisk. It seems that no well-defined correlation exists between population levels and the average size of observed broods.

TABLE 33.   July and August brood size by years.

Year	Nebraska	Minnesota	North Dakota	Iowa	South Dakota
1942	7.0*	....	6.47*	....	....
1943	5.1*	....	6.67*	....	....
1944	....	....	7.49*	....	....
1945	6.2*	5.5	....	....	....
1946	6.5*	6.1	6.70	....	5.29*
1947	5.1	5.5	6.37	....	5.47
1948	6.44	8.2	6.77	6.6	6.50
1949	6.27	7.9	7.20	7.2*	6.2
1950	6.43*	6.7*	....	7.2*	5.6*

* Years of comparatively good populations.

The average brood size has ranged from 5.1 to 8.2 in the five states over a 9-year period but there is a surprising uniformity in the general picture of brood sizes. At least, there are not the marked differences that one might expect if variations in brood size were a major factor influencing production.

Data from North Dakota, Iowa, and South Dakota show that about 9 young leave the nest. Since brood sizes by July and August are 6 to 7, a mortality of 25 to 30 percent is indicated. Studies of average brood sizes by weeks in South Dakota showed a decrease of 28 percent in brood size between hatching and the 8th week, and a probable maximum juvenile mortality of 35 percent by the time broods were 14 weeks old. The major part of the mortality occurs, as might be expected, during the first three weeks of life.

Studies in South Dakota, 1947-1950, in which over 4,000 broods were aged to the nearest week, showed that early-hatched broods averaged about 15 percent larger than late-hatched broods, a direct reflection of the smaller clutch size of late nests. Both early and late broods were found to average smaller in number than those hatched nearer the peak of hatching.

From available data, neither nest success nor brood size appears to be a prime factor determining production of young, so we must look to other aspects of reproduction for the answer. The first of these is the success of hens in producing broods. How many of the hens present at the start of the breeding season live through the season and produce young?

Information on the percentage of hens observed with young has been gathered by some states in recent years. A summary of this follows:

TABLE 34.   Percent of hens observed with young.

	1942	1945	1948	1949	1950	1951
Nebraska	65	80	82	81	74	..
Iowa	..	..	63	62	69	62
South Dakota	..	..	83	84	84	79

Comparing these figures with general population trends, we find that in Nebraska from 1942 to 1945, while populations decreased, the observed percentage of hens with broods increased. There are no data for 1946 and 1947 when pheasants were at a low ebb. During 1948-1950, years of population recovery, the percentage of hens with young declined. Data for Iowa for 1948-1951, also a period of recovery and higher density levels following the recent low, show uniform success, but at a lower level than either Nebraska or South Dakota. Success in South Dakota for 1948 to 1951, years of population growth, was uniformly high the first three years, dropping slightly in 1951 when pheasants reached their highest level since the 1947 low.

These comparisons suggest that if a relationship exists between population trends and the observed percentage of hens with young, it is an inverse one. In low populations, success is high and remains high as bird numbers build up, declining as the population reaches a maximum density.

The percentage of hens with young does not correspond with the age ratios found in bag checks the following fall. Increases in the percentage of hens with young are not always followed by higher age ratios, and vice versa. Age ratios fluctuate considerably during periods when the percentage of hens with young remains relatively constant.

The percent of hens with young is not easy to determine accurately. Data from large samples in South Dakota for 1948 to 1951, when the percentage of hens with young was determined each week from standardized observations, show that it increased from week to week during the summer. Similar data from Nebraska for 1948 show an increase through the first week of August, and a decrease in the succeeding three weeks.

TABLE 35. Percentage of hens with young by weeks.

Week of Observation	South Dakota—1950		Nebraska—1948	
	No. of Hens	Percent with Young	No. of Hens	Percent with Young
June 5-11	....	....	205	9
June 12-18	....	....	96	0
June 19-25	370	0.0	106	23
June 26-July 2	266	0.8	82	30
July 3-9	259	6.9	241	54
July 10-16	196	10.7	321	50
July 17-23	253	26.1	374	61
July 24-30	215	48.9	573	70
July 31-Aug. 6	257	45.9	446	82
Aug. 7-13	337	59.6	462	73
Aug. 14-20	288	75.3	368	69
Aug. 21-27	156	83.9	173	60
Aug. 28-Sept. 3	222	86.9	....	....

Obviously, the week or weeks when counts are taken greatly influences the percent of hens found with young. Spot checks made in a one-or two-week period mean little unless something is known of the progress of the hatch, and the seasonal pattern of success.

Obtaining a true picture of hen success is complicated by the fact that observed success continues to increase throughout most of the period when data can be collected. By early September, many young are difficult to distinguish from hens, and the break-up and intermingling of broods makes further counts unreliable. Where, on the ascending scale, the true success figure may be taken is not known with certainty. Nebraska and South Dakota studies suggest that the eighth week after the week of peak hatch may give the most reliable figure on percentage of hens with young.

There are several reasons why the percentage of hens with young cannot be determined *per se* from field observations. First, broods, especially young ones, are not always seen with the hen. Flushing all hens seen will overcome this difficulty to a great extent. Second, and more important, is the effect of changing behavior of hens through the hatching and brooding season. Hens that are incubating, hens which have very young broods, and hens which have completed nesting and brooding (successful or not), and begun to molt, do not appear along roads and are missed in field observations. Toward the end of the summer, there is a tendency for only successful hens to appear; unsuccessful hens are molting and have retired to cover. At that time, it is not uncommon for a week of observation in one area to show 100 percent of the hens with broods.

Perhaps the continued gathering of figures through a period of low reproduction and falling populations will prove the trends to be valuable in spite of shortcomings in technique.

We believe that information showing the percentage of hens with young is a logical place to look for causes of varying production in spite of the fact that the data now available are not strong. The persistence of hens in renesting and eventually bringing off a brood could well make the difference between good and poor reproduction, and is a factor which might be expected to respond to weather conditions, population densities, disturbance factors, or those physiological unknowns associated with cycles, if such there be.

Mortality

Finally, pheasant production may be affected by mortality, both of breeding stock and of juveniles. If the number of hens present at the start of breeding is reduced seriously during the season, production will be low in spite of normal or above-normal observed brood sizes, and percentage of hens with young. In regard to one important mortality factor, there is good information on hen losses from hayfield mowing.

TABLE 36.   Hens killed or injured in hay mowing.

	1941	1942	1943	1944	1947	1949	1950
Nebraska	33%	40%	1 ♀ :6.4	1 ♀ :6.5			
(alfalfa)			acres	acres			
Minnesota				30%			
Montana					1 ♀ :12.7		
					acres		
South Dakota						39%	32%

Hen mortality of this magnitude cannot help but reduce production, especially where hayfields provide the principal nesting cover for pheasants. The amount of mortality is influenced by whether or not the date of the first cutting of hay occurs before or after most of the nests are hatched. First cuttings ordinarily will find a high percentage of hens still incubating, but there is no analysis of the over-all effect of this type of mortality on populations. In recent years, pheasants have increased in this region, although the amount of hay mowing going on has not decreased to our knowledge.

Information on hen losses from other causes during the nesting and brooding season is practically non-existent. Indices of pre-breeding populations from census methods currently in use are not comparable and cannot be used to show hen losses. Something is known about the annual turnover to be expected in hens, but what portion of the year's loss represents breeding females has not been determined.

The final consideration in production is juvenile mortality. This has been considered in the discussion of brood sizes, where it was shown that in five states, over a 9-year period, broods in late July and August ranged from 5 to 8 birds. Juvenile mortality did not appear to be an important factor in production, or in population changes. A mortality of about 30 percent may be expected between the time the young hatch and when they reach two to three months old. Mortality to the hunting season would not be much greater, since most losses occur in the first few weeks of life.

Brood counts show mortality of the attritional type, resulting in progressive decrease in size. They do not tell anything about losses to production caused by entire broods being wiped out. Young pheasants are susceptible to chilling, and entire broods might perish if separated from the hen during cold, wet weather. It seems unlikely that mortality of this nature would be extensive enough to have any substantial effect on the over-all production. However, in heavily settled areas, with closely spaced farms and towns, and the accompanying greater amount of disturbances from man, dogs, cats, stock and other causes, an appreciable amount of such mortality might occur.

In summary, the data reviewed on nest success, brood sizes, percentage of hens with young, and hen and juvenile mortality, while not conclusive, suggest that the major determinant in production of young, and hence population increases, is the ability of hens to survive through the breeding season and bring off broods.

Density

Density in terms of birds per acre has been determined for various areas in the region by drive counts and aerial censuses.

In Minnesota, drive censuses in Martin County showed 32 birds per square mile in 1939, 63 in 1940, and 28 in 1941. In Scott County, there were 14 birds per section in 1939 and 30 in 1941. Drive censuses in February and March, 1939, showed 29 pheasants per section in the Fairmont region, 28 in the Belle Plaine area, 107 near Mankato, 25 at Mountain Lake, and 20 at Redwood Falls (censused in May).

Counts made during organized rabbit and coyote drives in Nebraska in late winter, 1943-44, showed populations of 8 to 133 pheasants per square mile and indicated a spring stocking in good range of 100 birds per section.

Aerial censuses in North Dakota in February, 1946, gave densities of 11 and 15 birds per section in two sample townships. Aerial count on the former township in 1947 gave 12

PLATE XLII.—*Upper.* A nesting hen that did not escape the mower (E. L. Kozicky, Iowa Cooperative Wildlife Research Unit). *Lower.* A nest in alfalfa, exposed by the mower (E. L. Kozicky, Iowa Cooperative Wildlife Research Unit).

birds per section. Aerial censuses in North Dakota in February, 1950, gave densities of 7 and 12 birds per section on two sample townships.

Populations on nesting study areas in North Dakota were 60 per square mile on an area in 1948, and 51 per square mile on a study area in 1947. In Iowa pre-nesting populations on a nest study area were 50 per section in 1939, 80 in 1940, 125 in 1941, 30 in 1949, 50 in 1950, and 60 in 1951.

In the Flathead Valley of Montana, walking-strip censuses gave populations of 672 birds per section in 1942, 832 in 1944, 416 in 1946 and 493 in 1947. Pre-season populations on the Fairfield Bench in 1949, determined by the Kelker index, were 298 birds per square mile.

Aerial censuses made in several South Dakota counties during the years 1948-1951 showed winter populations as follows:

TABLE 37.   Wintering pheasants per square mile—South Dakota.

County	1948	1949	1950	1951
Aurora	..	73	95	94
Beadle	104	..	152	..
Bon Homme	..	15	..	..
Corson	..	29	17	8
Deuel	8	..	..	..
Faulk	..	40	42	26
Sully	64	39	17	16
Walworth	..	52	19	10

These counts are average densities for areas of 80 square miles in most cases. Populations ran as high as 1,000 birds and more per square mile in local concentrations.

The plains and prairie states have maintained breeding populations ranging from 8 to 152 birds per section in recent years. During years of high populations, there probably were large areas in the Dakotas, Minnesota, Nebraska, and Iowa where breeding populations exceeded 100 and likely reached 200 or more birds per section. Average densities of 50 to 75 birds per section represent fairly good populations, which, with ordinary reproduction success, will furnish good fall hunting. Where breeding populations are 75 to 100 or more per section, pheasants are abundant, and good hatches will result in good hunting. Fall populations in the region during the years of pheasant abundance range from 300 to over 1,000 birds per section in the better habitat.

Sex Ratio

The proportion of cocks and hens in post-season populations is a reflection of hunting pressure, compensated possibly by other mortality factors.

Winter sex ratio counts of concentrations, the method which gives the most nearly accurate sex ration data, show the following ratios prevailing in this region in the past decade:

TABLE 38.   Winter sex ratios   (cocks per 100 hens).

Year	Minnesota	Nebraska	North Dakota	Montana	Iowa	South Dakota
1941	33	..	..	..	..	..
1942	..	100	..	50	..	..
1943	50	..	..	..	..	..
1944	..	75-100	..	..	..	..
1945	..	..	..	..	..	75-100
1946	43	..	..	20	..	75-100
1947	36	..	50	48	..	75
1948	77	..	50	31	48	48
1949	59	..	50	32	40	53
1950	32	..	58	40	34	47

With the population levels and hunting pressure that we have had in these states, pre-breeding sex ratios have not dropped below 30 cocks per 100 hens, and have been between 75 and 100 in a number of cases. In other words, this region has between 1 and 3 hens per cock, with a ratio of 2 hens per cock occurring commonly. In only one case (Montana in 1946), was a sex ratio of more than 3 hens per cock recorded, and that was not a state-wide figure.

Sex ratios at the hunting season should range from about 65 to 85 cocks per 100 hens, depending upon the reproduction. With a good hatch, the fall population would be composed to a large extent of juveniles, evenly sexed or nearly so, and hence the sex ratio of the entire population would tend to approach 1:1. Thus at the start of the hunting season, there should be no more than 1.0 to 1.5 hens per cock, and the apparent large surplus of hens that sportsmen sometimes complain about is not likely to exist.

Age Ratios

A third population characteristic, the proportion of young to adults in the fall, is a measure of reproductive success. Age ratios are determined by making bag checks during the hunting season. The following table summarizes age ratio data for this region.

TABLE 39.   Fall age ratio of cocks (young per adult).

	1943	1944	1945	1946	1947	1948	1949	1950
Iowa	..	..	..	..	..	5.26	4.82	5.96
Minnesota	2.5	4.6	7.4	..	..	..	4.50	..
Nebraska	4.8	..	3.0	1.41	4.15	2.39	4.94	2.58
North Dakota	..	2.2	2.0	1.88	3.05	3.62	2.04	4.78
Montana	..	..	..	..	..	4.20	3.70	4.50
South Dakota	..	..	1.09	1.51	2.98	4.29	3.12	5.34
South Dakota (corrected)	..	..	..	1.09	1.51	2.55	3.21	2.15	2.51

These ratios indicate that fall populations in this region may be composed of from 50 to 90 percent young birds, depending upon the success of the hatch. The lowest age ratios reported, ranging from about 1 to 2 young per adult, occurred in North Dakota for the years 1945 and 1946, and again in 1949; in Nebraska in 1946; and in South Dakota in 1945 and 1946. These low ratios (1949 excepted) came in the last year of the recent pheasant high and the first year of the decline. Although 1947 was the low point in pheasant numbers, age ratios were not unduly low and had risen from the previous year.

South Dakota age ratios, corrected for sex ratios, show a lowered age ratio at the time of the peak populations (1945), an increase in the years of the major decline and the lowest population (1946 and 1947), continuing as populations rose but tending to level off as populations approached high densities. The high 1945 population resulted from a large carry-over of adult birds from the still higher 1944 population. The decline came as a result of the low age ratios. Further studies of age ratios may prove more definitely that reproduction in pheasants, as in many animals, is linked closely with population density.

Production

Production, in terms of the number of birds hunters are able to get during the open season, may not be a population characteristic nor a biological feature, but it certainly is an important aspect of pheasant management. The following tables show what pheasant populations have produced for the sportsmen in this region in recent years, expressed in season bags, daily bags and hours required to bag a bird.

Our present knowledge shows that the average daily bag has ranged from slightly less than 1 to over 3 birds per day in the past 10 years. Season bags have varied from a little less than 3 birds to over 37. The time required to bag a pheasant has been as high as 4.9 hours and as low as 53 minutes. Data are incomplete and it would be interesting to have more information for the peak years in the early forties. It seems likely that during the best years in the Dakotas and Nebraska, daily bags averaged as high as 3 to 5 or more birds, and that the time required to kill a bird averaged as little as 30 to 45 minutes.

It appears that the better range of this region will produce average daily bags of 2 to 3 pheasants in years of "normal" populations. The poorest years will produce a bird or two per day, and the best years, 3 or more.

Winter Losses

Winter losses of significant magnitude usually occur in various parts of the plains and prairie region every year, especially in the northern sector. In the severe winter of 1935-36, a study on 4,900 acres in Winnebago County, Iowa, showed that approximately 1,000 pheasants were present in the fall (Green 1938). Of these, 501 were harvested by sportsmen, and 493 remained to enter the winter. On March 5, 1936, the termination of the study, 246 pheasants were left on the area. A winter loss of 238 birds, 48.2 percent, was known to have occurred, and only nine could not be accounted for. Starvation and predation losses were negligible, and the poaching loss was low. The highest loss came from freezing and choking during severe

Table 40. Pheasants killed per hunter.

State	Average Bag	1940	1941	1942	1943	1944	1945	1946	1947	1948	1949	1950
Minnesota	Daily	...	...	...	...	...	...	...	...	...	...	...
	Season	...	...	3.4	...	...	3.1	2.27	...	...	...	...
North Dakota	Daily	...	...	...	...	...	...	...	...	...	...	...
	Season	13.1	16.7	34.1	37.2	48.9	38.3	8.7	4.7	6.6	5.9	1.1
Nebraska	Daily	...	2.26	2.61	2.33	2.36	2.39	2.05	1.30	1.65	1.28	1.77
	Season	...	8.6	11.1	18.8	16.1	19.2	11.2	4.76	7.01	4.39	7.51
Montana	Daily	...	...	...	...	...	...	...	.95	.68—	...	1.0
	Season	...	...	...	...	...	...	...	...	1.59	...	1.2
South Dakota	Daily	...	...	...	...	...	...	...	2.17	2.14	2.74	1.76
	Season	...	...	...	...	...	37.2	17.7	11.7	14.1	13.2	...

Table 41. Time required to bag a pheasant (minutes).

State	1941	1942	1943	1946	1947	1948	1949	1950
Nebraska[1]	90	64	53	...	...	68	86	...
Montana	...	...	...	...	294	193	187	...
South Dakota	...	...	...	85	96	330	103	96
Iowa	...	...	...	...	...	198	210	180

[1] For Valley County, a better than average pheasant area.

weather. Survival was highest in the flocks that roosted in dense cover where it was not necessary to range over long distances to obtain food. Losses were highest in the flocks that roosted in open cover and were forced to range some distance in feeding. An analysis of the 238 winter losses revealed that 0.4 percent was due to starvation; 0.4 percent, predation; 4.8 percent, illegal shooting; 6.0 percent, pneumonia; 57.6 percent, freezing or choking; 16.0 percent, undetermined (snowed under); and 14.8 percent, strayed from the area. Starvation, as shown in South Dakota, occasionally results in localized mortality in significant magnitude, but it is unimportant in the over-all picture (Nelson and Jansen 1949).

The well-remembered Armistice Day storm in 1940 resulted in pheasant mortality of 10 percent or more. The sudden exposure of birds unaccustomed to weather conditions of midwinter severity was believed responsible for the spectacular loss (Scott and Baskett 1941). The amount of mortality was related closely to the heavy snowfall and high wind velocity. The latter was believed to have been of most consequence. Other blizzard conditions were reported in Minnesota in 1936, 1946, 1947, and 1951 (Erickson et al. 1951). South Dakota has had high storm mortality (50 percent or more) in some parts of the state in 1947-48; 1948-49, and 1949-50 (Kirsch 1951), the same as North Dakota and Nebraska (Miller 1948, McClure 1948).

Predation and Diseases

There is no evidence that predation on adults or juveniles is a limiting factor to pheasants in the plains and prairie region. Nests, however, are susceptible to predation and locally this might be a factor of consequence in the life cycle of the species.

The ringneck pheasant is remarkably free of known diseases. Of 278 birds autopsied in the parasitology laboratory at the University of Minnesota, only seven kinds of parasitic worms were found (Erickson, et al. 1951). *Heterakis gallinae*, a common parasite of domestic fowl, was the most common. Other roundworms recovered were *Capillaria contorta* from the crops of seven birds, and *Ascaridea* sp. from the intestine of one bird. The only tapeworm found was *Choanotaenea infundibulum*. Of the intestinal flukes, *Echinoparyphium recurvatum* and *E. contiguum* were the only two species found. Only two birds were found infected by *Eimeria phasianii*, a protozoan that causes coccidiosis. Ticks were found on one bird, lice on one, and mites on one. Only one case of pullorum disease was found. In another group of 96 birds, the most frequent causes of death were as follows: brain hemorrhages and mechanical injuries, 11 birds; exposure, 17; starvation, 8; tuberculosis, 1; aspergillosis, 3; and bumblefoot, 2. McClure (1949) discusses the prevalence of eyeworm (*Oxyspirura petrowi*) in pheasants in Nebraska.

Food Habits

In 1946-48, the South Dakota Department of Game, Fish, and Parks collected 1,679 pheasants and analyzed their crop contents. These birds were collected during every month of the year and from all kinds of habitat. Adult pheasants depend largely on farm crops, obtaining over four-fifths of their food from that source. Weed seeds make up 7 percent of the diet, insects 7 percent, plant foliage 7 percent, and mineral matter one percent. Corn accounted for 57 percent of the year's food; wheat, 20 percent. Of weed seeds, the foxtails were most important. Grasshoppers composed 2.3 percent of the crop contents. Other insects included cut worms, crickets, ground beetles, ants, millipeds, etc. Pheasants, like other gallinaceous birds, include much green leafy material in their diet. Almost three-fourths of the crops contained plant foliage, which composed 4.5 percent of the food for the year.

Young pheasants eat much the same foods as adults, but in different proportions. Their food habits change during the summer as the birds mature, and by fall, are similar to those of old birds. Juveniles eat a large amount of animal matter, consisting of one-third the diet in July and August, and one-fifth in September. Grasshoppers, crickets, and ants were the most common species consumed. Additional studies in Neb-

PLATE XLIII.—Pheasants seldom die of starvation, but on the northern plains, in severe winters, it may occur. This is the characteristic pose of a starved pheasant (Bernard A. Nelson, South Dakota Dept. of Game, Fish and Parks).

raska and Minnesota have found essentially the same relationship among the major food items (Swenk 1930, Fried 1940, Mohler 1949).

TECHNIQUES

The wildlife biologist sometimes is criticized for devoting too much of his time to the development of techniques of study. It is argued that time spent developing a new method of estimating population, determining age, or calculating movement does not contribute a single bird to the hunter's bag. Fortunately, this type of criticism is fading, because the administrator and the thinking sportsman have come to realize that techniques are the tools with which the field man must work. Unfortunately, the technician cannot, like the carpenter or plumber, purchase his implements ready made and century tested. Scientific game management is a young profession, and

PLATE XLIV.—*Upper*. In severe winters, direct killing by prairie blizzards may bring heavy local losses. This hen was caught out of cover by a storm and was close to death. The bird recovered quickly in a car trunk (James W. Kimball, South Dakota Dept. of Game, Fish and Parks). *Lower*. Narrow shelter belts and small cover patches can be winter death traps for pheasants (Bernard A. Nelson, South Dakota Dept. of Game, Fish and Parks).

practically the only methods available are those developed by contemporary workers. More and better ones are needed badly.

Winter Mortality Studies

As has been pointed out, over most of the plains and prairie states, blizzards occasionally cause serious mortality in local areas, and in the northern part of the region, severe winter weather is a limiting factor in maintaining pheasant populations. Various techniques have been used to measure the loss of pheasants from winter storms, and to determine the factors affecting survival. The most widely used method consists of car and foot surveys, which record both living and killed birds following each blizzard, and indicate the percentage of birds killed. This method is suitable for extensive application and is fast and economical, but accuracy varies with snow conditions and the nature of the storm. When dead birds are not buried in drifts, highly accurate results may be obtained.

An excellent means of determining storm losses is to make pre- and post-storm aerial counts of pheasants in a given area. This method has limited application because snow conditions must be right, and counts must precede, as well as follow, the storm. When used, it provides a check on other techniques of determining winter loss.

A third method is to determine, through periodic counts, the number of birds in a winter concentration, or in a given area. Then, counts made immediately following a storm should give the percent of mortality for that particular storm. In practice, this technique has not worked too well because of pheasant movements, inadequate sample where the storm strikes, and inaccessibility of the area following a storm.

In studies of winter mortality, the dead birds found should be checked for weight, injuries, sex, amount and nature of iceing, and location in relation to different cover types. Weather data for each storm should be recorded and compared with the degree of mortality resulting from the storm. By a study of cover and weather conditions in relation to pheasant losses, habitat deficiencies and the cover development necessary to carry birds through the winter can be determined. The amount of loss to be expected from blizzards of varying degrees of severity also will become known.

Starvation occurs occasionally during hard winters in the plains and prairie states, but it is of minor over-all importance as a mortality factor. Its occurrence is obvious to individuals making periodic observations in an area. Starving birds do not fly or run readily, and those that die are emaciated and often die in roosting forms.

Mortality from predators and from accidents is associated with winter storms and may be considered as indirect storm losses. Pheasants often are killed during blizzards by flying into trees, buildings, telephone wires, and power lines. Following a severe storm, they are more susceptible to predation, since they may be encumbered by balls of ice and snow, and because escape cover is filled with snow.

It should be remembered, however, that the "compensation" principle applies, and some storm loss may be replacing other kinds of mortality in a normal population turnover. A storm loss of 30 percent does not mean that the ensuing breeding population necessarily will be reduced proportionally.

Winter Sex Ratio Studies

Knowledge of the sex ratio of a pheasant population is useful in management and in studies of population dynamics. Age ratios of cocks in the hunter's bag mean little as a measure of reproduction, unless they are interpreted in terms of sex ratio. Sex ratio studies made after a hunting season show the effects of hunting and often make it possible to measure the degree of the kill. They likewise are necessary for interpreting population trends shown by crowing counts.

Accurate sex ratios are difficult to obtain during much of the year, because pheasant behavior during the breeding, nesting, brooding and molting periods results in a constantly changing "observed" ratio. Roadside counts are distorted by the more conspicuous coloring and bold nature of the males, which makes them much more conspicuous.

PLATE XLV.—*Upper*. In each region, weed seeds form an important part of the ringneck's diet. On the prairies, the wild sunflower is used commonly (South Dakota Dept. of Game, Fish and Parks). *Lower*. Crop residues provide abundant food in season. These wheat heads did not reach the combine (South Dakota Dept. of Game, Fish and Parks).

Winter is the best time to get accurate sex ratio data on a state-wide basis, especially when snow and other conditions are such that practically all of the population is concentrated in winter cover areas. It is possible to obtain an accurate sex ratio from counts of these concentrations; and samples from a sufficient number of concentrations will give the sex ratio pattern for an entire state.

Sex ratio counts should be made during cold or stormy weather, since mild weather induces individual cocks to range out from winter cover. Hens are apt to remain together, and, unless the sampling is thorough, an accurate sex ratio will not be obtained. Another reason for sampling a number and variety of cover areas in the same locality is the possibility of segregation of sexes in winter flocks. The extent of segregation is not constant, but where a choice is available, there is some indication that cocks will select tall but open cover, suitable to a running escape, while hens prefer a dense cover which affords better concealment. In South Dakota, such segregation was noted in some areas in 1945; on the other hand, mixed flocks appeared to be the rule in recent years. Where good winter cover is scarce, it appears that birds are more likely to concentrate in mixed flocks.

Other methods of determining winter sex ratios include observing and recording the birds moving between roosting and loafing areas, between loafing cover and feeding locations, or of pheasants spread out over feeding grounds. In some cases, roadside counts and rural mail carrier records are used, but these data are more valuable as an index of year-to-year trends in sex ratio than in providing actual figures on the number of hens per cock.

Reliable winter sex ratio information is necessary to any well-rounded pheasant management program, but obtaining it involves considerable work and a scientific approach. Incidental observations are of little or no value because of the possibilities for error.

Pheasant Census Techniques

Censuses, a vital tool in both administration and research, provide the data required for setting hunting regulations and for studying population changes. Methods used in this region are largely indices to relative abundance, although some progress has been made in obtaining actual population figures.

Of the 10 states and one province from which data were obtained, three (Wyoming, Kansas and Manitoba) make no pheasant censuses, relying instead on general observations of field personnel.

The census method used most widely is the crowing count, employed by all states that census pheasants. The fall roadside census is being used in the north-central region in every state except Nebraska and Missouri. The rural mail carrier's survey, a type of roadside census, is used in Nebraska, North Dakota, and South Dakota. Aerial censusing is done by North Dakota, South Dakota, and Montana.

Roadside brood censuses are made in Missouri on a limited scale, and in North Dakota and Montana. Transects are used by Montana only. South Dakota tried belt transects in 1950, but found them impractical. Other methods experimented with previously in this region include a field traverse used by Minnesota in 1947, and a one-minute crowing count, detonation counts, a transect by horseback, and scat counts used in Nebraska in 1941-1943 (McClure 1945).

The Missouri Office of River Basin Studies of the U. S. Fish and Wildlife Service in this region use crowing counts, roadside censuses, aerial censuses, drive counts, field traverses, and quadrats.

Roadside and rural mail carrier censuses

At present, the roadside census is being used in the fall by game commission personnel, and rural mail carriers make counts in spring, summer, and fall. Basically, these censuses are line counts made from an automobile, and are most successful when timed to coincide with daily and seasonal behavior of the pheasant. From about May through mid-October, pheasants tend to be distributed throughout their range; that is, there are no large social aggregations such as are found during late fall and winter. During early morning hours, pheasants move from roosting sites to other cover, and an opportunity is afforded, depending on the stage of the reproductive cycle, weather, and cover conditions, to observe a large segment of the population.

With this knowledge, biologists in Iowa developed a standardized fall technique to eliminate some of the variables, such as time of day and year, weather, and cover conditions (Bennett and Hendrickson 1938).

As an example of differing opinions, and applications of such a method in different states, Iowa is convinced that the fall roadside census conducted by conservation officers in the primary range of 33 counties in northern Iowa depicts annual population trends (Stiles and Hendrickson 1946, Kozicky 1952, Kozicky *et al.* 1952). Minnesota, North Dakota, and South Dakota believe the fall roadside census to be useful chiefly in showing state-wide trends and distribution. Montana feels that it is inconsistent and a poor method but that it indicates the minimum number of birds present (Fisher *et al.* 1947). Personnel of th eMissouri Office of River Basin Studies comment that the roadside census is too variable to be an actual census, but it does indicate distribution and comparative populations. Missouri discontinued this method because, in their opinion, it was worthless in censusing low populations. Nebraska discarded it in favor of the crowing count and rural mail carriers survey, although they believe it to be satisfactory if the sample is large and the census is made by competent personnel.

In summary, the utility of the fall roadside census depends upon the sampling design and size, observers, proper timing, topography, weather conditions, and agricultural practices.

To make the most of the potential volume of data at a low cost, Kimball recruited Nebraska rural mail carriers in 1944 to conduct roadside censuses at specified times. At present, Nebraska, North Dakota, South Dakota, and Iowa use the rural mail carrier survey. Missouri and Montana tried the method but discontinued it because it did not give a satisfactory meas-urement of low or irregularly distributed populations.

The rural mail carrier census involves the keeping of records by carriers of all the game they see on their mail routes over a designated number of days. The number of carriers cooperat-ing in the survey is 300-400 in North Dakota, 500 in South Dakota, 800 in Iowa and over 600 in Nebraska. The system is inexpensive and has a public relations value because of the large number of carriers cooperating in it. To date, the relia-bility of the rural mail carrier count has not been determined. It is subject to variations resulting from weather conditions, time of day and year, type of cooperator, cover conditions, and sampling.

Crowing count census

The crowing count census was used experimentally from 1942-47 in Nebraska. The method in use currently was devel-oped in Nebraska by Kimball (1949), who gave it its first extensive application in South Dakota in the spring of 1946. It is in use now in every state that makes pheasant censuses in the area.

The method is standardized more than any other in general use, which is fortunate, because it facilitates direct comparison of population indices between states.

It is based on the fact that under the right weather condi-tions, cock pheasants crow consistently for a period of an hour and a half each morning during the height of the crowing season. The number of calls heard from one spot during a specified time gives a good index to the number of cocks present. In practice, established routes are run, and stops made at regular intervals, to count the number of calls which can be heard. The average count of all the stops is the population index for the route.

Census routes usually are 20 miles long, and are located randomly, or stratified by counties, in major pheasant ranges. The number of routes varies from 198 in Iowa, 100 in North Dakota and 71 in South Dakota to 5 in Missouri. The listening period is 2 minutes in all states, and stops are made at mile intervals except in North Dakota, which uses a 2-mile interval. Censuses are not made when the wind exceeds 8 miles per hour. The time of morning for making counts is from 30 to 45 minutes before sunrise to 30 to 60 minutes after sunrise. Censuses are conducted in April, May, and early June, with May being the best month.

Initial attempts to derive bird-per-square-mile figures from crowing counts have been made by South Dakota. A study of the relationship of crowing counts to aerial census data, from the same areas, gave a conversion coefficient of .311. That is, the number of cocks per square mile is equal to the crowing count multiplied by .311. The total breeding population then can be determined by adding the female component of the population determined from sex ratio data. The formulae for obtaining population figures from crowing counts are:

$$C \times .311 = c \quad \text{(Cocks per square mile)}$$
$$c \times \frac{100}{SR} = h \quad \text{(Hens per square mile)}$$
$$c + h = P \quad \text{(Total population)}$$

where C = crowing count, SR = sex ratio in cocks per 100 hens and c, h and P equal cocks, hens and total birds per square mile, respectively.

Aerial census

Pheasants are censused by airplane in North Dakota, South Dakota, and Montana, and in Missouri by the Office of River Basin Studies. North Dakota first used the technique in 1947. Piper Cubs, or similar aircraft, have been found most suitable for observing birds. Flying is done at speeds of 60 to 80 m.p.h., and at altitudes of 75 to 200 feet. Sample areas are flown, which vary in size from 36 to 105 square miles, and in shape from long narrow strips to squares. The method of counting birds is to traverse the area at intervals close enough to scan all cover areas, locate concentrations of pheasants, and count the birds.

The right snow and weather conditions are essential to making accurate counts from the air. There must be sufficient snow to fill weedy and grassy cover, so that the birds cannot hide. The weather must be such that the birds are concentrated in winter cover, where groups may be segregated, and each concentration counted. This condition occurs in cold weather and following winter storms. Mild weather encourages pheasants to scatter along roadsides and fencerows in poorer cover, where they are difficult to locate and count.

Areas having groves of trees are more difficult to census than those with few trees and a greater proportion of shrubbery cover.

The outstanding feature of the aerial census is that it is a total count of birds on a given area rather than an index. Actual population figures are of great value, since they can be related to production, mortality, and harvest, better than can indices. Population figures for areas censused by air can be rated to the results of other sampling methods and conversion factors obtained to derive total population data from indices.

Drive count

This method is used in Missouri River Basin work and is primarily a Kelker index. A group of 6 to 12 biologists walk through sample plots, which vary from 2 14 acres in size and are bounded on three sides by roads, ditches, plowed fields or other barriers. As many pheasants as possible are flushed and counted. By making pre- and post-season counts, sex ratio differences can be used in conjunction with kill figures to give the pre-season population. Sex ratios are believed to be accurate, if based on a sample of 300 to 400 birds.

Field traverse

The field traverse is used by the Missouri Office of River Basin Studies. It is a walking cruise, following established routes which are covered at least once in the early spring, and twice in the fall (before and after hunting seasons). The census is conducted by one biologist who follows a circuitous route, sampling the best cover and "edges" to observe as much game as possible. The routes average about 1.5 miles in length, and form circuits so the biologist returns to his starting point without deadheading.

Plate XLVI.—*Above and below.* Aerial counts are a highly accurate method of determining storm losses (Bernard A. Nelson and Eldon H. Smith, South Dakota Dept. of Game, Fish and Parks).

General

Census methods, dependent upon observing birds, are affected by the amount and nature of the cover present. Identical pheasant densities may yield varying indices depending on differences in cover conditions. Those variations may occur from area to area, and from year to year, and probably produce some distortion in distribution and trend data.

In crowing counts, roadside censuses, rural mail carrier censuses, and probably in most other methods, there may not be a straight-line relationship between pheasant densities and the indices obtained. That is, a census index from one area may be twice that from another area, but that does not mean that one population is twice as high as the other.

Timing is important. In spring censuses, the number and sex composition of the birds that can be seen from the road is dependent upon the stage of breeding activity, and also on the progress of vegetation growth. In early spring, cocks are more widely dispersed than hens, and are conspicuous because of their crowing behavior. As the season progresses, cocks acquire harems, and the proportion of hens seen increases steadily until nesting and incubation begin. Unless breeding behavior data are obtained, upon which to base the time of a survey, differences due to poor timing well may be greater than those in population density.

The crowing count census must be made during the period in the spring when crowing intensity is near the peak and is relatively constant for several weeks. Counts made before or after this period are low. The proper time is determined by gathering data on crowing intensity throughout the season.

Late summer surveys must be timed to measure reproduction accurately each year. The hatching peak, the time when most of the young come off, may vary several weeks from year to year. Censuses should be made a few weeks after the hatching peak, when the majority of young birds are old enough to show up along roads. Broods are not seen easily until they are two weeks or more old. A census that is made too early misses many of the young birds, and hence does not measure the largest part of the population.

The timing of summer censuses in many cases is decided by the date upon which game departments must have information for setting the hunting seasons. This frequently is in mid-August, which is too early to permit getting the best population data. The time required to get licenses and regulations printed, and the prior notice of the hunting season that is required by law, are responsible in most cases for the early dates on which seasons are set. Some states have found ways to overcome these difficulties, however, and it is believed that most of them eventually will find it possible to set their seasons late enough to make full use of the data available.

Brood Studies

Since the bulk of the birds available for hunting in the fall are young, it is important in setting hunting regulations, as well as conducting population studies, to know how successful the hatch has been. Ordinarily, a late-summer or early-fall picture of reproductive success is desired, to be used as a measure of the population available to the sportsmen. Production at this time is well expressed by a young-per-hen figure, which involves, but does not show, the combined effect of the average brood size, plus the percentage of hens which succeeded in bringing off broods. The latter figures are not essential to measuring production, but must be known to determine the whys and wherefors of good or poor production. Brood size depends on clutch size, egg hatchability and juvenile mortality, between the hatching dates and the time when production studies are made. The percent of successful hens is a function of such factors as nest desertion, destruction, renesting, and loss of entire broods.

Brood studies of an extensive nature, designed to give production data over large areas, usually involve roadside counts. These may be standardized counts made at regular intervals along the specified routes, or they may be observations made whenever the opportunity offers. Brood data also are obtained in conjunction with summer censuses.

A standardized method of obtaining brood data is used in South Dakota by which each observer follows the same procedure. Figures thus obtained are analyzed more easily, and provide a basis for comparison between different years and areas. Collection of data on a standardized basis over a period of weeks produces a good picture of the progress, distribution and success of the hatch. It enables the game manager to detect significant renesting efforts, important in total production, which may be missed in surveys of only one or two weeks duration. The date upon which most of the birds will be mature enough for hunting can be determined and used as one of the factors in setting the open season.

The ages of broods are estimated in the field on the basis of size, flying ability, molt and plumage patterns. Biologists collect young birds occasionally and age them by the molt of the primaries as an aid in keeping age estimations accurate. A series of photographs of young pheasants at weekly age intervals, also helps in aging broods seen in the field.

Two gaps remain in data obtained from brood studies. First, it is difficult to determine accurately what percent of the hens succeed in bringing off a brood. Early counts show this percentage to be low, but it increases steadily through the weeks and eventually appears to approach 100 percent, a degree of success which obviously is not attained. Unsuccessful hens probably molt earlier than those with broods and, because of their retiring nature during the molt, are not seen on roadside brood counts. It appears, from four years of South Dakota data, that the most reliable figure on the success of hens bringing off broods is that taken about 8 weeks after the peak of the hatch.

The other hiatus is the fact that production data from brood studies are for only those hens still alive at the time the studies are made. The success of hens at that time cannot be applied to the breeding population without reservations, since a portion of the breeders have perished by late summer. Thus a high percentage of reproductive success in observed hens, and large broods in August, do not necessarily mean high production. It may be that 80 to 90 percent of the hens present in August have broods, but if only 10 percent of the spring population lived until August, production still would be low.

These weaknesses and difficulties in brood studies should not discredit them, but rather should encourage efforts to fill the gaps in existing knowledge of how to interpret and use them.

Determining Hunter Success

Many factors other than pheasant populations enter into hunting success. Some of these are: fall cover density, which changes annually because of summer moisture, and the date of the first fall frost; age of young birds, which varies with the time of hatch, extent of renesting, and date of the hunting season; degree of pheasant winter concentration, which has occurred by the time the season opens; weather during the shooting season, which affects the activities of both the bird and the hunter; and possibly (pure theory, of course) the pheasant itself may be more sagacious and wary during certain phases of population fluctuations. It has been suggested that the pheasant may be a warier bird during population upswings.

Persons charged with estimating pheasant populations prior to the setting of the hunting regulations sometimes find themselves grasping desperately such ideas when hunting success does not verify population estimates. There may or may not be a straight-line relationship between pheasant numbers and hunting success, but, to the sportsman, hunting results still are the most widely accepted, if not the best, index to pheasant abundance.

A technique for determining hunting success and harvest is a must in the business of game management. It is the part of the bookkeeping which shows disbursements, and it tells us whether or not we are satisfying the customers.

The need for this information has resulted in many studies of sampling techniques (Hjersman 1951, Hunter 1949, Barnes

1946, Sondrini 1950, Gordon 1941). The methods of obtaining hunter success and kill figures can be separated into three broad categories: personal interviews, postal questionnaires, and field checks. Each method has inherent advantages and disadvantages.

The personal interview method, as conducted in Colorado and reported by Gilbert Hunter, is ideal for obtaining a mass of detailed information, but the cost is high, and it does not insure against exaggeration or lapse of memory on the part of the sportsman.

Questionnaires sent through the mail are used extensively in determining hunter success and kill. This method is inexpensive and, where license stubs are available from which to obtain names and addresses, a good random sample can be obtained. Some states have used a card attached to each license, which is to be filled in and returned at the close of the hunting season. The percentage of hunters returning this report usually is small, however, and there always is the possibility that the successful hunters are more prone to make reports. These objections are overcome, at least partially, by mailing questionnaires to a randomly selected group of hunters at the close of the season. The return from such questionnaires is much higher, and follow-up work indicates that good and poor hunters reply about equally well.

The mailed questionnaire cannot obtain the extensive and detailed information of the interview method, and it, too, must rely upon the memory and honesty of the hunter. However, recent studies indicate that the results obtained from the two methods are of comparable accuracy.

Bag checks, conducted in the field at the time and place of hunting, probably are the most accurate in determining hunter success for a particular time and place. This technique is used extensively in Iowa, South Dakota, and other states throughout the pheasant season. It has the advantage of yielding immediate results for each day of the pheasant season, whereas the results obtained from post-season surveys are not known for several months after the season ends. The immediate results

PLATE XLVII.—The measure of successful management (South Dakota Dept. of Game, Fish and Parks).

have proved valuable, particularly in the public relations field. However, while field bag checks yield daily hunting success, they do not reveal the number of times a hunter goes afield, or an estimate of his season kill of birds.

Where it is possible to contact all hunters using an established area, the bag check has been used to determine the accuracy of previously mentioned sampling techniques. The majority of such studies indicate that hunters, like fishermen and brilliant children, may have well-developed imaginations. The sampling techniques in common use may give exaggerated results, but because the exaggeration probably is a fairly constant factor, the surveys still show relative hunting success from year to year, and between areas.

Aging Pheasants in the Fall Bag Check

The method of separating adult from juvenile pheasants which is accepted as the most accurate is the bursa examination (Gower 1939). The bursa (bursa of Fabricius) is a sack-like structure lying above, and opening into, the posterior end of the large intestine. At the time of the hunting season, it is present in young birds, but usually not in adults (Linduska 1943). Occasionally, an adult will retain a bursa until the second hunting season. However, this probably causes little inaccuracy in the aging technique prior to the first of January if the birds with bursas measuring less than 10 mm. in depth are classified as adult.

The pheasant "age gauge" was developed for the purpose of collecting mass data on the age of pheasants. Like the bursa method, it is intended only to separate birds of the year from adults. Also, because it is based upon spur length, it is usable only on cock pheasants. The principal advantage of the age gauge is its simplicity and speed, plus the fact that no training in its use is needed.

This device was first developed in Nebraska in 1943, and is used extensively now in many of the plains and prairie states (Kimball 1944). In addition to its use by game managers, it can be made simply and used by any hunter. Rumor has it that the gauge finds application in separating the old, tough birds, which are presented to the landlady, from the young, tender birds for Ma's oven. The gauges are made from $3/4''$ metal washers, called bushing or packing washers, which are obtainable in many hardware and farm supply stores. They have an inside diameter of 19.5 to 20 mm. These are converted into age gauges quickly by cutting a segment out of one side with a hack saw. In use, the leg is slipped into the gauge through the slot. If the gauge then slips over the spur, the bird is young; if not, it is old. Over 25,000 pheasants are being aged annually in South Dakota with this gauge, and approximately 5,000 are aged by both the gauge and bursa for accuracy checks. In that state, the compensated accuracy of the gauge is approximately 97 percent. As would be expected, accuracy decreases as juvenile birds increase in age; therefore, the gauge is less accurate in January than during October. It should not be used in other sections of the country without first comparing results obtained with bursa examinations.

The error in any aging technique is magnified as the proportion of one age group to the other increases (Petrides 1949).

Thus, where approximately equal numbers of adults and juveniles exist in the population, a small error in aging is not important, but where the number of young may exceed the adults by 10 to 1, a small error in aging can result in a significantly inaccurate age ratio.

A major problem in obtaining fall age ratios during the hunting season is that of obtaining a large, well-distributed sample throughout a state's pheasant range. In South Dakota, an attempt to accomplish this is made by placing foot collection containers in the major pheasant processing plants throughout the pheasant range. Cooperating plant operators dump the feet from processed birds into these containers, which are picked up and aged by use of the gauge. Thus, a well-distributed sample of 25,000 to 30,000 birds is obtained. During the same period, trained technicians examine 5,000 birds in the same general areas served by the processing plants. The latter birds are checked for age by both the gauge, and the highly reliable bursa method, thus providing a correction factor to be applied to the larger foot collection sample.

Determining the Hatching Date of Juvenile Pheasants

In addition to the separation of juvenile birds from adults, techniques now have been developed for determining the age and hatching date of young pheasants, at the time they are harvested (Trautman 1950). These dates can be correlated with spring weather records, and any other factors which might influence the time or success of hatching. The information is useful also in checking against previously predicted hatching dates and success, thus improving the accuracy of such predictions.

The method used is based on the fact that young pheasants molt and replace their primary wing feathers in a regular manner at known ages. The order of molt and replacement starts with the innermost feathers, numbers 10 and 9, and proceeds outward to number one, the distal primary. These feathers are replaced at the rate of approximately one per week, thus making it possible to construct a "step-ladder" type of aging chart—using feathers which are undergoing their most active growth.

In using the chart in Table 42, begin with the outermost primary, number 1, and work inward until the first immature feather among those listed in the chart is encountered. Immature feathers have a blue shaft. Measure in millimeters the length of this feather from its tip to the point where it enters the skin. If this measurement is not contained within the chart, proceed to the next feather. When the range is located, which encompasses the measurement, the age of the bird is stated in the age column.

TABLE 42. Juvenile Pheasant Age Determination Chart.

Age (Weeks)	Primary Feather-Length Ranges in Millimeters					
	Fea. No. 1	Fea. No. 2	Fea. No. 3	Fea. No. 4	Fea. No. 5	Fea. No. 8
1	....	....	....	1-28	....	....
2	....	....	....	29-47	....	....
3	....	....	....	48-68	....	....
4	6-25	....	....	....	....	....
5	26-50	....	....	....	....	....
6	51-73	....	....	....	....	Molt
7	....	....	....	....	....	33-81
8	....	....	....	....	....	82-117
9	....	....	....	....	Molt	118-144
10	....	....	....	Molt	31-76	....
11	....	....	....	....	77-113	....
12	....	....	Molt	....	114-142	....
13	....	....	55-87	....	....	....
14	....	Molt	88 121	....	....	....
15	....	....	122-147	....	....	....
16	Molt	77-107	....	....	....	....
17	....	108-123	....	....	....	....
18	....	124-150	....	....	....	....
19	92-112	....	....	....	....	....
20	113-129	....	....	....	....	....
21	130-145	....	....	....	....	....
22	146-159	....	....	....	....	....

MANAGEMENT

Every successful business must keep a record of goods acquired, amount of sales and losses, and must conduct an annual or continuous inventory of stock on hand. The business of managing pheasants or any other game species is no excep-

PLATE XLVIII.—South Dakota biologists get age-ratio statistics from a collection of pheasant legs obtained at a locker plant (South Dakota Dept. of Game, Fish and Parks).

tion. The bulk of what we call pheasant research deals with gathering and compiling the facts that are considered essential in the operation of any successful enterprise.

The researcher must realize, however, that his job is not finished when the facts gathered have been compiled, tabulated and filed. He must sell his wares to administrators, and often directly to the public. What he has learned becomes of value only when it finds application in management.

Figure 13 presents a graphic calendar of the major activities and basic facts required in a pheasant management program. The data contained in the graph are approximately average for latitudes 44° and 45° north in the central section of the country. However, these dates will change from area to area, and from year to year, and can be ascertained only by running the surveys indicated, or by application of other techniques.

Regulations

Regulation of the harvest is among the oldest of tools in the game management profession. Inasmuch as the pheasant is polygamous, and the sexes are distinguished easily, controlling the kill of hens is an important management tool. As pointed out by Allen (1947), it virtually is impossible to overshoot cocks. This fact has made open seasons possible where populations are low, and also has maintained high annual harvests where birds are abundant. Hen pheasants should be harvested only for the purpose of reducing the population when, and only when, crop depredations or surplus populations warrant such action.

The establishment of the daily bag limit should not be based solely on the abundance of pheasants. An unobtainable daily bag limit on cocks sometimes is claimed to increase both the intentional and unintentional kill of hens. The psychological aspect of a sportsman obtaining his limit is important. A hunter having succeeded in filling a two-bird limit is more content than the individual who fell one short of obtaining a four-bird limit. Some consideration also should be

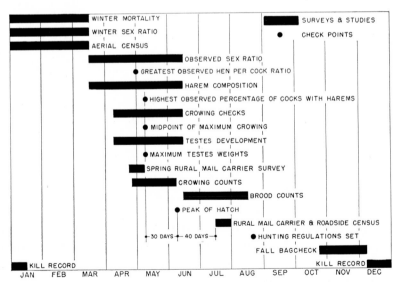

FIGURE 13.—Calendar of major activities required in pheasant management.

given to the average time necessary to bag a pheasant. If past records show that it will take a sportsman about two hours to harvest a bird, and only four legal shooting hours are contemplated in any one day, the daily bag should be established at two birds.

The point of diminishing returns for hunters in the plains and prairies region appears to be reached when the sex ratio has been shot down to one male to three females. In many eastern states, such as Pennsylvania, where hunting pressure is greater, post-hunting season sex ratios reach one male to six or more females (Randall 1940), indicating a closer harvest of available cocks.

The practice of restricting pheasant shooting to afternoons is gaining popularity. It invariably is favored by farmers, and it frequently appeals to sportsmen once they have become accustomed to afternoon shooting. Four to six hours afield can provide sufficient time for an enjoyable hunt, and free mornings allow a hunter enough time to reach the desired location. To make it unanimous, there is little doubt that the pheasants enjoy unmolested mornings.

A relatively long, but late, open season generally seems desirable. Except where pheasants are very plentiful, the majority of the harvest takes place on the opening three days, and the first two weekends (Allen 1947). A long season tends to relieve the pressure at any one time, and permits more sporting days afield. A mid-October or November opening reduces the kill of "squealers" (immature young), and generally provides better hunting weather for man and dog (Mohler 1943). Crop harvesting is advanced, and escape cover is less abundant. In the Dakotas, however, a late season may be cut short by inclement weather.

In setting regulations for harvesting cock pheasants, it should be remembered that the surplus of cocks seldom if ever is harvested fully. A high percentage of the unharvested surplus will not live to see a second hunting season, and thus will not serve man's purpose.

Stocking

Stocking continues to receive stress as a phase of ringneck pheasant management in some states, and not in others. About six thousand 12-week old birds were released in Iowa in 1950, but no expansion of game-farm facilities or stocking is contemplated. Minnesota released 73,793 young birds, and 3,186 breeders; 42,177 day-old chicks were distributed to farmers and sportsmen for rearing purposes. The state game farm in Nebraska releases from 10 to 15 thousand pheasants annually. During the past five years, Kansas has released about 20,000 birds annually. Stocking is not part of the management program in North Dakota, South Dakota, or Missouri; the latter state does not have an open hunting season.

Many people believe that pheasant stocking throughout the plains and prairie region is unnecessary, but those who support it claim a two-fold purpose: to provide breeding stock in areas where the wild population has been decreased by severe winter storms, and to satisfy the sportsman's demand for birds. The rearing of young pheasants by sportsmen organizations helps maintain interest during the closed season, and gives the club members an incentive for meeting during the spring and summer months.

Public Information

Education's part in pheasant management is to keep the public abreast of the biological principles that form the basis for management. Management practices are not implemented easily, when the public is apathetic to their need or opposed to them through ignorance of their value.

As in any field of science, the layman lags behind the professional in his knowledge of pheasant biology. For example, biologists have shown conclusively that harvesting up to 90 percent of the cock pheasants is good management, yet the rank and file of sportsmen still believe that a light harvest, or none at all, automatically will be followed by a boom in the pheasant population. The public equally is far behind in its thinking on restocking programs.

Some of the more pressing points which an educational program should include are discussed below:

1. *Population turnover.* The average life span of a pheasant is short, and it is not abnormal for about three-fourths of the birds present at any one time to have perished by the following year. It therefore is impossible to save pheasants and stockpile them from year to year merely by not hunting them.

2. *Adequate harvest.* It is possible to harvest 75 to 90 percent of the cock pheasants each year without harming future population levels. In some of the prairie states, it is difficult to obtain an adequate harvest, especially during years of lowered numbers, because sportsmen are reluctant to shoot a low to moderate population.. The people need to know that they can shoot, if they wish, even very low populations, if they take only cocks. In conjunction with this idea, the principle of not shooting hens, except when pheasants are very abundant, must be impressed upon the sportsmen.

3. *Effects of hunting.* Too many people still believe that game populations rise and fall in direct response to hunting pressure. The public should be made aware that many interrelated factors enter into game population fluctuations, and that hunting is one of the less important of these factors.

4. *Stocking programs.* Except under special circumstances, the raising and stocking of pheasants are ineffective and economically unfeasible.

5. *Carrying capacity.* Sportsmen need to be informed on the habitat requirements of pheasants. Understanding those requirements, they will not expect large populations where the habitat is unsuitable, and they will understand that changing habitat results in changing population levels.

6. *Predators and bounty systems.* The public generally has a biased conception of the relationship of predators to

pheasant populations. Ample evidence is at hand to demonstrate that, in most cases, pheasants in suitable habitat will maintain satisfactory numbers in spite of predators. If and when adequate studies indicate that control of predators is required, more efficient methods than the bounty system should be used. Years of experience with the bounty system in many states have proved it to be costly and ineffective.

7. *Confidence in wildlife administrators.* Every hunter is an authority on pheasant management. This attitude often is a stumbling block to good administration. Confidence in a game administration can be built by basing management on sound biological data, and by getting such information to the public.

8. *Farmers and sportsmen.* In the more densely populated states, the problem of farmer-sportsmen relationships is paramount. Certainly, the individual sportsman must assume the responsibility of improving those relationships. In Iowa, as a means of promoting mutual understanding, a successful campaign is being directed at the sportsman throughout the state by radio, newspapers, and brochures on "Ask the farmer first." The future of farm-game management depends to a large extent on the attitude of the farmer toward game and sportsmen. If his experience with hunters has been a happy one—there are many such examples—the farmer will encourage game and permit hunting; if not, there will be less game and more "no hunting" signs.

Habitat Improvement

In the past, the principal tools of the game manager have been three: control of the harvest, predator control, and artificial propagation. Each of these tools has had a place in the management program, but it is evident that no known measures can increase or maintain a game population in an unsuitable environment. Accordingly, management of the habitat promises to be the most effective implement in the game managers' tool chest.

Man-made alterations in habitat have brought about many accidental changes in animal numbers; and hunting in the future will depend largely on the way in which man influences wildlife habitat. Planned, not accidental, improvement in game habitat promises to be the most effective tool in maintaining shootable pheasant populations. This fact has been recognized, and most states in this region have cover development programs. For the most part, these are aimed at providing winter cover for pheasants, but some states also endeavor to supplement nesting cover and food.

The bulk of the planting stock used in this work is obtained from commercial nurseries, although Minnesota is developing three state nurseries from which they had an output of two million trees and shrubs in 1952. Nebraska started cover development work in 1940 and is continuing an expanded program. South Dakota got started in 1947 and now is planting a million trees and shrubs a year, with plans for further expansion. North Dakota more recently has instituted a program which provides seed and tree and shrub seedlings to interested farmers. In Kansas, over a quarter-million trees and shrubs are being set out under a habitat restoration program started in 1949. Under the farmer-sportsman plan, developed in 1948, Iowa is planting 750 acres. Another 125 acres are being developed in Iowa under the farm-game habitat improvement plan inaugurated in 1950.

Many states are cooperating with the U. S. Soil Conservation Service in procuring sites and doing the planting; most of such work is being carried out under Pittman-Robertson projects. The majority of plantings are made on marginal or submarginal agricultural land, but some states, notably South Dakota, have been able to secure desirable planting sites at no cost to the state. In most instances, a 20- or 25-year agreement, easement, or lease is executed between the landowner and the state conservation department.

It generally is agreed that best results are obtained where

the landowner makes the greatest contribution. However, the extent of this will vary with land values, the need and desire for trees and shrubs, and the interest in wildlife. A Dakota farmer will provide a good planting site of 5 to 10 acres, prepare the ground, fence, cultivate, and generally maintain the area in exchange for a supply of trees and shrubs well planted. Farther east, where the need for trees is less acute, and land values are higher, the problem increases.

The species of trees and shrubs planted vary with location and weather conditions. Multiflora rose is planted extensively in Missouri and appears to be successful in Kansas, southern Iowa and southern Nebraska. Farther north, this valuable plant must give way to more hardy, drought-resistant species such as wild plum, Chinese elm, chokecherry, American elm, Russian olive, and many others.

Any cover development program should be preceded by, and operated with, a progressive pheasant research project. Without such guidance, the program has little chance of being effective. Research first must determine which environmental factor is exerting the greatest pressure on the pheasant population. Next, it must determine the minimum requirements of this factor. And, third, working with the development project, it must determine the most economical means of fulfilling those requirements.

Using South Dakota as an example, it has been learned that winter storm mortality, due to deficient winter cover, is of major importance. Based on rather extensive winter surveys, the estimated number of pheasants lost in that state for the past four years is as follows: 1947-48, 275,000; 1948-49, 250,000; 1949-50, 775,000; 1950-51, 36,000. This loss of potential spring brood stock is important locally.

The need for additional winter cover in South Dakota long has been recognized. Early plans called for the development of 40-acre, state-owned tracts; or for a smaller cover area on every farm, or at least one or two per square mile. Calculations quickly revealed the expense of such programs to be prohibitive The time required to developed an appreciable portion of the range also would be beyond reason.

Fortunately, research in both of the Dakotas and Iowa (Weston 1950) revealed that pheasants in that section of the country make seasonal movements of several miles between summer range and winter concentration areas. It also was learned that cover areas, five acres in size, can accommodate 500 to 1,000 birds, if the areas are located adjacent to cultivated fields, where food in the form of waste grain is available. The best of cover areas are used little if the food supply is half a mile or more away. It has been learned that 86 percent of the wintering birds use cover which has food not more than a quarter-mile distant.

Out of this knowledge emerged the present South Dakota cover program, which calls for only four cover areas per township (36 square miles). With coverts spaced at three-mile intervals, no bird need travel much over one and one-half miles to a wintering area.

The width of a winter cover area is of great significance. The 100-foot-wide shelterbelt is a boon to wintering pheasants in Nebraska, of questionable value in South Dakota, and a death trap in North Dakota. During winters of heavy snow and severe blizzards, the 100-foot-wide belt is not sufficient, even in Nebraska. To insure protection throughout severe winters, South Dakota plantings all are being made 300 feet in width.

As previously stated, the first steps in inaugurating a habitat restoration program are to determine the key limiting factor, and to determine if and how a remedy can be applied. From the previously cited winter losses, it is logical to conclude that winter cover deficiency is one of the more apparent limitations in the Dakotas. Compared to other habitat requirements, winter cover also is a relatively simple requirement to supply. South Dakota studies indicate that $\frac{1}{2}$ of 1 percent of the land properly developed will fulfill the winter cover needs of a reasonable pheasant population. By contrast, nesting cover is a more difficult habitat requirement to fulfill, because pheasants are distributed quite evenly over their range during summer months.

The third step in setting up a habitat development program is to test, with the best data at hand, the economic feasibiliy of conducting a proposed program.

Over the past 10 years, South Dakota has harvested an average of 3,000,000 pheasants annually from its 30,000,000-acre pheasant range, for an average of 10 birds harvested per 100 acres. The total cost of establishing a seven-acre cover area under South Dakota's Pittman-Robertson project 19-D is approximately $400. Spacing the plots at three-mile intervals, the cost per 100 acres of pheasant range is $7.

Assuming the developed areas will have a useful life of 20 years, the cost of development is 35 cents per 100 acres per year. It follows that, if cover development increases the bird population and resulting harvest by only 10 percent, one bird per 100 acres, pheasants are being added to the hunter's bag at a cost of 35 cents each. If a 20 percent increase follows development, pheasants will be produced for half as much.

The third job of research in a habitat development program is to determine, through every census survey and technique at hand, whether or not the development actually is accomplishing what it set out to do; and here it should be remembered that the use of a cover area by pheasants is not proof that the over-all population has been increased.

Finally, it should be emphasized that habitat restoration, and winter cover development in particular, is not a cure-all. The crash decline of pheasants throughout the plains and prairies during the early forties does not correlate with excessive winter mortality, and cannot be correlated definitely with any known environmental factors. Such mass fluctuations in abundance probably will continue, at least until further knowledge reveals the cause. The lack of this information should not inhibit use of the information at hand, however. Scottish grouse, for example, remain cyclic, but, through management of the heather, the grouse population at all stages of the cycle has been increased materially. Habitat development may do the same for pheasants.

PLATE XLIX.—*Above.* A one-year-old game cover planting made as a part of South Dakota's federal aid habitat improvement program. The open strip will be planted to sweet clover or other herbaceous cover (Robert Gage, South Dakota Dept. of Game, Fish and Parks). *Below.* Large-scale shrub and tree planting is done with a tractor-drawn planter (James W. Kimball, South Dakota Dept. of Game, Fish and Parks).

LOOKING AHEAD

The fabulous stories of pheasant abundance in these plains and prairies during the early forties are true. They are true because the birds actually were so abundant that no room was left for exaggeration. Most of the stories originated in the Dakotas, but pheasants were in great abundance throughout the region. Iowa resorted to spring shooting one year, and reducing pheasant damage was a problem in several states.

This pheasant "epidemic" was brought about by a coincidence of favorable conditions which could, but probably will not, occur again in our lifetime. Abundant waste land, plentiful food, and favorable weather are conditions we can enumerate. Then, of course, there is the much debated subject of cycles. If there be an intangible, undefinable something that causes a species to become temporarily more prolific and prosperous it certainly played its part in the pheasant bonanza.

Following the boom came the bust. The low in 1947 was brought about by several years of poor reproduction. Now, pheasants have increased to reasonable (there is no normal) abundance; and hunting—by present-day standards, is good.

Only one unfavorable change is taking place in the plains and prairies, and that is basically economic. We cannot feed the world from sweet clover patches, idle marginal land, marshes, and sloughs. Intensified agricultural use, wise and foolish, is destroying pheasant habitat. The drainage of marshes and potholes is almost as destructive to pheasants as to waterfowl.

But the picture is not all black. Pittman-Robertson funds are enabling the states to replace at least a portion of the habitat which intensified agriculture is destroying. Then, of course, there always is the hope of a future program of truly sound land use, land use which looks to fertile soil in the future, rather than increased farm income today; which recognizes wet lands, high water tables, and wildlife as valuable natural resources and, above all, land use which does not set the stage for another "dust bowl." Under such a land-use policy, pheasants would continue to be a prominent and thriving feature of the plains and prairies.

CHAPTER 6

RINGNECK PHEASANTS IN THE GREAT LAKES REGION

By ROBERT A. MCCABE, RALPH A. MACMULLAN,
AND EUGENE H. DUSTMAN

T he pheasant is the most sought-after upland game bird
in the Lake States. In the early 1940's it probably provided more hours of good hunting than any other game species.
Like most game animals, however, it never has been abundant
enough to satisfy all sportsmen and conservation departments.
In the mid-1940's pheasant numbers dwindled, leaving an un-
precedented number of impatient upland game hunters. Since
this depression, pheasants have been steadily, although sometimes slowly, recovering. While the Lake States region now has
good pheasant shooting, in no state does it equal the pre-de-
pression days. Efforts made toward understanding this depression and recovery have eclipsed the results, some of which
will be analyzed in the pages that follow.

In some cases, the pheasant was introduced directly from
the Orient and, in others, indirectly via English and continental stock. It is impossible to list a pedigree for Lake States
pheasants, since records of private and public plantings are
wanting in many instances. It seems certain that the Chinese
ringneck either was released in greatest numbers, or it survived best and genetically absorbed other varieties. Our bird
usually has the white neck-ring and the grayish-green rump
and lower back of the pure Chinese pheasant *(Phasianus colchicus torquatus)*.

Between 1860 and 1910, the Lake States were cultivated more and more intensively. Fertile lands were being cleared of timber. Wheat production was surpassed by corn, and small unit dairy farming became commonplace. Small farm units and intensive cultivation, together with increased hunting pressure from rapidly growing urban settlements, caused the native prairie chicken to diminish rapidly. Its decline progressed westward through grasslands of the Lake States. Woodlots were reduced in size and number, and under economic pressure many were grazed. The ruffed grouse dwindled with its habitat. Today, in the Lake States, it is important as a game bird only in Michigan, Wisconsin and eastern Ohio. Most of what had been productive ranges for native grouse were changed vastly and ready for the pheasant.

First Introductions

The decline of native birds may have prompted certain private groups and persons to begin the introduction of pheasants. Early releases in Ohio were made by individuals and local groups before the turn of the present century (Hicks 1938). Accurate records are lacking and numbers unknown. The State Fish and Game Report issued in 1900 mentions a "pheasantry" near Van Wert which sold and shipped birds to many points throughout Ohio. Another, established near Celina in 1896, was one of the first game farms in the United States. Pheasants were released in the vicinity between 1893 and 1896, but without success. By 1903 repeated plantings in many areas had been effective, for Dawson (1903) mentions the species as established in 10 counties.

In 1893, a sportsman's club near Holland, Michigan, bought a few birds and bred them for several years until they had a stock of more than 200. In the spring of 1895, these constituted the first release of pheasants in the state. Other efforts followed, and there was some breeding in the wild, but following abandonment of the project in 1899, the birds disappeared. Failure was blamed on poaching, perhaps with reason, for this area later became known as good pheasant range.

Schorger (1947) pointed out that while the large Pabst plant-

Table 43. Ringneck Pheasant Stocking in the Lake States.

Year	Wisconsin Eggs & Chicks	Wisconsin Pheas. Adult	Michigan Eggs & Chicks	Michigan Pheas. Adult	Illinois Eggs & Chicks	Illinois Pheas. Adult	Indiana Eggs & Chicks	Indiana Pheas. Adult	Ohio Eggs & Chicks	Ohio Pheas. Adult
1918	.....	.....	27,000	2,396	.....	.....	.....	.....	.....	.....
1919	.....	.....	42,300	3,800	.....	.....	.....	.....	50,000	5,431
1920	.....	.....	38,463	4,861	.....	.....	.....	.....	.....	353
1921	.....	.....	20,650	5,824	.....	.....	.....	.....	.....	7,683
1922	.....	.....	31,387	6,730	.....	.....	.....	.....	.....	9,472
1923	.....	.....	34,000	6,400	.....	.....	.....	.....	52,800	9,123
1924	.....	.....	18,213	2,803	.....	.....	.....	.....	27,100	11,807
1925	.....	.....	10,785	6,043	.....	.....	.....	.....	22,850	8,500
1926	.....	.....	30,040	6,591	.....	.....	.....	.....	6,800	11,000
1927	.....	.....	29,750	7,421	.....	.....	1,674	.....	6,500	14,050
1928	.....	.....	16,235	3,875	40,492	8,080	10,040	.....	6,500	10,940
1929	4,006	1,717	7,744	8,792	39,628	1,500	14,248	4,998	6,500	11,005
1930	18,899	8,799	6,560	8,431	28,452	?	9,625	8,055	3,693	9,871
1931	26,932	7,439	12,090	8,263	52,036	3,122	3,975	7,387	.....	18,231
1932	18,575	7,360	27,589	6,942	41,475	8,122	.....	.....	8,628	26,400
1933	73,458	4,131	22,736	4,259	.....	11,366	.....	.....	7,165	27,520
1934	48,936	12,126	20,228	6,006	.....	13,199	.....	.....	13,262	29,670
1935	107,932	2,791	21,160	5,615	.....	14,381	52,102	22,732	14,000	34,175
1936	83,443	11,050	24,493	3,321	.....	12,481	53,057	16,100	?	38,228

Year										
1937	105,523	28,250	21,617	2,458	16,649	10,443	115,801	14,993	?	25,625
1938	122,555	69,671	30,775	2,990	24,179	11,050	139,366	17,349	37,485	32,690
1939	156,749	97,403	24,077	2,863	35,250	11,106	80,000	45,295	52,000	32,727
1940	199,168	96,486	26,838	2,194	50,020	23,589	119,741	103,8?9	28,859	71,000
1941	281,430	36,525	26,149	2,339	54,170	25,845	133,331	86,666	?	?
1942	217,793	39,865	18,220	1,067	57,296	31,304	90,317	7,993	?	?
1943	189,812	29,333	8,485	187	46,675	12,905	124,776	14,962	?	?
1944	200,781	30,345	4,665	2,740	56,911	13,938	165,221	6,782	?	?
1945	195,181	36,692	10,380	4,984	72,100	20,600	80,352	9,664	?	?
1946	188,915	49,621	24,630	9,021	86,618	31,443	94,327	18,459	42,903	26,637
1947	192,968	46,432	33,113	9,380	72,029	23,315	82,920	10,491	36,368	17,409
1948	203,110	50,206	87,020	28,412	71,065	32,129	59,145	8,820	32,555	29,850
1949	224,744	55,657	62,344	28,896	69,700	20,806	73,484	11,567	30,000	34,993
1950	233,213	51,527	52,400	19,628	59,628	21,672	47,527	20,431	11,408	45,657
1951	170,872	68,723	......	7,001	40,514	21,562	65,080	30,713	......	42,824
1952	175,947	61,819	......	4,793	45,051	26,912	76,684	12,973	......	39,133
1953	239,178	67,007	......	4,692	54,440	44,854	74,123	30,292	......	62,819
	3,680,120	970,975	872,136	242,018	1,114,369	455,724	1,766,916	510,541	497,376	744,823

Indiana: over 3500 birds were released between 1900 and 1918.

Ohio: some birds were released in 1915 but no records are available.

Wisconsin: eggs only 1926 through 1935.

.. = no program.

? = program active but no data available.

ings in southern Wisconsin began in 1911, "pheasants were liberated much earlier than has been assumed." He cites newspaper records of at least ten individuals and groups who released pheasants prior to 1900. The extent of stocking between 1900 and 1910 is not known.

The first state-sponsored introductions on which figures have been recorded were as follows: Indiana 1908; Michigan, 1918; Ohio, 1919; Illinois, 1928; Wisconsin, 1929. State releases were made as early as 1910 in Illinois, but no statistics are available, and doubtless the same occurred elsewhere. Leopold (1931) estimated that between 1900 and 1930, in a region comprising Indiana, Illinois, Iowa, Ohio, Michigan, Minnesota, Missouri, and Wisconsin, 224,436 pheasants were released at a cost of $750,000; and in addition, some 742,000 eggs were distributed (for hatching and rearing) at a cost of about $150,000.

In the individual states of immediate interest to this account, Leopold's figures give the best available record of birds stocked and eggs given to farmers and sportsmen in official programs through 1930:

	Indiana	Illinois	Wisconsin	Michigan	Ohio
Pheasants ..	7,498	9,580	19,800	67,520	86,296
Eggs	25,962	108,572	44,500	313,037	112,743

Not all plantings were successful, but the end result was firm establishment of the pheasant in all of these states by 1930. Release figures to date are given in Table 43. In all, a minimum of 2,400,000 pheasants were stocked in the region prior to 1950, and in many areas plantings undoubtedly continued long after birds in the wild had reached a satisfactory huntable population.

Pheasant history in the province of Ontario, Canada, is not unlike that in most pheasant states. The first pheasants were released in Ontario prior to 1892; sporadic plantings by private individuals followed. Eventually a provincial pheasantry was established, which aided in the early plantings, and pheasants were considered sufficiently abundant in the Point Pelee area and in the Magra peninsula by 1910 to have a two-week open season. Range limitations in Ontario appear to be the same as those in northern Wisconsin and Michigan, namely no winter foods to sustain even a small population (Clarke and Braffette 1946). This report concludes further:

1) "Anything up to 50 inches (of snowfall) may be thought of as optimum conditions for pheasants." Interesting also is their corollary statement: "The isopleth determining the northward growth of seed corn almost exactly agrees with the 50 inch snow-fall line."

2) "The areas having at least 50 percent of the occupied land in crops are the best regions for pheasants. Anything less than 50 percent would seem to be deficient in food supply for the birds."

3) The correlation with density of woodlots is not clear-cut.

The present range boundary of Ontario pheasants is virtually coincident with the 50-inch snowfall line. The habitable area now is occupied, and according to present knowledge, the birds fall into the pre-hunting category of less than 10 per one hundred acres (Fig. 15). There are small, local areas along Lakes Erie and St. Clair where the density is greater than this and these areas are counterparts of Michigan and Ohio's best pheasant range along the lakeshore. Pelee Island is part of Ontario and the phenomenal pheasant densities there are so unique that they are dealt with at length in another section.

Pheasant Range and Numbers

Pheasant range in the Lake States has expanded and contracted locally with changes in land-use, weather conditions, and food supply. The general trend over the past 20 years, however, has been one of growth. Today the pheasant occupies about 65 percent of the land area in the Lake States.

The first map (Fig. 14) of pheasant distribution in the region was made by Leopold (1931). From 1929 to the present, the range has increased[1] about 36 percent (Fig. 15).

---

[1] Areas were obtained by planimetering the ranges from Figs. 14 and 15.

In Figure 15 the relative numbers of pheasants are shown within the ascribed range. The percentage of the range in each abundance category is as follows:

More than 50 birds per 100 acres	1.5 percent
10 to 50	13.6
Less than 10	49.9
No birds	35.0

It is clear that half the occupied range is populated with fewer than 10 birds per 100 acres. Unoccupied range, constituting 35 percent of the total area, lies in southern Indiana and Illinois and in northern Wisconsin and Michigan. If we assume that the present range has about reached its limit, what, then, limits the northern and southern range extension, since there are still many pheasantless areas in the Lake States?

In the north, the problem appears to be one of food and, to some extent, cover. The pheasant is granivorous and hence relies on seeds of cultivated and wild plants. It is restricted to agricultural areas and fails to thrive in forested regions. Ruffed grouse and sharp-tailed grouse are adapted to forested areas because they can subsist on the winter buds of many trees and shrubs, a food supply that never is snowed under.

In the south, high air and surface temperatures have been postulated (Yeatter letter to Aldo Leopold 1945, Yeatter 1950, Graham and Hesterberg 1948) as causing low hatchability of pheasant eggs and therefore limiting the range southward. However, there are areas of pheasant abundance in southern California where air temperatures are considerably higher than those used in Yeatter's experiments. This might be explainable on the basis that California birds were of southern Asiatic origin and hence "more tolerant of higher temperatures." If this is true, then the logical game management recommendation would be to import birds from the southern-most edge of the Asiatic range and release them in our pheasant-free South Central States, an idea worth investigating.

Although Yeatter's research indicates that pheasant embryos are vulnerable to high temperatures during the laying period, other environmental factors have not been ruled out in limiting the southern distribution of pheasants.

Habitat Requirements

Pheasant range in the Lake States does not hold an even distribution of birds. Even within the gross categories of the range map, there is wide variation. What must the habitat have to make it suitable for pheasants? This question can be answered only in the broadest terms; pheasants have certain requirements in the way of food, cover, breeding grounds, and weather. Not only must these habitat requisites be present in quantity, but their arrangement must be proper. For example, winter cover is of little value unless near a food supply.

What is good pheasant habitat?

What pattern is there of climate, land, and human activity that makes for good pheasant hunting? Parts of this pattern are obvious. Good pheasant range always is good farmland. In this region, pheasant range has a certain look about it— prosperous farms on flat, heavy soil with corn as a major crop.

A closer examination shows other, less-evident characteristics. Usually associated with corn are soybeans, cereal grains, and sugarbeets. Cover is a varying thing, and often the best range has the least cover. In general, the landscape consists of broad fields with occasional woodlots or swamps, frequently with shrubby fencerows between the fields. Often the fencerows are bare, and sometimes they are replaced by large drainage ditches.

When the many characteristics of pheasant range are tabulated, the pattern becomes more definite. It looks something like this:

First, some basic climatological or geological criteria must delineate the broad outside limits of pheasant range in the Lake States (as shown in Fig. 15). These criteria are discussed later. Secondly, within these broad limits, pheasant range is on the more fertile soil. In general, the best soil supports the most pheasants. Third, on this good soil are active farms,

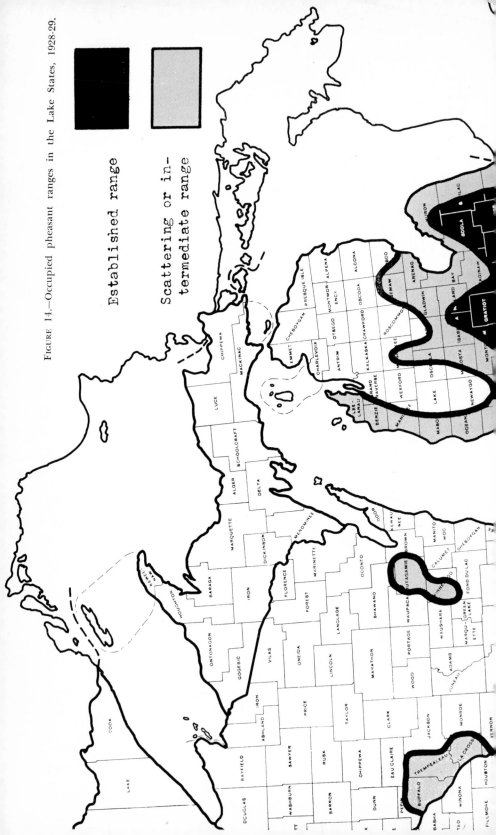

FIGURE 14.—Occupied pheasant ranges in the Lake States, 1928-29.

Established range

Scattering or in-
termediate range

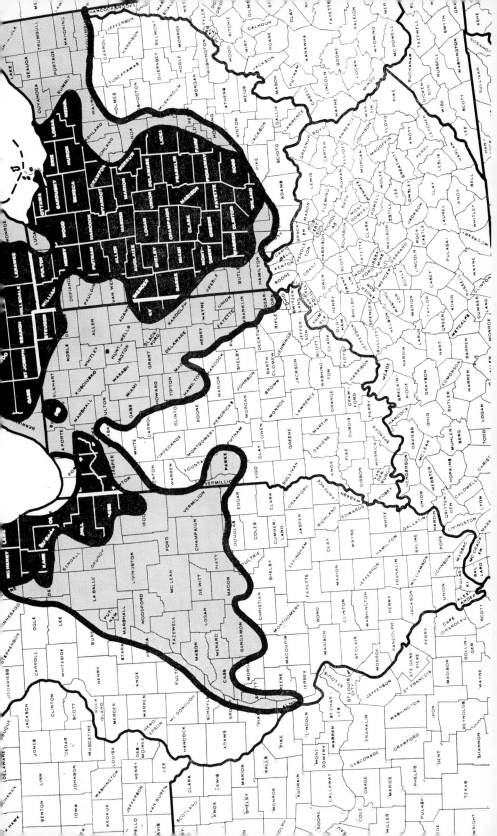

and these farms devote much space to cereal grains and corn.

So if we wanted to state the habitat affinities of pheasants in the Lake States in a single short sentence we could say: "Given a (1) certain climate and geology, pheasants thrive on (2) good soil which (3) supports active farms which (4) grow cereals and corn."

Why pheasants have an affinity for good soil is still a moot question. It is being studied and it is increasingly apparent that fertility of the soil on which the foods of an animal grow can affect (1) its productivity, and (2) its ability to survive. It seems possible that fertile soil may impart to a pheasant stock vigor that is lacking on poorer soil.

Why pheasants like farms is somewhat more evident. The best pheasant range today originally was poorly drained hardwood swamp, upland hardwood, or prairie. Draining and clearing this land made nesting cover, and grain crops and their associated weeds provided food.

Corn is especially valuable as food, particularly where it is available above the snow during winter months in quantities to support the large flocks that pheasants form at that season. Small grains and soybeans are no small diet items, but in late winter when food is in its shortest supply, corn is the staple.

In this respect, a point of possible significance concerns the northern fringe of pheasant range. In northern Michigan, for example, there are pockets of good soil that support fairly prosperous farms, but the frost-free period is so short most years that corn cannot mature. These areas support a sprinkling of pheasants, and probably would support more if there were enough corn standing above the snow as a food supply.

One fact is unmistakable. Pheasants are not a wildland bird in the Lake States. They tolerate people, and are closely dependent on an agricultural economy. This provides a stimulating challenge, for pheasant numbers undoubtedly can be manipulated by the farmer's handling of his land.

Managing Pheasant Habitat

Plants obviously are a major component of any habitat. Communities of wild plants are in a constant state of change.

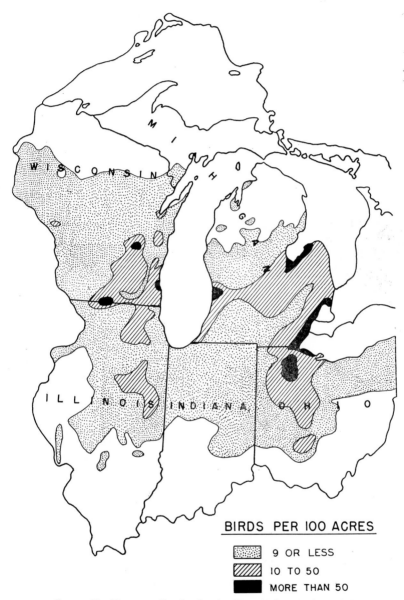

BIRDS PER 100 ACRES

9 OR LESS
10 TO 50
MORE THAN 50

FIGURE 15.—Pheasant distribution in Great Lakes Region, 1952.

PLATE L.—Aspects of Lake States pheasant range. *Above.* This flat and fertile lake bed plain in Lenawee County of southeastern Michigan supports a prosperous agriculture and produces abundant pheasant crops. *Below.* Drained lake bed soils on the eastern margin of the state are Michigan's best pheasant range (Ralph I. Blouch, Michigan Dept. of Conservation).

Bare ground left idle will first support annual weeds, followed by perennial herbs and grass, then shrubs. Finally trees will top the brush. These changes occur slowly and with overlapping of the various stages. Each stage has a somewhat different value to pheasants. A combination of cover types, rather than any single one, is desirable on a year-around basis.

Man-made alterations of the landscape, through farming, initiate many plant-succession changes beneficial to the pheasant. Important in this regard is the production of field weeds in cultivated grain, particularly corn. Food and cover, side by side, are to the pheasant what a snug cabin, well provisioned, is to a trapper.

The pattern of land and vegetation, man-made and natural, is not uniform throughout the Lake States, and its influence on pheasants is variable. For example, in Wisconsin and Michigan where winter temperatures are most severe, winter cover is of greatest importance. Here marshes, swales and tamarack swamps are used extensively. In Ohio, woodlots are the chief winter cover. The difference probably is a matter of availability. In Illinois and Indiana, where winter is not so critical a period, the birds are scattered more widely along roadsides and in fencerows, river bottoms, and woodlands.

Available knowledge of plantings beneficial to pheasants is scant. Any such management has a close relationship to the economy of the farmland concerned. Hence, to a large extent, habitat improvement in the Lake States will be in the form of modifications of farming practices, or in the use of small areas which the farmer is willing to devote to pheasants.

Unfortunately there is no rule of thumb on procedure or ready list of plants to be used reliably for food and cover plantings throughout the Lake States. Habitat improvement must involve diagnosis of local range deficiencies and is no job for an amateur. Nevertheless, for those who are interested in doing something for pheasants, the following discussion can serve as a background of what is known and the principles involved in habitat improvement. State conservation departments and the Soil Conservation Service can be of aid to individuals or groups in setting up a habitat improvement program best suited to local needs.

Cover improvement

Experiments with cover plantings for pheasants in the Lake States largely have been discouraging. Early attempts were shots in the dark, and too much effort undoubtedly was expended in trying to improve the quality of cover in areas that, as far as the pheasant was concerned, already had adequate cover. Over the years, many biologists have concluded that perhaps the most logical and justifiable management is in highly agriculturalized areas, which can support good pheasant populations, but where cover may be inadequate as a result of intensive cultivation.

Few plants fulfill all the desirable characteristics of a cover plant in being vigorous, quick-growing, and resistant to disease, fire, drouth, grazing, shade and insect injury. Such stock must produce suitable shelter for birds, and the cost of planting must not be prohibitive. Site, soil, moisture, temperature, planting method and maintenance requirements must be understood for each species used.

It is evident that the cover value of woody species, coniferous and deciduous, is not uniform throughout the life of the plant. In the lake region, plantation evergreens offer good cover conditions when trees are young, grassy undergrowth and lower branches forming excellent protection against weather and predators. But as such a stand matures, grass is shaded out, lower branches die, and cover value declines.

The opposite situation occurs with a shrub or vine type of vegetation which produces negligible cover in the first years after planting. But as such plants mature and the low canopy is formed, cover value becomes high. Maturing vines not only become more leafy and spreading, but they incorporate any adjacent bush or tree as a natural arbor, thereby adding to the amount and quality of cover.

Although cover planting programs commonly employ woody species, excellent cover can sometimes be produced with herbaceous plants. Discing a piece of idle land will create a seed

PLATE LI.—*Above*. Michigan's "Prairie Farm," in Saginaw County has produced some of the state's highest pheasant populations and supported some
of the heaviest hunting pressure. The fertile organic soil produces an abundant growth of annual weeds on uncultivated dykes and ditch banks (Ralph
I. Blouch, Michigan Dept. of Conservation). *Below*. Brush cover near a food
source makes ideal wintering conditions for pheasants in Dane County, Wisconsin (Robert A. McCabe).

Plate LII.—*Above*. Excellent winter cover in one of Ohio's pheasant concentration areas, Wood County. Topping of largetooth aspens by ice storm will improve herbaceous and shrubby ground cover (Eugene H. Dustman, Ohio Cooperative Wildlife Research Unit). *Below*. Winter covert in Jefferson County, Wisconsin, of a type characteristic of the northern lake states. Willow, dogwood, elderberry, and bog birch are common shrubs. (Robert A. McCabe).

bed for weeds and perennial herbs. This soil disturbance, if done early enough in the spring, will produce a crop of weeds for food and will afford good fall and winter cover for pheasants.

A corn field that has had only early cultivation or herbicidal treatment will support a heavy growth of weeds by fall, and the combined food and cover value thus created is excellent for pheasants. Other herbaceous plants also form both food and cover. Alfalfa is good nesting and brood cover, and a source of spring, summer, and fall food (leaves and insects). Unharvested soybeans make good summer, fall, and winter cover, and the beans are eaten from fall to spring.

Clean-farming practices have been in vogue in the Lake States for the past 30 years and greatly have reduced roadside and fencerow cover. Travel lanes and loafing and roosting cover near food frequently have been eliminated, rendering food supplies for all practical purposes non-existent to the pheasant. The need in such cases is less a matter of cover planting than of allowing a fencerow or roadside to grow its own cover naturally.

The current threat to roadside cover is the indiscriminate use of herbicides on a broad scale. In Wisconsin alone, in 1950, and estimated 2,000 miles of roadside was debrushed or sprayed, thereby reducing or destroying available game cover (Swift 1951). Debrushing is primarily to reduce snow drifting on roads. This is an important loss of pheasant cover in Wisconsin and Michigan and occurs in all the Lake States. Such work is of particular importance in prairie lands, such as those of Illinois, where fields are extensive and closely cultivated and fencerows few, leaving roadsides one of the main sources of cover.

Habitat improvement notwithstanding, it appears now that the first concern is not so much a matter of creating cover as of preventing its destruction.

Drainage

The most important loss of cover in Wisconsin, and, to a lesser degree in Indiana, Michigan, and Illinois, is the drainage of seasonally wet areas not normally tillable. Marshes and borders of tamarack swamps are excellent wintering grounds for pheasants. Turning them into areas of more game food, at the expense of cover, may destroy their usefulness in the habitat pattern.

Drainage is the end result of a complex of social and economic factors. Of concern here is the fact that it adversely affects one of our most important game birds and that it is increasing. One index to the amount of drainage is shown in payment records of the Production and Marketing Administration (Fig. 16). Several points must be kept in mind when reviewing these data: (1) This is not a complete picture of Lake States drainage. The Soil Conservation Service and other public and private drainage projects are not included here. (2) Not all the drainage recorded has damaged pheasant cover. (3) The principal point of interest in the PMA data is the magnitude of change in the amount of drainage over the period shown.

Drainage increased rapidly after the second year of the subsidy program. In the three-year period 1948-1950 an aggregate of more than two million acres was drained under the PMA program alone. Much of this land was not cultivated, so it represents a considerable loss of cover. The price of corn probably prompted drainage also, for PMA drainage payments rose with the corresponding rise in corn price. How long these two statistics can rise together remains to be seen; in the meantime, however, game habitat is being destroyed at a rapid rate.

In periods when farm income is high, fly-by-night drainage rigs become active in wet areas of the Lake States. When farm prices drop, much of this drained land becomes idle again. Vegetation taking over such a location may make inferior cover for pheasants. Eventually, when ditches are silted in or the tiles broken, water levels become re-established and much of the original vegetation may come back. This is a slow process, and in the meantime, cover is inferior or absent.

Blouch and Eberhardt (1953) have reported the case history

PLATE LIII.—Typical aspect of Michigan's medium quality pheasant range. *Above.* Gently rolling till plain in Clinton County farmland. Unpastured wheat stubble offers food and cover in fall and spring. *Below.* There is food, abundant cover, and birds in this central Michigan area (Ingham County), but the state's best pheasant populations are in more intensively cultivated areas (Ralph I. Blouch, Michigan Dept. of Conservation).

PLATE LIV.—Fencerows and pheasants. *Above.* This weedy fencerow in Washtenaw County, Michigan, was used throughout one winter as a travel lane between roosting cover and a feeding area (Ralph I. Blouch, Michigan Dept. of Conservation. *Below.* This wide, brushy fenceline in Wood County, Ohio, probably is used by more pheasants than any other fencerow in the state. In December, 1951, an estimated 2,000 birds were using the adjacent 320-acre refuge (Eugene H. Dustman, Ohio Cooperative Wildlife Research Unit).

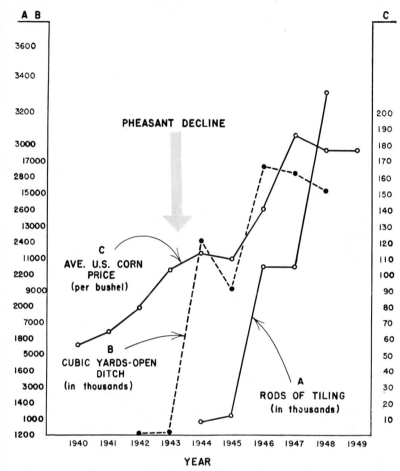

FIGURE 16.—Relationship of Lake State drainage to corn price.

of an area which has run the gamut of drainage. The Prairie Farm, in Saginaw County, is in the heart of Michigan's best pheasant range. When its poorly drained clay soil was cleared and drained, pheasants prospered as they did in the rest of the state, reaching a high and then sinking to a low in the late '40s. By 1952 pheasants had recovered to about 75 percent of their former abundance in the rest of Saginaw County, but pheasants on the Prairie Farm recovered to only 15 percent of their former high. In the words of the authors, "Some continuing misfortune has befallen them." This continuing misfortune is chiefly drainage and the intensive cultivation associated with it.

The Prairie Farm was 30 percent cultivated in 1937, but 83 percent of it was cultivated in 1953. While drainage and clearing were going on, pheasants had a heyday. There always were fallow fields and abandoned crops. Drainage ditches and spoil banks were allowed to grow up to weeds and brush. Today drainage is virtually completed and these inefficient farming practices have disappeared; ditches are kept open, fields are rarely left fallow, and fall plowing is common. Of the 17 percent left in cover, much is grazed woodlot which is of little value to pheasants. Drainage that first created excellent pheasant habitat, later, when carried to its greatest efficiency, ruined the excellent habitat it had made.

One of the areas (Bird Marsh, Jefferson County, Wisconsin) used by Buss (1946) in his Wisconsin pheasant survival studies has been drained so completely that roughly 90 percent of the natural cover of that area has been lost and there is little or no hunting in the marsh proper. The photograph in Plate LV shows a ditching rig in action. This skid shovel is capable of digging a 14′x5′ ditch at the rate of 27-38 rods per day, depending on the site and subsoil. The cost to the farmer for a ditch of this kind is about $3.00 a running rod. Such rigs are not required to report their activities.

Drainage is not always detrimental to pheasant habitat. In northwest Ohio and along the Lake Erie shore, and in southern Michigan adjacent to Lakes Erie and Huron, there were large areas of waterlogged soil with poor drainage and a high water table. This land was worthless to agriculture and hence to pheasants until drainage, usually by a combination of tiling and ditching, made it highly productive of both crops and birds. Agricultural development broke up the solid blocks of cover with cultivated fields and the resulting interspersion of food and cover made ideal pheasant habitat. It is in this land that Michigan and Ohio now have their greatest pheasant densities, although in certain localities reclamation has

PLATE LV.—A skid shovel digging a drain in what was once an excellent pheasant marsh, Jefferson County, Wisconsin (Robert A. McCabe).

been so complete that there actually is a need for pheasant cover.

Summarizing the role of cover as a necessary part of pheasant environment, these deductions appear valid: (1) cover is needed at all seasons of the year for protection against weather and predators; (2) during inclement weather it is essential that food be near cover; (3) the greatest need in the Lake States is less for planting cover than for preventing its destruction.

Food

One of the basic differences between native grouse and the introduced pheasant is in winter feeding habits. Pheasants do not eat the buds on which grouse rely for winter fare. Both grouse and pheasants augment their main diet with other items, such as occasional greens from wintering plants, insect eggs, invertebrates, and grit.

If food for pheasants ever is in short supply, it is during late winter and early spring. At other seasons, grain, fruits, green parts of plants, insects and berries are plentiful. Of course, proper foods, like adequate cover, must be available and accessible when needed most.

The five most important foods for each state in order of their importance are listed in Table 44. It comes as no surprise that corn is the chief food and that second in importance are small grains. Both form part of the legume-corn-grain crop rotation so common in the Lake States. The seed-producing weeds associated with this rotation are likewise valuable as pheasant food. Ragweed is common in grain fields and new seedings; foxtail and smartweed are abundant in corn fields, especially those not check-rowed.

TABLE 44. The Five Most Important Winter-Spring Pheasant Foods By States.

Item	Wisconsin	Michigan	Illinois	Indiana	Ohio
Corn	1	1	1	1	1
Small grain	2	2	3	5	3
Ragweed	3	3	4	2	4
Smartweed	4	—	—	3	5
Foxtail (grass)	5	5	5	4	—
Soybean	—	—	2	—	2
Wild grape	—	4	—	—	—

Illinois foods rated by Willet N. Wandell and Ralph E. Yeatter.
Indiana foods rated by William E. Ginn.
Michigan foods from Dalke, 1945.

In the extensive dairy region of the Lake States much of the grain eaten in winter comes from standing corn and spread manure. In years when most of the corn crop is brought in from the field, manure is a principal source of food, without which pheasant survival in areas of dairy farming might be poor. Here is a case where the mechanization of farms has been a boon rather than a detriment to pheasants. Rubber-tired equipment allows manure to be spread throughout the winter, whereas the old iron-rimmed spreader bogged down in deep snow and slipped on icy fields. Manure was stored in the barnyard to wait for weather suitable for spreading, and stacks usually were well away from cover and often protected by the farm dog.

Starvation has occurred in wild pheasants involving from a few birds to half a given population (Nelson and Janson

1949, Trautman *et al.* 1939, Errington 1939, Bump 1937, Sharp
and McClure 1945, and Kirsch 1951). Lack of proper food in
the winter also could contribute to other causes of mortality.
Hunger alone, prior to any physical evidence of starvation, is
a stress factor. When such stress is coupled with any one or a

PLATE LVI.—Pheasant tracks in snow reveal where the birds leave heavy
cover to range onto adjacent cropland to feed on waste corn and soybeans
(Eugene H. Dustman), Ohio Cooperative Wildlife Research Unit).

PLATE LVII.—*Above*. Machine-picked cornfield in central Michigan, Clinton County. Pheasants make good use of such fields through the winter (Ralph I. Blouch, Michigan Dept. of Conservation). *Below*. Cutting and shocking corn leaves much less food and cover. The use of pickers is increasing, thus favoring the ringneck (Eugene H. Dustman, Ohio Cooperative Wildlife Research Unit).

combination of extreme cold, high wind, rain, pursuit by predators, reduction of cover, or deep snow, it may render birds
more vulnerable or cause death (Selye 1949).

It is true, however, that pheasant starvation is generally uncommon and almost unknown in the Lake States. Although
starved birds would be difficult to find, enough interest is
shown in pheasants so that any widespread mortality would
be made known by people demanding that "something be
done." Die-offs of muskrat, skunk, and beaver have been recognized quickly. Of the Lake States, Illinois, Indiana and Ohio
are least likely to have conditions causing this kind of winter
loss.

The ringneck pheasant is known to be a hardy bird, as
borne out by controlled starvation experiments (Gerstell 1942,
Latham 1947, Kozlik 1949). In captivity, pheasants repeatedly
have survived several weeks without food and it is unlikely that
a few days without food would cause any wholesale mortality
in the wild. This is rather remarkable in view of the fact, that,
in general, birds burn up energy quickly and many of our
smaller birds must feed every day or so in order to stay alive.
There seems to be some relation between the weight of a bird
and its ability to survive starvation, and the larger size of the
pheasant seems to stand him in good stead.

In any appraisal of food available to wild pheasants, quantity, quality, and accessibility must be considered. Quantity
and accessibility usually are easily determined. The quality of
food is less evident. It seems to be true that soil fertility, or
something associated with it, may have sufficient influence on
the quality of pheasant foods grown upon them to affect pheasant abundance. An example in Michigan will illustrate this.

Sanilac County is in Michigan's "thumb." Here large corn
fields provide food, but cover may be scarce. Excellent pheasant populations are supported on its flat, lakebed-clay plains.
Cass County, in southwestern Michigan, on the other hand, has
but few pheasants. Yet cover is more abundant and food (corn)
is available in quantity, and presumably quality, equal to
that in Sanilac County. Cass County is principally outwash

Table 45. Method of harvesting corn for grain, by states, 1938, 1943, and 1946 [1].

State	Corn harvested for grain			Percent of acreage of corn for grain that was						
	1938	1943	1946	Harvested with mechanical corn picker			Husked or snapped by hand from standing stalk or shock		Husked with husker shredder	
	1,000 acres	1,000 acres	1,000 acres	1938 [2]	1943 [3]	1946	1943 [3]	1946	1943 [3]	1946
				Percent	Percent	Percent	Percent	Percent	Percent	Percent
Wisconsin	1,164	1,302	1,247	5	20.6	37.0	37.5	28.0	41.9	35.0
Michigan	1,240	1,043	1,335	5	22.4	37.0	45.4	36.0	32.2	27.0
Illinois	8,073	8,023	8,553	43	64.7	75.0	33.7	24.0	1.6	1.0
Indiana	4,003	4,114	4,445	22	53.8	65.0	40.3	30.0	5.9	5.0
Ohio	3,350	3,186	3,405	12	34.5	55.0	46.0	30.0	19.5	15.0

[1] Brodell, A. P. and J. A. Ewing, 1948.
[2] From data published in the July 1939 Labor Release.
[3] B.A.E. report F. M. 49 "Harvesting the Corn Crop." U. S. Dept. of Agricuture (processed).

plains and moraines, and so the soil has much lower fertility.

This same situation is repeated over much of southern Michigan, for distribution of pheasants seems to follow directly the distribution of good soils. Roughly, we can say that, in southern Michigan, the most pheasants are on the best soil; further, that Michigan has islands of moraine and outwash plains (poor soil) surrounded by excellent pheasant populations on good soil. These poor soil areas (which usually have more cover) often provide good wintering grounds, but alone they appear incapable of supporting much of a pheasant population.

No one knows why the better soils seems to support more pheasants. Possibly foods grown upon them are more nutritious, or possibly more intensive exploitation of the good soils somehow affects the habitat and indirectly the population. In any event, soil fertility may be related to the effectiveness of a food or cover planting, as it is to habitat requirements in the wild.

Many kinds of seed-producing plants have been used in foodpatch experiments (Allen 1938, Leopold *et al.* 1939), but it is generally agreed that the main source of winter food in the Lake States comes from some form of standing or machine-picked corn. Soybeans and sorghum are the only other crops that stand up well under winter conditions and still maintain their food value. Shocked cereal grains also are good, but may require hand labor to make them available as food and are particularly vulnerable to mouse and sparrow pilfering. Weeds can be grown as a source of food by working up the soil. However, not all weeds produce food, and what grows on any plot will depend on the kinds of seeds stored in the ground or that fall on the plot after the soil has been worked up. The best way to determine what these may be is to examine adjacent croplands or fallow fields. It is axiomatic that land too poor for most crops is not likely to produce a heavy yield of weeds.

The best way to assure a food supply for pheasants is to leave standing corn near areas of good winter cover. However, a machine-picked corn field usually is sufficient, and the economics and need for special measures to feed the ringneck must be appraised locally.

Vitamin A deficiency was reported in game-farm quail by Nestler (1946), but studies on wild pheasants and quail by Schultz (1948) and Thompson and Bauman (1950) failed to uncover any such condition in Ohio and Wisconsin. It is doubtful that a Vitamin A deficiency in Lake States game birds ever exists in the wild. Corn, staple winter food of the pheasant, is rich in provitamin A.

Pheasants, like domestic chickens, retain grit in their gizzards to help grind the seeds they eat. Grit is naturally retained in the gizzard during periods when the bird is unable to obtain it, and hard seeds may function as a substitute. When the hard seed coat is worn off, this kind of grit also supplies nourishment. Snail shells which are eaten may serve as a combination of food and grit.

Edges of plowed roads become favorite feeding and grit-gathering sites in winter. During the nesting period when the hen requires considerable amounts of calcium for egg production, calcareous grit provides one of the main sources of that mineral.

Pheasants need water, and there is an adequate supply in dew, succulent fruits, and insects if free water is wanting. Water and grit are important physical needs of pheasants, but nowhere in the Lake States is a shortage of them considered to limit the number or distribution of pheasants.

Knowledge of how to manage pheasant food and cover on a practical and effective basis is far from complete. Biologists are experimenting and learning—but results are extremely difficult to measure. Of course, the food and cover that is now an integral part of the Lake States pheasant range was provided unwittingly by man as he carved his farms from the original cover. Thus, it is evident that managing the land can manipulate pheasant populations, up or down; but it is not clear that this can be done on a scale that is economically feasible when more birds are the principal objective.

PLATE LVIII.—In Illinois, drainage ditches are important as nesting and roosting areas (Illinois Natural History Survey).

TABLE 46.   Pheasant kill report for the Lake States[1].

Year	Michigan	Wisconsin	Indiana	Ohio
1941	1,254,725	646,959	206,138	....
1942	1,200,595	801,999	109,026	....
1943	1,368,039	720,679	83,105	no data
1944	1,401,076	446,996	91,993	....
1945	1,055,350	470,596	65,426	....
1946	904,367	437,428	71,913	868,000
1947	452,934	294,929	closed	592,000
1948	632,698	299,143	52,721	707,000
1949	863,959	383,882	52,851	1,042,500
1950	797,543	414,487	57,763	920,150

[1] These figures (adjusted to a 100 percent return) were arrived at as follows:
Michigan: about 10 percent of hunters' reports (compulsory).
Wisconsin: about 18-20 percent of hunter's reports (compulsory).
Indiana: a random sample of 1 hunter in 25—voluntary questionnaire.
Ohio: a random sample of 30,000 hunters (4-6.5 percent of the total)—
voluntary questionnaire.
Illinois: no reliable statistics available.

The Pheasant and the Farmer

The state has the sovereign right to hold wildlife in trust for all the people. In the case of the pheasant, the farmer implements this right. He has become the custodian of most of our Lake States pheasants. On his activities, economy, progress and land-attitude depend the pheasant's food and cover essentials. Some of the land-use influences in which the farmer has a part have been discussed earlier.

Hay-mowing

The evolution of the farmer's tools has had a profound effect on the welfare of the pheasant. One case, that of the manure spreader, has been discussed.

Thirty years ago, hay-mowers were slow-moving, horse-drawn machines. But today, most haying in the Lake States is done by tractors, often with power take-off cutters. This means greater speed in cutting, and therefore a greater likelihood of killing a nesting hen and destroying her nest or brood. Such accidents are frequent because pheasants use hayfields as preferred nesting cover (Buss 1946, Wight 1933). The mortality of nesting hens and juvenile birds caused by hay mowing may be a key limitation to pheasant populations. In many areas,

PLATE LIX.—Woods borders and woodlots, with thick understory, are important cover types in Ohio (Eugene H. Dustman, Ohio Cooperative Wildlife Research Unit).

it is likely that losses through this farming practice deprive the hunter of larger shootable populations. Under some conditions, hayfield mortality is the only loss factor that can be measured accurately.

TABLE 47.   Some hunter, land, and kill statistics for the Lake States.

State	Ohio	Michigan	Wisconsin	Illinois	Indiana
Total pop.[1] (thousands) .	7,899	6,309	3,421	8,712	3,921
Percent Urban	70.2	71.0	57.8	77.6	59.9
Total Land[2] Acreages ...	26,318,080	36,494,080	35,040,640	35,806,080	23,171,200
Estimated[3] Acreages Available to Hunting	20,995,911	32,394,698	30,469,631	30,617,802	18,963,858
Percent	79.8	88.8	87.0	85.5	81.8
Estimated Area of Pheas. Range (acres)	26,318,080	18,995,168	25,212,672	18,952,157	12,512,448
No. of Resident Small Game Hunting Licenses[4] (1950)	689,000	620,192	474,430	491,796	397,512
Estimated Pheasant Kill (1950)	920,150	797,543	414,487	150,000	57,763
Pheasant kill per Small Game Hunter (1950) ..	1.34	1.29	0.87	0.31	0.15

[1] Preliminary reports, U. S. census, 1950.
[2] World Almanac, 1950.
[3] Miller and Powell, 1942.
[4] This represents *total small game* hunters, not all of whom are *pheasant* hunters.

A second innovation in hay cutting is the use of lights on the tractor to make night operation possible. In some parts of Ohio and Michigan, cut hay is artificially dried at a mill. This "mill-cut hay" is high quality and excellent for commercial sale. Cutting can be done whenever the hay is ready, since there is no reliance on weather curing. Dustman (1950a) reports that mill-cutting causes much more damage to pheasants than ordinary methods of haying. The difference for three cuttings in 1948, in terms of mortality of adult hens and young birds, was as follows:

PLATE LX.—*Above.* The mowing machine is the most efficient pheasant "predator" by far in the Lake States. *Below.* After the hay mill mowers, come the choppers, who pick up the alfalfa and blow it into trucks for hauling to the dehydrating plant (Eugene H. Dustman, Ohio Cooperative Wildlife Research Unit).

	Total Casualties 100 Nests	Casualties 100 Acres
Mill-cut	93.6	27.6
Farmer-cut	34.9	5.9

The profit is greater, the hay better, and a great deal of valuable time is saved, so it is doubtful whether killing six out of every 10 nesting hens will influence the argument against mill-cutting hay. A small-scale attempt to buy hayfield nest cover in Ohio proved too expensive. Fortunately, so far, only a small fraction of Lake States hay is mill-cut. Strangely enough, a *reduction* in the amount of livestock in these areas could result in an increase in mill-cut haying, since mill-processed hay is a cash crop. A workable solution to the problem of hayfield mortality could have far-reaching importance in pheasant management, but experimentation to date has been only partially successful.

The flushing bar, which is attached to the mowing machine or tractor ahead of the cutter bar, is designed to frighten nesting hens and young pheasants from the path of the onrushing knives. Incubating hens so saved have the opportunity to establish another nest; and young birds which manage to escape contribute to the fall population.

Flushing bars of various types have been used for many years, but only recently has one been designed for high-speed power mowers. Such a bar has been developed in Ohio (Warvel 1950), and studies in this state showed that its use reduced hayfield mortality of nesting hens by 45 percent and of young pheasants by 70 percent.

Although these figures demonstrate the value of such bars, they are not in wide use. Main reasons are difficulty in mounting and adjusting, and the cost, which varies from 12 to 15 dollars per bar installed. The latter objection has been overcome to some extent in Ohio by encouraging sportsmen's clubs to contribute funds for the bars, which are made available to farmers agreeing to use them. The State Division of Wildlife also promotes the use of flushing bars by furnishing them to farmers without cost and assigning personnel to aid in mounting them on the tractors. Not infrequently the user is discouraged when pheasants refuse to flush and are killed in spite of the flushing bar, and also when no birds are found in the hayfield. Research workers presently are seeking new methods for reducing mowing losses.

The small combine now has largely replaced the traveling threshing-rig. In general, the introduction of combines has been a benefit. Grain to be harvested is allowed to ripen on the stalk, and hence some wastage is caused by shelling out during the harvest. The legume seeding under the grain often is protected by cutting the grain high, and in areas where straw is not used, only the heads and a small portion of the straw is threshed. Field weeds also go uncut, and this allows seeds to mature. Often late-nesting hens, nests or broods are saved because of the high-set cutter bar.

Stubble clipping, however, nullifies some of the advantages

PLATE LXI.—In the wake of the mower (Robert A. McCabe).

of combining. Stubble is cut with a mower and quite often baled and removed from the field (Dustman 1949). The reasons for this added operation are (1) to reduce shading of hay seedings, (2) to eliminate the spread of plant disease by cutting and thus promoting the decomposition of grain stalks, and (3) to keep old stubble out of the first cutting of hay the following summer. This procedure reduces important brood cover and eliminates field weeds that make excellent fall and winter pheasant foods.

Corn harvest

The corn picker can be regarded as a boon or bane to pheasant existence. Fields picked mechanically have considerable wastage (Wandell 1948, Leedy and Hicks 1945), and this grain is available as pheasant food until covered by snow. It becomes available again in spring when the snow melts. If such corn were ordinarily husked during the winter or in the spring, and hence available all winter, machine-picking in the fall would be undesirable. If, however, corn were hand-snapped or cut as silage, wastage would be much less and machine-picking therefore advantageous. The same holds true for cover: picking creates cover inferior to standing corn, but obviously superior to *no cover*. The corn harvest for the Lake States is shown in Table 45. Space does not permit a detailed evaluation of the data, but correlations between pheasant welfare and crop management are clearly evident. There is little doubt that the welfare of Lake States pheasants depends greatly upon corn agriculture and corn economy.

Woodlot grazing is harmful to pheasants, since it destroys both food and cover. The agricultural desirability of woodlot grazing has long been challenged. Roadside, fencerow, ditchbank, and marsh burning likewise ruin much-needed cover in order to accomplish dubious farm benefits.

In some parts of the range near areas of good winter cover, pheasants in spring are known to pull young corn plants (up to 6-8 inches tall) in order to get what remains of the kernel. A serious loss of corn can result, which can at best be remedied

PLATE LXII.—Unclipped grain stubble serves as excellent cover from fall to spring in Ohio. The presence of many such fields keeps pheasants scattered, and results in more equal utilization of the range. The practice of clipping is increasing, since it benefits the oncoming hay crop (Eugene H. Dustman, Ohio Cooperative Wildlife Research Unit).

by replanting. Repellents and preventive measures have been tried, but without uniform success.

Many Lake States farmers are indifferent toward pheasants. Some have sacrificed time or produce in an effort to increase them, while others are openly hostile toward the bird because of its corn-pulling habit and because pheasant hunting invites trespass. On the other hand, state conservation agencies until recently have given little more than lip service to the farmer. It is imperative that the farmer's interest and cooperation be solicited relative to game matters, for he is the custodian of the pheasant and without his permission to hunt, our hunting licenses are meaningless pieces of paper.

The Pheasant as a Game Bird

The ultimate test of a transplanted game bird is its ability to multiply and provide good hunting over a period of years. In this regard, the pheasant has a unique advantage over other Lake States game birds. It is polygamous, and cocks can be distinguished readily from hens. Thus, a large percentage of males can be removed by hunting without affecting next spring's breeding potential.

In most cases the spread of pheasants from the various plantings was rapid, and therefore public shooting was possible less than a decade after the first official releases. In Wisconsin, the first state releases were made in 1928 and the first open season to embrace more than one entire county was in 1932, at which time eight entire counties and parts of one other were open to pheasant hunting. The kill of cocks was 40,500. In Michigan the first state releases were in 1918, and the first season was held in 1925.

Lake States hunters took quickly to pheasant shooting, and within a few years they surpassed in numbers all other kinds of game-bird enthusiasts.

Sometimes it is difficult for the individual hunter to see where he and his fowling piece fit into the over-all picture of pheasant hunting. Some statistics for several Lake States are given in Tables 46 and 47. Ohio has the greatest number of hunters, the largest area open to pheasant hunting, and kills the greatest number of birds. This state is highest in birds killed per license holder as well. Only Ohio and Michigan kill more than one pheasant per license holder (1.34 and 1.29 as of 1950). Indiana is lowest both in total kill and kill per license. On a basis of acres of range per license holder, Wisconsin ranks highest, as shown in the following summary:

Wisconsin	Illinois	Ohio	Indiana	Michigan
53.1	38.5	38.2	31.5	30.6

Effects of hunting on pheasant numbers

Hunting pressure is controlled in part by a number of economic and social conditions, including the national economy, war restrictions on guns and ammunition, accessibility of cover by good roads, timing of the open season with week-ends and holidays, and the simultaneous opening of the season for a number of game species on the same day. Of course, the prime governor for outdoor recreation is weather, a topic which needs no elaboration.

Any factor affecting hunting pressure will have its greatest effect on opening days. Leedy and Hicks (1945) show that on a study area in Wood County, Ohio, hunters exerted the greatest gun pressure and killed the most birds during the first two days of the season. From this high point, hunting pressure and kill diminished steadily to the end of the season, showing a slight recovery during weekends and holidays. This same principle of diminishing hunting pressure and kill has been substantiated by public hunting ground checks made by the Wisconsin Conservation Department (Kozlik 1949), and by Michigan workers.

In 1937, Michigan began two studies that determined not only the pattern of hunting pressure day-by-day for the season, but also the effects of shooting on pheasant populations in subsequent years.

One of the study areas was the 9,000-acre Prairie Farm in some of Michigan's best and most heavily hunted pheasant range. Biologists followed the pheasant populations on this

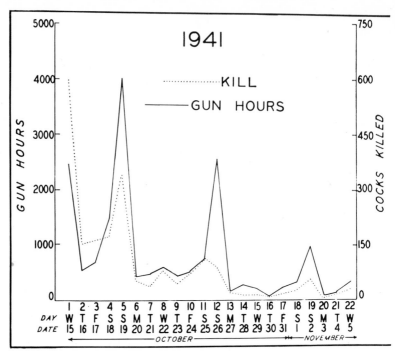

Figure 17.—Distribution of gun pressure and pheasant kill on Prairie Farm.

area for three years and have obtained hunting information for fifteen consecutive years up to the present time (Shick 1952). The other study was conducted on the Rose Lake Wildlife Experiment Station, established in 1937 to study wildlife relationships to farm practices, and also to study the effects of hunting on small game. This station is located in average pheasant range in south central Michigan, near Lansing. Here, too, pheasant populations were watched carefully from season to season. This study, which is still active, has been reported on by Allen (1946, 1947).

From these two studies has evolved the well-known "you can't shoot 'em out" philosophy. In short, this principle states that hunting pressure, as we know it in the Lake States, has virtually no effect on subsequent pheasant populations. Since this principle has become the core of the policy for setting hunting regulations in Michigan and many other states, it is worth briefly reviewing what these biologists found:

Figure 17 shows the typical pattern of pheasant hunting and kill during a Lake States season. While both the Prairie Farm and Rose Lake were hunted many times harder than surrounding farm lands, the pattern on private farm lands is much the same: heavy pressure on opening days and weekends, and the bulk of the kill in the first week of the season.

These two areas of exceedingly heavy hunting pressure consistently had a large percentage of the cocks removed by hunting. The Prairie Farm, for example, had an average sex ratio of about 1 cock to 10 hens followed the season, indicating removal of about 90 percent of the males!

It had been a matter of frequent concern to sportsmen that such an unbalanced sex ratio might leave hens unmated and thus affect production the following year. But pheasants stayed at a relatively high level on the Prairie Farm year after year despite this ratio. Even though single cocks were seen with harems of 16 to 18 hens, at no time was there any indication that production was suffering. In California, under comparable hunting conditions (Harper *et al.* 1951) a postseason sex ratio was recorded that varied from about 1:7 to 1:20. Shick (1947) reported that confined birds bred with no excessive loss of fertility in ratios of 1 cock to 50 hens. Undoubtedly even more than 90 percent of the cocks could be removed safely.

It was estimated that Rose Lake's hunting pressure went up to 5 times as heavy as surrounding areas, and Shick calculated that pressure on the Prairie Farm was equivalent to 1 man spending 11 hours every day of the 22-day hunting season on the same 100 acres of ground. It seems almost inconceivable that pheasants could stand that sort of pressure, until we look at the statistics. Every hunter knows it is easier to shoot pheasants at the beginning of the season than at the end. Few realize how much easier. On heavily hunted areas where a bird may be bagged every few gun-hours on the opening day, it may

take literally hundreds of gun-hours to bag one at the end
of the season. When numbers reach this low level, variations in
gun pressure have little effect on the kill, and almost   no
amount of added hunting increases the bag very much.
Pheasant hunting has a built-in safety valve, which illustrates
again the universal law of diminishing returns.

The Prairie Farm study showed that when cocks had been
reduced to the point where only about two remained per
hundred acres, hunting interest dropped off and few more
were taken. By that time in the season, the survivors have
become more wary also, which helps to reduce further the
returns from hunting. All evidence indicates that hunting
pressure, as it is known in this region, will not wipe out cock
pheasants in any extensive area of good cover.

In light of this situation, hunting pressure obviously adjusts
to the size of the available pheasant crop. When there are
more birds, hunting effort tends to hold up until the surplus is taken. When the crop is small, the surplus disappears
quickly and hunting tapers off. It is evident that length of
season and daily bag limits have little effect on the total
pheasant kill. These restrictions help primarily to spread the
pheasant take among more hunters.

Shick (1952) calculated the rate of turnover of the pheasant
population at the Prairie Farm. He found a shrinkage of 84
percent of the birds from midsummer to the following spring.
This is on an area from which about 90 percent of the cocks
were removed by hunting.

Leopold et al. (1943) had also calculated a shrinkage of 84
percent in young birds from hatching to winter trapping in an
unhunted pheasant population. About four-fifths of the pheasants must die from one cause or another during their first
year—whether they are hunted or not. A closed season one year
could not add appreciably to the next year's shooting by holding over birds, and to close the season in a low year just to
"give the birds a rest" seems unwarranted. The history of
pheasant numbers at the Prairie Farm for a three-year period
is shown in Fig. 18.

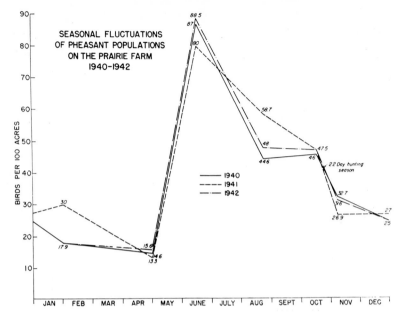

FIGURE 18.—Three-year record of changing numbers on Michigan pheasant ranges.

Rarely do Lake States hunters harvest 90 percent of the cocks. Post-season sex ratios usually are around 2 to 4 hens per cock, indicating a kill of from 50 to 75 percent. Since it is known that at *least* 90 percent of the cocks can be harvested safely, it is obvious that most of the Lake States range actually is undershot. Further evidence of the pheasant's ability to stand heavy hunting pressure is strikingly shown in the chapter on Pelee Island.

Many administrators and research workers believe that longer seasons would be practicable were it not for the illegal killing of hens. It is fairly well established that as cocks become harder to find, the illegal hen kill begins to increase. While some hens undoubtedly could be killed some years in certain areas, legal hen shooting in the Lake States could reduce pheasant populations seriously (Kozlik and Kabat 1949).

The effectiveness of easing hunting pressure on pheasants

by simultaneous opening of the hunting season with several other game species depends on the number of "buffer" species available to the hunter. The possibilities in such buffering in this region are shown in Table 48. Except for two species of fox, furbearers are not treated in this table. Mourning doves are hunted only in Illinois, but no kill records are available. In point of individuals bagged, the pheasant rates as follows: Wisconsin, 4th; Michigan, 2nd; Indiana, 8th; Ohio, 3d. Cottontails rated first in all Lake States except Wisconsin, where ruffed grouse was the number-one game species. Ohio and Michigan have no open season on quail. The inter-species buf-

TABLE 48.   Comparison of Pheasant kill with that of other species in the Lake States—1950

Total Kill in 1950	Wisconsin	Michigan	Indiana	Ohio
PHEASANT	414,487	797,543	57,763	930,150
Cottontail rabbit	768,189	1,796,898	3,426,144	4,664,530
Snowshoe hare	154,428	336,011	***	***
Jackrabbit	26,701	***	***	***
Gray squirrel	732,672	51,830	465,408	695,890
Fox squirrel	404,894	610,442	1,442,764	1,233,310
Bobwhite quail	18,487	***	1,132,817	***
Ruffed grouse	798,932	479,665	***	?
Sharptail and prairie chicken	66,851	33,588	***	***
Woodcock	22,791	78,095	7,717	?
Hungarian partridge	48,919	***	20,020	***
Bear (hunting only)	1,276	1,179	***	***
White-tailed deer	168,294	116,420	***	2,146
Ducks	399,751	383,404	103,740	?
Geese	16,118	24,483	4,178	?
Coot and gallinules	151,983	43,349	19,029	?
Red fox	21,953	13,805	38,108	?
Gray fox	6,489	***	12,067	?

*** no open season, or species does not occur in the state.

Michigan and Indiana do not collect kill statistics on gallinules. The question marks in the Ohio column indicate that the sampling system returns were too small to calculate a total kill. There are no game harvest figures for Illinois. Wisconsin and Michigan calculate the total kill by adjusting to 100 percent the kill sent in on hunters' report cards. In Michigan 10-15 percent return a kill report. Ohio and Indiana obtain a sample kill by sending questionnaires to about 15 percent of the licensed hunters. This figure is then adjusted to a 100 percent return.

fer action is complex, particularly when so many kinds of game are hunted during a single season. The chief interest in this table is the great variety of species buffering the pheasant and their relative abundance within each state. There is much to be said for concurrent hunting season openings. In brief, no one is denied his favorite hunting while at the same time crowding of the cover is alleviated and pressure on each hunted species dissipated.

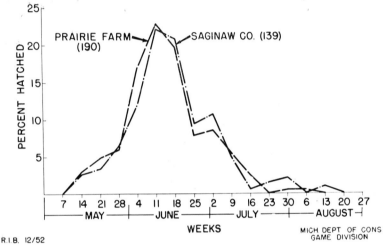

FIGURE 19.—Pheasant hatching distribution in Michigan, 1951.

Regulation Problems

Shooting seasons and bag limits for our native game birds have progressed from no limitations to our present restrictions. In the case of an introduced species like the pheasant, current restrictions have developed from complete protection to generous bag limits and long open seasons. South Dakota had the ultimate in liberal regulations in 1943 with a 120-day season and daily bag limit of 7.

Not many years ago the setting of regulations was largely

guesswork. Wardens and public officials were quizzed or volunteered impressions and hearsay information on the season's reproduction. Often these impressions were accurate, especially when the field observations were numerous. But since the advent of the trained game technician, and Federal Aid funds that put him in the field, much has been learned about the effects of hunting and how to inventory game.

Today biologists in the Lake States are continually appraising the number of pheasants. An index to the breeding population is arrived at by crowing cock transects. The number of pheasant cock crows heard per 2-minute period every mile along 20 miles of all-weather roads is tabulated. These transsects are set up and run to give maximum efficiency (Kimball 1949). The average number of crows for each route can then be compared with other routes or the same route in other years.

Roadside counts in summer are made by game wardens and field personnel and these, plus similar tallies by rural mail carriers, produce numerical data on total number, sex ratios, brood size, and broodless hens. Since the supply of pheasants for each fall's hunting season is an annual crop which depends largely on the productivity of that summer's breeding season, a measure of this productivity is important. In Michigan, for example, the relationship between the number of broods seen in late July and the reported fall kill of pheasants was studied over a period of years. This relationship proved to be so consistent that it allowed a prediction of the fall kill of pheasants before the season was opened. Since 1946 the predictions have been made and used by the Michigan Department of Conservation in recommending bag limits and lengths of seasons. The test of these predictions is shown in Fig. 19. The consistently low margin of error affirms the faith placed in this management tool.

New techniques are constantly being devised by research workers. For example, obtaining a winter census and sex ratio has long been a perplexing problem. When snow is deep, more pheasants are seen and the *observed* sex ratio is low for

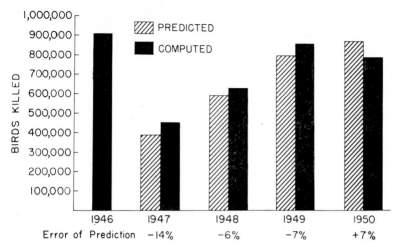

FIGURE 20.—Michigan pheasant kill, 1946-1950.

the cocks, who seek heavier cover and are harder to see. A comparison of snow depth with numbers of pheasants observed each day by conservation officers uncovered a consistent relationship between snow depth and the birds observed (Fig. 20). Thus, by taking snow depth into consideration, *observed* sex ratio and numbers can be converted into a more nearly actual population count and sex ratio.

Throughout the Midwest, tens of thousands of birds in hunters' bags have been examined by biologists and information gathered has been of great value. Often much can be learned through questionnaires or the collection of inedible parts, such as wings and legs, of animals bagged. Statistical studies have been made possible by hunter cooperation through the mails. Returning the yearly kill report is the minimum participation the state asks of sportsmen in managing the game resource.

The gathering of various kinds of information on pheasants, through observation and statistical treatment, plus the constant efforts made to improve these methods, is manifestation of the progress from guesswork to scientific management. Space does not permit a recitation of all the facts that game research has uncovered, but these facts are guiding most of the game administration in the Lake States (and the United States) today.

Cyclic behavior?

One problem that has puzzled the hunter and intrigued the technician is the "cyclic" ups and downs of some of our game species, particularly grouse and snowshoe hares. Despite much research, the cause of these cycles is not known, and the rise and fall in numbers cannot be checked or controlled.

About 1943, pheasants in the Lake States began to decline drastically in numbers, so that by 1947 a low point for the 1940's was reached. In Indiana this prompted a closed season

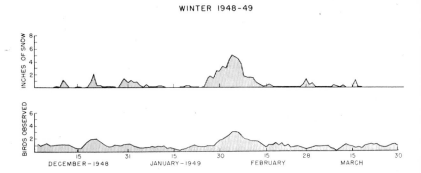

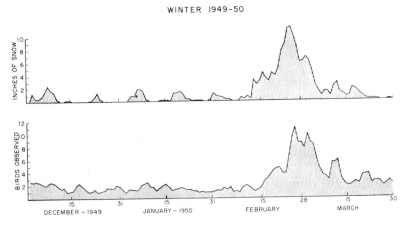

FIGURE 21.—Daily snow depth compared with number of pheasants observed.

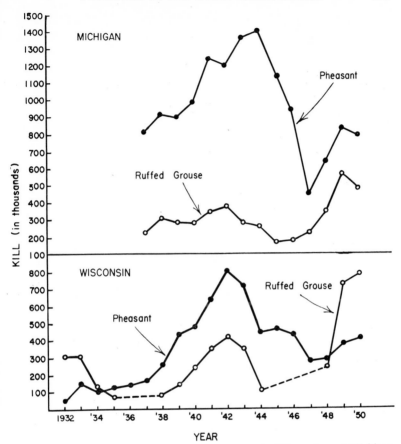

FIGURE 22.—Fluctuation in pheasant and grouse kill in Wisconsin and Michigan.

in 1947. Michigan and Wisconsin peaks of abundance, according to kill statistics (Table 46) occurred in 1944 and 1942 respectively, declining to a low in 1947. A ruffed grouse peak and depression occurred in the Lake States during the same period (Fig. 22). Only Michigan and Wisconsin kill enough ruffed grouse to make a comparison. Wisconsin closed its season on these birds during years of extreme low population, but the parallel paths of the various curves suggest a common causative agent. Minnesota kill statistics show essentially the same trends as the Wisconsin data.

Enough of a synchronization existed, at least during a peak

PLATE LXIII.—Sprout-pulling pheasants thinned the stand in this Wisconsin cornfield. In areas of abundance, this is one of the nuisance values of the ringneck.

and a low, to suspect the Lake States pheasant of fluctuating with the ruffed grouse during the forties. Of course, speculation that the pheasant *may* be cyclic answers no questions. Ordinarily, a game bird is considered to be cyclic when peaks and lows in population come with *reasonable* regularity. If the term, "cycle" were used with the same mathematical connotation it has in physics, there is doubt whether any biological phenomenon, much less game abundance, could be considered cyclic. There is also little likelihood of all local or regional populations being abundant or scarce at the same time. Complete geographic synchronization seldom, if ever, occurs. Local weather phenomena, land use and other factors can radically change local pheasant populations, but when numbers decline from the Dakotas to the Atlantic Coast, spanning climatic and geographic regions, the cause is difficult to identify. Whether or not the pheasant continues as a cyclic species remains to be seen, but from the information available, it has been as cyclic as the ruffed grouse for the past 15 years.

The Pheasant and Adversity

Animals living in the wild follow a difficult road from one generation to the next, and few of the young born each spring live out the year to reproduce a subsequent generation. To allow for heavy losses, the pheasant is endowed with a high reproductive capacity. Each spring many more young are produced than are needed to maintain the population, and it is one of the principal jobs of investigators to learn what happens to those that are lost. The part that food, cover, and farm operations play in the survival of pheasants has been discussed. Two other factors that are commonly suspected of limiting pheasant numbers are weather and predation. Both need realistic appraisal.

Weather

At the Thirteenth North American Wildlife Conference, a meeting attended by wildlife specialists from all parts of North America, James Kimball of South Dakota (1948) reported on the suspected reasons for population decline in pheasants. He solicited the opinion of 12 research workers doing active field work. The reasons varied geographically, as might be expected, but the common denominator in 11 cases was inclement weather during the breeding season. The climatic rigors of the winter season were recognized as important but were not considered as causing the widespread decline of pheasants in the forties.

Robert F. Perry (1946) considered that abnormally cold and wet breeding seasons caused the reduction of pheasants in New York State. These conditions would be considered unfavorable in most of the Lake States as well. Just how excessive precipitation and low temperatures affect pheasants can be deduced only by analogy in most instances. Abandoned and flooded nests, poor hatchability, chilling of young birds, and disease are possible causes of this lowered production, and all can be brought about by weather conditions.

Michigan workers (MacMullan and Eberhardt 1953) attempted to test some of the effects of low temperatures and rainfall on pheasant eggs during various stages of incubation, by simulating these conditions in pens. When their tests were

PLATE LXIV.—A law inforcement officer has many jobs. In Iowa, one of them is collecting pheasant legs for age-ratio studies (Jim Sherman, Iowa Conservation Commission).

completed, they concluded that, "The tolerance shown by pheasant eggs in these experiments was considerably greater than popularly supposed. For much of the incubation period, tolerance is great enough that widespread mortality from unseasonal cold spells would not likely occur in the wild."

One other lead uncovered, but by no means substantiated, is the possibility of abnormal behavior of hens in certain years that might be reflected in a lack of broodiness. This could make for frequent or severe chilling of eggs and thus lead to poor reproduction generally.

Even within a geographic area the size of the Lake States, given weather factors may have opposing effects. A cold, wet spring, which was blamed for poor pheasant hatch in Wisconsin and Michigan, was thought to provide good conditions for pheasants in Illinois (Moore and Cowan 1947). Similarly, Bergeson (1949) reported satisfactory reproduction in Montana despite an excessively wet breeding season. Glading implies the same for California pheasants (in Wandell 1949). Kimball (1948) concluded that in spite of one of the coldest and wettest springs in South Dakota, the 1947 crop of pheasants was three times as great as in 1945, and twice as great as in 1946.

Charles and Elizabeth Schwartz (1949) report pheasant range in Hawaii where as much as 300 inches of rain falls annually.

In Ohio, Dustman (1949) found that heavy rains caused considerable flooding of nests in the years 1946 and 1947. In two counties in northwestern Ohio, 15 to 20 percent of the land was under water. Flooding alone accounted for 41 percent of the nest destruction in 1946. This impairment of nesting was followed by lowered rates of hatchability in May and June clutches. The number of hens with broods was likewise lower in 1946 and 1947 than in any other year in Ohio pheasant investigations. The Ohio findings show that renesting may not compensate for the failure of earlier nesting attempts.

In addition to its direct effect on pheasants, weather may have an even more potent influence indirectly. It has been mentioned previously that hay mowing often is responsible for heavy losses of pheasants. There is a good possibility that spring weather conditions may have their most significant effect through the timing of such farm operations as hay mowing or sod plowing. If the peak of mowing came a week after

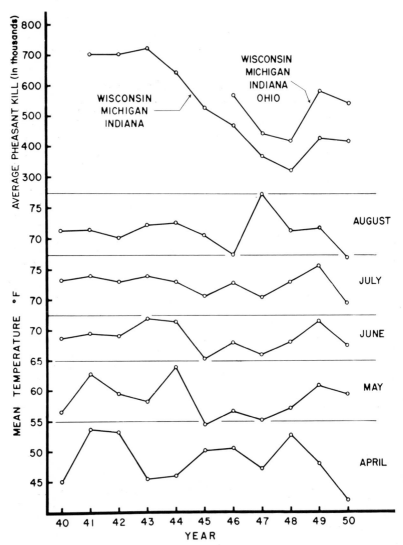

FIGURE 23.—Mean monthly temperature in Lake States and average pheasant kill.

instead of at the peak of pheasant hatching, it might change radically the brood mortality rate.

Here, then, is a source of confusion that results from comparing a series of local studies of a bird with a large geographical range. Each worker uses the words colder, hotter, drier, or wetter, relative to local conditions. On a range-wide basis, such terms have little meaning. This confusion may be eliminated if the situation is viewed thus: In parts of the pheasant range where high temperature and low moisture tend to limit annual production, a year of relatively cold, moist weather will be conducive to increased production of young birds. The opposite holds true in areas of normally cool, moist breeding seasons where relatively warm and dry conditions are considered ideal.

The mean monthly temperatures and precipitation for the Lake States are shown in Fig. 23 and Table 49 respectively. There is no obvious correlation between these two weather factors and pheasant abundance.

One interesting but not unexpected aspect of Lake States temperatures (and rainfall) is the consistent similarities between Michigan and Wisconsin and among Ohio, Indiana and Illinois. This is illustrated in Fig. 24. What it may indicate is that Lake States climate during the pheasant breeding seasons is a combination of two distinct climates.

TABLE 49.   Lake States Average Mean Precipitation.
(in inches)

Year	April	May	June	July	August	Ave. Total	Combined Kill Michigan & Wisconsin*
1941	2.52	2.98	4.18	2.90	3.31	15.9	1,901,684
1942	2.54	4.58	4.65	4.13	3.22	19.1	2,002,594
1943	2.80	6.67	4.27	3.74	3.09	20.6	2,088,718
1944	4.30	3.80	3.50	2.06	3.53	17.2	1,848,072
1945	4.21	4.87	5.30	2.88	3.41	20.7	1,525,946
1946	1.41	4.83	4.85	2.29	3.26	16.6	1,341,785
1947	5.50	4.83	4.91	2.84	3.24	21.3	747,863
1948	3.24	3.25	3.77	3.79	1.98	16.0	931,841
1949	1.95	2.84	4.59	4.37	2.90	16.7	1,247,841
1950	4.30	2.65	4.66	4.32	3.06	19.0	1,212,030
Average	3.28	4.13	4.47	3.33	3.10		

* Only states for which the 10-year record was available.

Fig. 24 includes all reporting weather stations and tends to exaggerate the mean difference. It is obvious that at the border regions between the states the temperatures would show little variance. When weather data from stations in the southern-most counties supporting pheasants in Illinois are compared with those from the northern tier of Wisconsin counties within the established range, the average mean temperature difference is about 8.50. This is about the same magnitude of difference shown in Fig. 24. In an area the size of the Lake States (about 700 miles long and 500 miles wide) no uniform climate can be expected. Even climatic extremes are not area-wide, nor do they occur uniformly in time and place.

The correlation of weather factors with pheasant abundance for certain states has been made (Banko in Kimball 1948, Ginn 1948, Allen 1946, 1947), but as the size of geographic units increases such correlations become less striking and often disappear. It seems that local pheasant abundance may be explained by the occurrence of weather extremes, but range-wide comparisons must of necessity rely on means. Climographic studies dealing in means and comparing temperature and precipitation of native and introduced ranges (Cahn 1938, Graham and Hesterberg 1948) have indicated that pheasants probably would not thrive south of 40° North latitude under conditions of normal temperature and rainfall. The limitation is considered to be high temperatures during the breeding season. This same idea was expressed by Bennitt and Terrill (1940). However, the existence of pheasants in certain hot and arid regions of the west would cast some doubt on this deduction, were it not for the fact that pheasants in these areas (e.g. the Imperial Valley in California, intermountain valleys in Utah and Colorado) are found near irrigation (Yeager et al. 1951). Thus it seems that high temperature alone is not detrimental and that relative humidity or a temperature: moisture ratio may be of importance.

The climatologist Thornthwaite (1948) in his attempt to classify the climate of the United States uses a term called "evapotranspiration," which is defined as combined evaporation from the soil surface and transpiration from plants. In short, it is the process whereby water is put back into the atmosphere, or the reverse of precipitation. His classification, however, is based essentially on "potential evapotranspiration" which he explains as follows:

"The vegetation of the desert is sparse and uses little water because water is deficient. If more water were

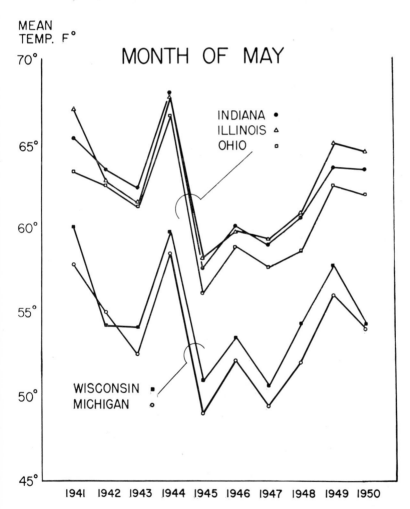

FIGURE 24.—Comparison of mean temperatures for May in Lake States.

available (locally), the vegetation would be less sparse and would use more water. This is a distinction, then, between the amount of water that actually transpires and evaporate and that which would transpire and evaporates if it were available. When water supply increases, as in a desert-irrigation project, evapotranspiration rises to a maximum that depends only on the climate."

Using potential evapotranspiration as an index of thermal efficiency, Thornthwaite has prepared a map of U. S. climates. The category *Mesothermal B1* (Fig. 25) with a potential evapotranspiration of 22.44 inches is an almost perfect correlation with the distribution of Lake States pheasants. This we consider to be more than just coincidence. How potential evapotranspiration affects the range is not known. There is no apparent correlation between the Mesothermal B1 zone and soil, vegetation, or agricultural practices in the Lake States. If the climate-moisture relationship affects the pheasant directly, how and when likewise are not known. Obviously, there is a dearth of investigation along the lines in question.

In summary, these ideas appear to be important relative to the pheasant and weather: (1) Cold and wet spring weather that may be detrimental in one part of the Lake States range may be beneficial in another. (2) High temperatures alone do not limit distribution. (3) Some relationship between temperature and moisture (*e.g.* potential evapotranspiration) governs suitability of pheasant range and perhaps yearly productivity. (4) What to the pheasant are ideal climatic conditions are not necessarily those measured by weather stations, although a recent climatic classification (Thornthwaite *op. cit.*) of the Lake States shows a striking correlation with current pheasant distribution.

In relation to pheasants, weather is still a favorite subject for discussion, but too little work has been done to clarify the situation fully. Until it is known how weather factors operate against pheasant production or range extension, listing weath-

MESOTHERMAL B₁

PHEASANT RANGE

FIGURE 25.—Thornwaite's climatic classification in relation to pheasant range.

er as a limitation tells very little. There is a need for well-designed experiments in this field of investigation.

Foxes, hawks, owls, and pheasants

The fox alternately has worn a halo or a crown of thorns, depending entirely on who was pleading his case. The upland game and rabbit hunter prefers to see his hide tacked to the barn door. Fox hunters gladly would trade pheasants for foxes and point enthusiastically to Reynard's qualities as an object of the chase.

The fox often has been accused of causing, or at least hastening, the decline of Lake States pheasants in the 1940's. Foxes are predatory and pheasants are prey. When pheasants went down, there was some logic in suspecting the fox.

The possibility that foxes might limit pheasants has been studied thoroughly. Since almost every creature either eats or is eaten by other animals, a sizable part of our game research has been aimed at finding out what effect predators might have on game species. Usually, this research has been along one of two different lines: (1) finding out what foxes eat, and (2) comparing the ups and downs of pheasants with the ups and downs of foxes to see if there could be any cause and effect relationship.

The diet of foxes has been fairly well determined in a number of states and encompasses a wide variety of plant and animal food. Choice is largely a matter of availability, which is in turn, dependent on the season. Almost without exception food studies have shown that on a year-round basis mice and rabbits form the chief diet of foxes (Errington 1937, Scott 1947). Even these animals thrive in spite of being the fox's favorite dish. No study has shown the ringneck to be a staple item of diet. Seldom are pheasants so abundant as to be more available than mice and rabbits, and if they were, those eaten probably would not be missed by the pheasant hunter.

One study of fox food habits was made by David A. Arnold (unpublished) in southern Michigan. Foxes were tracked over fresh snow for an aggregate of 760 miles. Following these tracks, bioligists found 1467 instances in which a fox killed or attempted to kill an animal. Mice accounted for 1204 of these kills or attempts. Of these, 163 were definitely established as kills, and it is estimated that about 500 of the remaining attempts were successful. Second on the list were 45 rabbits killed. There was evidence that 23 pheasants were taken by foxes. It is noteworthy that 19 of these were killed in the vicinity of the Fennville State Game Area which had a winter concentration of about 250 pheasants per square mile. A large part of the area was a refuge where no hunting was allowed. This high localized kill represents one of those unusual situations which provides the basis for popular denunciation of the fox as a pheasant killer. Viewed dispassionately, it illustrates the principle that foxes (and other predators) are influenced by availability—the more pheasants there are, the more likely they are to be taken. The Fennville area has a high local pheasant population surrounded by largely submarginal lands that are inferior pheasant range but excellent for foxes. Pheasants are not hunted, and little hay mowing is done on this area. It is not surprising that some of the annual surplus of birds ends up as fox food. If hunters had taken the surplus, foxes might find other prey more readily available than pheasants.

Arnold's works gives good information (760 miles of fox tracking is a significant sample) on what foxes actually kill, as well as what they eat, and other studies have been made of the contents of fox stomachs and scats. Hair, bone fragments, and teeth remain undigested in the stomach and are passed out in the droppings. Of course, if a fox eats carrion, it usually cannot be distinguished from something the fox killed. Investigations almost invariably show small rodents as the staple, with pheasants an occasional or incidental item.

Other research has been based on food remains found around fox dens. Such observations are rather inconclusive, since one is likely to find remains of anything from a dead horse to fish heads around a fox den. When foxes are denning, the parents are hard put to gather food for the young, and they frequently scavenge around manure piles and garbage pits. Moreover, the remains that are found represent only a part of the story. For example, mice are eaten whole, and no remains are left around the den.

A seemingly obvious approach to fox-pheasant relationships is to compare their population trends. Many states now get some idea of the number of foxes and pheasants from hunters' reports and bounty records. These figures leave something to be desired, since bounty payments and fur prices sometimes affect the fox take, and since the reliability of kill statistics is in some cases questionable. However, they should indicate the trends of populations. For example, Wisconsin kill statistics

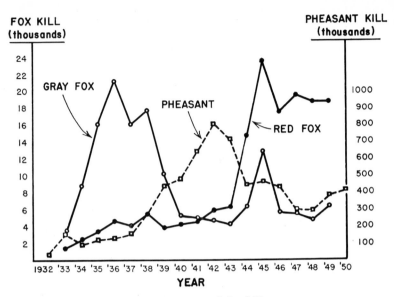

FIGURE 26.—Pheasant and fox kill curves.

(Fig. 26) show an inverse relationship between pheasant and fox abundance. This suggests cause and effect and makes a *circumstantial* case against the fox. It is circumstantial because true relationships are masked by the fact that the poorest and best fox and pheasant counties are "lumped" in this graph.

If, over a period of years, fox populations were growing at the expense of pheasants, then areas of high pheasant populations should produce progressively greater numbers of foxes, and the pheasants should decline. Conversely, areas of low pheasant populations might be expected to lose the abundance of foxes.

Two groups of Wisconsin counties where there are both foxes and pheasants are compared in Fig. 27. Group A represents five of the best fox counties and group B five of the best pheasant counties. The graphs are not a direct comparison of the number of foxes and pheasants, but they show population trends on an adjusted scale. The fact that pheasants followed the same ups and downs in counties where foxes were numerous and in counties where they were few indicates

that Reynard was not directly involved in what actually determined the numbers of ringnecks.

In reference to this relationship, Arnold (1951) stated that
"The distribution of foxes and pheasants in southern Mich-

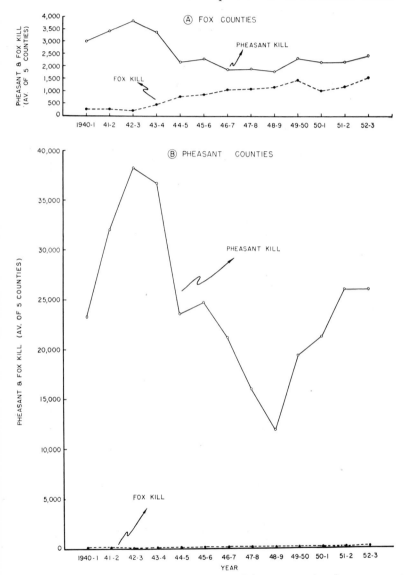

FIGURE 27.—Relationship of kills of pheasant and foxes on good and poor range.

igan is such that many foxes are not regularly found in the best pheasant habitat. Even at the peak of Michigan's fox population the majority of these animals occurred in what is considered poor pheasant range." He observed further, "The numerous food habit studies that have been made on foxes add even further to the evidence that fox predation was probably a very minor factor in the decline of Michigan pheasants —if it was a factor at all."

In Illinois, two years of bounty records[2] show no correlation between the number of foxes taken and the pheasant range. On a basis of the fox kill per square mile, there were good and poor catches within the best pheasant range and also excellent catches in parts of the state where there are no pheasants. As in Wisconsin and Michigan, the heaviest fox population in Illinois does not occur in the better pheasant habitat. Throughout this region fox abundance occurs on land with steep slopes and less intensive agriculture, and these conditions undoubtedly are of greater importance than the numbers of a relatively unimportant food species. In summary, there is no evidence that an abundance of foxes reduced the pheasant population in the Lake States in 1943 or at any other time.

In lesser degree, hawks and owls also are accused of having a part in pheasant depressions, but food habits studies show that most of these birds eat pheasants even less frequently than do foxes. About a dozen species of hawks and owls spend at least a part of the year in Lake States' pheasant range. Although numbers undoubtedly fluctuate, birds of prey are a permanent part of the fauna. The fact that pheasants became established so quickly in ranges frequented by hawks and owls would suggest that avian predators do not have much influence on ringneck numbers, despite the fact that, as pheasants become established, they naturally become a part of the prey population.

Several detailed studies have been made pointing out the role of hawks and owls in relation to game birds. One of these

---

[2] Furnished by L. S. Weber of the Illinois Coal Strippers Association, who compiled these data from records of the county clerks.

(Einarsen 1942) showed that on 400-acre Protection Island, off the State of Washington, where two cocks and six hen pheasants were liberated in 1937, the population had an average annual increase of 277 percent in the next five years. No hunting was allowed, and an undetermined number of at least five species of hawks and owls were present and they too were not molested. Similarly the phenomenal pheasant population on Pelee Island, Ontario, was unaffected by winged predators. No excessive concentration of hawks and owls was attracted to either of these islands.

In one study in Pennsylvania, (Luttringer 1938) 2817 hawks' stomachs were examined during a 13-year period. The only species found to have taken game birds were the accipiters, the sharp-shinned, Cooper's and goshawks. Only 89 stomachs out of 1925 examined (4.6 percent) contained remains of ruffed grouse and pheasant.

Perhaps the most thorough and detailed ecological study of hawks and owls was made in Michigan (Craighead and Craighead 1950). An area of 36 square miles was studied the year around for density, activity, movement, mortality and productivity of both the raptors and their prey. It was concluded (relative to game birds), that (1) predation alone could not control the prey population, and (2) no single prey species (i.e., pheasants) can draw sufficient predation pressure to keep its population level dangerously depressed. It should be remembered also that there are persons who do not use a gun and who enjoy seeing the graceful darters. These people are entitled to enjoy a share in the public ownership of all wildlife, including creatures that hunt and those that are hunted.

A single observation of a cock pheasant killed in the field always makes better conversation and stays in one's mind longer than a larger number of inconspicuous and rarely seen rodent kills. Yet, without exception, studies to date indicate that no predator depends on the ringneck as a staple food, and no evidence has been found that predators are influencing Lake States pheasants seriously.

PLATE LXV.—*Above*. Spring floods sometimes seriously interfere with pheasant nesting. *Below*. The mowing and burning of roadsides destroys valuable pheasant cover in Ohio farmland (Eugene H. Dustman, Ohio Cooperative Wildlife Research Unit).

This fact can be understood better when we realize that every established wild species produces a number of "extra" young each year. A part of this surplus goes to the sportsman during the hunting season; but since the game harvest is only a part of the annual loss, it is not necessarily true that every pheasant killed by a predator means one less bird to shoot that fall, or one less brood the following spring. Similarly, pheasants taken by predators are part of the regular annual turnover of numbers, and they are such a small part that even if all predators were eliminated we might expect little, if any increase in the Lake States pheasant kill.

Illegal hen kill

Illegal killing of hens and poaching may be a greater cause of local losses than wild predators. In Ohio, Leedy and Hicks (1945), found that in one county 40 hen pheasants were illegally killed for every 100 cocks legally bagged. They state that, "All evidence indicates that this loss of hens is a typical and regular occurrence." On excellent range, the population may be able to tolerate such abuse, but in other areas it might ruin the hunting. In Wisconsin, it has been postulated that illegal killing of hens was the reason why pheasants did not regain their numbers after the slump in 1943 (Kozlik and Kabat 1949). While there is no full agreement on this, the problem undoubtedly is serious.

Hen-killing sometimes is a matter of mistaken identity, sometimes careless identification, and sometimes willful violation of the law. In each case little thought is given to the role the female plays in producing good hunting. Realizing that most hunters are essentially sportsmen, the state of Iowa carried on a campaign of enlightenment. A strong appeal was made to the hunter's sense of fair play and sense of economics. Posters in public places, newspaper articles, and talks before interested groups telling of the harm done by the illegal killing of hens have paved the way toward understanding. While no measurement of the number of hens saved is likely to be available, the Iowa Conservation Department has considered the effort highly successful. Similar educational campaigns probably would help to reduce killing of hens in the Lake States.

Pheasant Hunting

The dollars and cents value of a day in the field after pheasants differs among individual hunters. There are some who consider pheasant hunting an inferior pastime (Knight 1947), although hunting statistics show this group to be a minority.

Most modern-day recreation is costly, and hunting is no exception. Several states have used questionnaires in attempting to find out what a hunter spends on his sport each sea-

PLATE LXVI.—Hen killed by Cooper's hawk. Predation rate is highest when birds concentrate in winter (Eugene H. Dustman, Ohio Cooperative Wildlife Research Unit).

son. In a 1947 inquiry (Leedy and Dambach 1948), over 4700 Ohio hunters reported spending $41.88 each on clothing, guns, ammunition, gas and oil, hunting privileges, meals, lodging, refreshments, decoys, and dog expenditures. This excludes the cost of a license. There were 689,000 licensed hunters in Ohio, and the sample questioned reported that 69.9 percent of them hunted pheasants.

Dollar values of wildlife are elusive, but it is of interest to get some idea of the cost of a wild-grown pheasant in the bag. There were 481,611 licensed pheasant hunters in Ohio in 1947 (69.9 percent of 689,000). If their expenditures are adjusted to 1951 standards,* they spent $24,807,783 on all forms of hunting ($51.51 annual cost per hunter x 481,611, the number of pheasant hunters). The percentage of a pheasant hunter's expense that can be allocated to the pursuit of his favorite bird varies with the individual, abundance of pheasants, abundance of other game species and similar conditions. Any of the following proportions might be realistic in a given year for determining the cost of harvesting a bird:

1) 75% of his expense = $18,605,837 or $27.00 per bird
2) 50% of his expense = $12,403,892 or $18.00 per bird
3) 25% of his expense = $6,201,946 or $9.00 per bird
4) 10% of his expense = $2,480,778 or $3.60 per bird

Such an evaluation leaves much to be desired, but it is obvious that pheasant hunting is an expensive sport. Cursory examination of the pheasant range map and hunting statistics will indicate that Ohio is not unusually high in the cost per pheasant to the hunter. Indeed the cost may be less in Ohio than in other Lake States.

Farmers and sportsmen

Each state, in its own way, has attempted to eliminate farmer-hunter friction, and to increase the use of available hunting land. Some of the first efforts were initiated by the farmers themselves. The Williamston area in Michigan (Wight

---

* Cost of living index shows a 12.3% rise between 1947 and 1951 (Dept. of Labor: Midyear Economic Report of the President, July 1951, p. 248).

1931), and the Plain Church area in Ohio (Lytle 1935), are examples. The Williamston plan originated in Ingham County, Michigan, in 1929, with the primary purpose of eliminating trespass during the hunting season. A group of farmers opened their lands to hunters on a free-permit basis. A hunter had to receive permission, and a permit, from one of the farmers before being allowed to hunt on the area. The hunter's car was parked in the farm yard, and no roadside parking was permitted. Refuge areas and closed areas were set up and respected. Only four permits were issued to each farmer, and new hunters were allowed on the land only after one or more permits had been returned. All boundaries were marked clearly, so that "ganging up" was infrequent. The Michigan conservation department acted as a silent partner in this plan, offering advice, publicity, and material to aid the organization.

Similar cooperatives are being formed today on a modified Williamston pattern. Many of the early areas dropped out of the plan (Hill 1940), although for some years the general idea and organizational program continued to grow. More recently, the plan has not expanded in the face of the every-man-for-himself type of hunting now prevalent in the Lake States. Following is the number of Williamston-type cooperatives in Michigan over a period of years:

1936	1937	1938	1939	1951
1	34	61	110	47

The principle of organizing against trespass has been tried many times in the rural areas of other states. Some cooperatives have worked, and others failed, but the basic idea continues to produce new attempts to improve farmer-sportsman relations.

The Plain Church group, organized in Ohio, used essentially the same system as the Williamston plan, except that the permittees were required to pay a fee. The money was placed in the church building fund. As of 1951, there were 12 similar associations in Wood County, Ohio. The stimulation for those enterprises comes from a financial need of the community Schools, churches, town halls or some other civic project are the beneficiaries. While this particular set-up worked well, fee hunting in general has not been attended by any great success elsewhere.

Another kind of paid-for hunting is that exercised under the *licensed shooting preserve* law* in Wisconsin. There, a group of persons who have a suitable piece of land under their control, by ownership or lease, may apply for a license. The fee is five dollars for an area of 320 acres or less, and ten dollars for an area up to 640 acres, which is the maximum allowable. There is no minimum acreage stipulation. This license requires that:

(1) All boundary signs be standardized and purchased from the Conservation Department.

(2) All such areas be stocked with pheasants, and the kill shall not exceed 75 percent of the stocked birds. The stocking ratio of males to females released between April 1 and 20, shall be of the ratio 1:8. A "credit" of 3 additional birds towards the allowable take shall be given for each hen stocked at that time.

(3) An area is accepted for a preserve, if it is not a wintering area for pheasants, is not too close to a refuge or public hunting ground, and does not in any way impair the hunting of the general public.

(4) The season runs from the opening of the general pheasant season to the first of February. Cocks and hens may be taken.

(5) All birds taken on the area must be marked by special wing tags, which are issued in accordance with the number of stocked birds.

These are the main regulations, although minor stipulations have not been included. The regulations are appraised each year, and changes are common. Preserve shooting appears to be put-and-take hunting, but it also forms the basis for in-

---

* The Wisconsin Licensed Shooting Preserve Law. Section 29.573 of the Wisconsin Statutes Order No. M-102 (Revised 6).

dividual and group efforts to manage the land so that it will "hold" and produce more birds. In one instance (Riley Preserve, Dane County, Wisconsin), farmers and town members planted evergreen cover, built feeding shelters, and allowed standing corn to remain in the fields near winter cover. To strengthen further the social bonds, farm members were the dinner guests of the town members at the annual business meeting.

In Wisconsin, the number of preserves has changed little as shown by the record from 1943 to 1953:

1943	1944	1945	1946	1947	1948	1949	1950	1951	1952	1953
67	63	67	72	63	69 .	68	67	69	68	67

Recently, the state of Ohio has used a similar system, and some of the major restrictions are given for comparison with those in Wisconsin:

(1) The area must not exceed 500 acres, and must be in a single block. (Wisconsin maximum is 640 acres.)

(2) It must be fenced with woven wire to a height of 6 feet, and the wire mesh may not be larger than two inches. (Wisconsin requires a single-strand wire fence.)

(3) An annual fee of $100.00 is required. (Wisconsin's fee is $5.00—320 acres or less; $10.00—over 320 acres.)

(4) All birds released must be banded. (Wisconsin requires a "gentle release" for spring breeders, but banding is optional.)

(5) Preserves must release at least one bird per acre, or a minimum release of 500 pheasants on their own lands. (Wisconsin has no minimum release, but not more than 75 percent of the number of birds released may be shot.)

(6) Only banded birds may be shot. If a wild-reared bird is taken, a banded pheasant must be released immediately on the open range by the preserve as a replacement (Wisconsin allows a kill of 75 percent of

PLATE LXVII.—A policy of "ask the farmer first" will do much to keep pheasant lands open to hunters (Jim Sherman, Iowa Conservation Commission).

the number of stocked birds, and the remaining 25 percent are in a sense "donated" to spread in open range.)

(7) Only one preserve per county is allowed. (Wisconsin has no per county maximum — each application is evaluated individually as to suitability and location.)

Thus, two neighboring states differ widely in the handling of the same game-management problem. Whether this is a result of hunter attitude or land-use factors is difficult to tell. At present, Wisconsin has had over 20 years' experience with its preserve program (67 active preserves as of 1953). Ohio's system is new. Michigan had a preserve law from 1929 through 1936, but a 1937 amendment caused the system to become defunct.

The history of the Williamston Plan, and of shooting preserves indicates that the desire and enthusiasm, plus the physical and economic energy put into one of these enterprises cannot be maintained indefinitely. Eventually, some of the presently active preserves and farmer-sportsman organizations probably will lose momentum and become inactive. At the same time, it should be expected that the basically sound idea of cooperative effort in producing and improving good hunting will take hold elsewhere and give birth to new group undertakings.

Plate LXVIII.—Hunt's reward (Jim Sherman, Iowa Conservation Commission).

Public hunting grounds

Public hunting ground systems have developed to counteract the reduction of shooting areas by posting, to alleviate congestion on private lands open to hunting, and to prevent the posting of additional acreages. Either leased or owned by the state, they help to insure a place to hunt for the average license holder. The administration of publicly controlled lands varies among the states depending largely on the size of the area, quantity of game, and number of hunters.

In Ohio, there are about 500,000 acres of public hunting land—82 separate areas. These are owned by the state divisions of Forestry, Parks, and Wildlife, the U. S. Forest Service, and the Muskingum Water Conservancy District. Illinois has 10 state-owned public shooting areas serving the Chicago area primarily. Indiana has had its state forests open to public hunting since 1944. There are 15 state forests so used, plus several other tracts purchased by the state (*e.g.* the Willow Slough Game Preserve and Hovey Lake Game Preserve). The Hoosier National Forest Purchase, which totals 115,000 acres, likewise is open to public hunting.

Michigan has about 225,000 acres of state-owned pheasant range that is open to hunting. This includes a series of "recreational areas" and "state game areas," plus a few state parks and one state forest. They are for the most part submarginal farm land, and include everything from excellent to poor pheasant range. A large percentage of this acreage is available to the Detroit metropolitan area, and is hunted heavily. In 1950, for example, a sample of 70,000 acres received an estimated 135 man-hours of hunting per hundred acres. This heavy hunting pressure assures more efficient harvest of game than on many private farmlands. On this 70,000 acres, over 11,000 small-game kills were made, and in addition, 121 deer and an unknown number of fur animals were taken.

Wisconsin has 257,000 acres of public hunting grounds open to pheasant hunting. State parks and refuges are not open to hunting. Leased areas of suitable size have been selected for available cover, variety of game, and nearness to the hunting population. The rental fee paid by the state for such lands is about 20 cents an acre. No restrictions are placed on the land, other than that it be open to the public for hunting without permission from a landowner. The conservation department then undertakes to post the boundaries of the grounds and the closed areas around buildings, furnish warden patrol, and pay for any damage which can be attributed to public hunting. Cover conditions usually are good, although winter food conditions frequently are such that supplemental feeding stations and food patches are used. Cover improvement sometimes has been undertaken where it can be included in watershed improvement.

In some areas, public hunting-ground shooting is largely put-and-take; in others, as with shooting preserve stocking (Leopold 1940), the surviving hens contribute to production of pheasants on the grounds and in the surrounding area, particularly if such areas are devoid of birds. Spring releases of hens are made for the same purpose, but there is little conclusive information as to what they contribute to the fall bag.

Wisconsin public hunting grounds often are congested on the opening day of shooting, causing undesirable and somewhat dangerous hunting conditions. Nevertheless, a reasonable kill usually is made, and a good measure of enjoyment is realized by the participants. Those who prefer this type of shooting on public hunting grounds are thus eliminated from the natural coverts frequented by the hunter who wishes to shoot a "wild" bird with a minimum of competition.

Game Farms and Stocking Programs in the Lake States

The state game farm, and the value of propagated birds, are points upon which there is no unanimity of opinion among sportsmen, administrators or technicians. It is obvious that without initial stocking, we would have had no pheasants. Most, if not all, Midwest pheasants were game-farm birds initially. To what extent subsequent releases in a given area were necessary for establishment is a matter of opinion. In some instances, the newly established population remained

low, and in many cases had, in a short time, died out completely, so that subsequent plantings were necessary (Leopold
1931). Few, if any, measurements were made on the growth and
spread of plantings. It is common knowledge, however, that an
established population usually was of low density during its
early years (Schorger 1947).

In some cases, continued planting, even up to the present,
has failed to create a self-supporting population. In others,
numerous large plantings were needed before a population
became established, but in most areas an initial planting was
sufficient to establish a self-supporting population. Probably
most people would agree that, if the population created by
the original stocking was large enough to create satisfactory
hunting, then further releases are a waste of time, birds, and
public funds.

Each of the Lake States has developed its own policy concerning stocking methods as to how, when and where they
should be used. The reasoning behind, and the evolution of,
those policies may not be clear, and only conjecture can piece
together a composite picture for the states involved.

Early releases

The first releases in all the Lake States were made by individuals or local groups before the turn of the present century.
The cost usually was assumed by private funds, and there was
little if any record-keeping. From 1900 to 1925, private and
state releases were conducted in trial-and-error fashion over
most of the region. Success was indifferent. In Ohio, the region
along the Lake Erie shore was the first to have an established
population. The natural spread from that area accounts for
most of Ohio's pheasant population. Some of the more rugged
areas of southern and eastern Ohio still are unpopulated in
spite of natural spread, or the direct planting of game-farm
birds.

After the establishment of Michigan's game farm in 1916,
pheasants were distributed systematically throughout the state.
This program was reported as highly successful only three
years after the first game-farm birds were released, and in six

years, the first open season was declared. Local clubs and individuals also participated in the release program. Releases from 1918 until 1947 averaged about 5,000 pheasants annually.

Indiana had eager private participation in the planting program, although state releases were slower than in other Lake States. By 1930 the program was well under way, and a few areas in northern and eastern Indiana had established populations.

Prior to 1930, Illinois had about 35 plantings of pheasants throughout the state, largely from private sources. Most releases, however, were made on the western and southern edges along the Mississippi River. As in Indiana, the state began to stock birds about 1930, and state and private plantings continue up to the present. The northeast corner of the state, in which the early populations were said to have been established, is the area that today supports a shootable population of birds. The southern areas where early plantings were made are pheasantless today.

The State of Wisconsin began to release pheasants in 1929, about 13 years after the Pabst plantings in southeastern Wisconsin were established and spreading. Wisconsin has one of the largest state-operated game farms in the United States, and undoubtedly the most ambitious program. Some of the earlier releases, however, were wild-trapped birds from other states. Eggs, day-old chicks, and grown pheasants are distributed. The day-old chick program was not started until 1936, when 5,700 birds were distributed. Presently about 160,000 chicks are turned over to various groups annually.

Current stocking programs

In 1951, Michigan curtailed its pheasant release program. Distribution of pheasant eggs to farmers and sportsmen and general pheasant releases were discontinued. The game farm was put on a stand-by basis, and pheasants now are released only for experimental purposes, or for field trials.

The original reason for setting up the game farm was to establish the pheasant in Michigan, and for many years releases were made in all sections of the State. When it became obvious that the pheasant habitat was restricted, for the most part, to the southern third of the State, stocking was concentrated in that section. By 1951, it had become apparent that pheasant releases no longer were helping to extend the range, or to increase pheasant numbers. Thus, the game farm had fulfilled its primary purpose.

In the meantime, another use for the propagation plant was considered. Assuming that reared birds were no longer useful in increasing wild populations, could game-farm pheasants be used to relieve high hunting pressure? Michigan has a large system of public hunting areas. Was it economically feasible to increase shooting on these areas by releasing pheasants?

Whether Michigan should engage in a "put-and-take" program—releasing pheasants ahead of the gun—was more a matter of economics than a biological question. For many years, Michigan had banded almost all of the released pheasants. Many experiments had been carried out to determine the best strain of pheasants to stock, and such things as the survival of released birds, and the best age, method, and time of year to release pheasants. Biologists concluded that, at best, it would cost several dollars each to get artificially reared birds into the hunter's bags. In general, the more money spent on the care and method of release, the more pheasants that survived to end up in a hunter's bag. When the least amount of money is spent on planting pheasants, the cost per bird is lower, but fewer are returned to the hunter's bag; so no matter how it is done, it still costs several dollars to bring a game-farm bird to bag.

Michigan decided against such a put-and-take program, on the basis that it could not be financed justifiably by license fees, in the face of the shooting offered by wild birds. It may be significant that popular feeling in Michigan had ruled out the *private* shooting preserve law several years before; Michigan people apparently also are against the principle of *public* preserve shooting.

As an alternative to a subsidy of put-and-take pheasant shooting, Michigan has substituted its habitat improvement program, on the assumption that the money spent to increase pheasant shooting can best be used to improve production of pheasants and other small game species in their natural habitat—a more permanent investment than an annual expenditure to release birds before the gun.

Wisconsin has the largest state program for egg and day-old chick distribution, and mature bird stocking in the United States. The propagation efforts are geared largely to the day-old chick distribution program, which is being evaluated currently. The state also raises birds for stocking public hunting areas. A three-month old bird released on such areas costs the state about $1.10.

Wisconsin was one of the first states to check its stocking program intensively for public hunting areas in order to shed some light on the general problem of stocking in the state.

Buss (1946) ran a series of experiments on Wisconsin shooting preserves from 1936 to 1940 and found that from 3 to 27 percent of the stocked birds were shot. This is a low return in light of the excellent cooperation on band returns from preserve members. In a special study in Dunn County, he released 3,500 eight-week-old cocks during the summers of 1941 and 1942. Postcards (2,500) were sent to most of the counties' 3,000 hunters. These cards, and newspaper publicity during the shooting period, produced a return of 11 percent of the cards sent. The data gathered showed that 277 hunters killed 241 of the released pheasants. Correcting to a complete return for those unanswered cards indicated a return of 77 percent of the released birds in 1941, and under a similar procedure, 84 per cent of the 1942 release. Buss discounted this high return as a result of the questionnaire method of survey where the successful hunters would be more likely to return their questionnaire cards than the unsuccessful hunter. Whether this bias rules out the results of this carefully planned and executed experiment completely is a matter of conjecture.

More recent research by Kabat, Kozlik, Thompson and

Wagner (1955) indicates that band recoveries from stocked birds on areas open to public hunting show an excellent return, if measured intensively.

Although a number of factors affect the recovery of stocked birds, the one most important in the formation of a stocking policy is the method of gathering band-recovery information.

Leg banding of stocked birds in Wisconsin is optional, but all state-controlled experiments on stocking have been undertaken with banded birds. Numbered leg bands identify the released birds that turn up in hunters' bags. The measure of success in stocking has been figured in two ways: the percent of stocked birds in the total bag, and the percent of the birds released that are bagged eventually.

It is common knowledge that not all bands from shot birds are returned. A number of studies have been made on ways and means of increasing the band return by hunters. One waterfowl investigation (Bellrose and Chase 1950) showed that a "reward" band increased the returns 290 percent over the ordinary hunters' voluntary return. This figure seems high even for a migratory group like the ducks, but it illustrates the reluctance by the hunting public to return bands voluntarily. One of the ways to increase efficiency is to surround an area where banded birds have been released with a crew large enough to check each bag individually. This can be done only on a limited scale because of the obvious manpower difficulties.

The 100-percent check is in reality something less, since even with a large crew and season-long vigilance, a few hunters will go unchecked. The Wisconsin Conservation Department (Kabat *et al., loc. cit.*) has been conducting 100 percent checks in areas stocked with game-farm birds since 1940. The results of those checks are shown in Table 50. The percentage of bands recovered under comparable conditions is higher than has been reported by other states. The intensity of checking is claimed by Kabat *et al.* to account in the main for this high recovery rate. Table 51 presents the results of less intensive coverages and substantiates the importance of 100 percent checks in obtaining a clear picture of the kill. In Indiana, Ginn (1947) found that of 4,203 club-reared birds released throughout the state, only 6.4 percent were reported recovered in the bag. This is close to the 5.7 percent received from Wisconsin hunters under similar circumstances, but is far below the 50 percent recovered during Wisconsin's 100 percent checks on areas open to public hunting. Such checks are expensive, but when administration policy is dependent on accurate figures, the inadequate voluntary reports cannot be relied upon.

To attempt range-wide or even state-wide recommendations on the basis of a single year's work, or even a single study, would be presumptuous if not unwise. Stocking has been shown to be a management tool in Wisconsin, but one must keep in mind that it cannot be applied everywhere, nor is it necessarily the best game management technique.

Ohio's stocking program appears intermediate between those of Michigan and Wisconsin. The egg and co-op chick program have been discontinued since 1951, but Ohio releases "mature" birds from its two game farms. The Ohio conservation department estimates that the cost of rearing a game-farm bird to eight weeks is about two dollars.

Another form of pheasant stocking practiced to a limited extent in Ohio has been that of live-trapping and transplanting wild birds. The first trapping for transplant purposes was done during the winter of 1931-32 and has been continued to a limited extent to the present. Surplus birds on refuges have been an important source of supply. This method of stocking serves: (1) to relieve population pressure and food problems, (2) to make poorly populated areas more productive for hunting, and (3) to provide a bird superior in stocking value to birds propagated artificially. Between 1922 and 1940, 11,734 birds, 23 percent of which were males, were live-trapped on three refuges in Wood County. These birds were heavier and stronger than most artificially reared birds. Such birds already are acclimatized and well adjusted to natural conditions and therefore have a high rate of survival. Contrary to artificially propagated stock these birds tend to colonize and, if shot, usually are taken near the point of release.

The live-trapping and transplanting method, although superior in many ways to artificial propagation, is limited by the success of natural production and the unpredictable results of winter trapping. Surpluses therefore are variable, and a constant supply of birds from year to year is not assured. The cost per wild, transplanted bird is about 35 cents.

The Ohio Division of Wildlife is aware of the two opposing policies relative to stocking and state game farms that are evident in Michigan and Wisconsin. Until more of the unknowns concerning stocking are resolved, the present position of releasing garm-farm birds will be maintained in areas where chances of increasing low population appear likely and where "put and take" alleviates excessive hunting pressure in surrounding areas.

Indiana, with its two game farms, has had an egg distribution and stocking program since about 1930. The state parcels out birds to the various counties from a central point, from which conservation clubs distribute them to suitable locations. In most cases the birds are released directly from shipping crates. Spring and fall liberations are made. The spring releases usually are statewide, whereas the fall-released birds are cocks only, and are confined to the northern counties.

Releases from club-reared birds usually are local, and the number varies from 8 to 200, but as a rule, most are less than 20 birds each. A total of 27,219 juvenile pheasants were released by conservation organizations during the 1953-54 fiscal year. No cost records are available for either state- or club-reared birds.

In general, Indiana sportsmen demand a stocking program, although the sporting public probably is unaware (as in most states) of all the facts and conditions involved.

Illinois has three game farms which carry on a cooperative program of day-old pheasant rearing, plus a stocking program of mature birds. Pheasants are released in about 50 counties throughout the state, but the day-old-chick program includes only 31 counties in the northeastern quarter. The estimated cost to the state of a seven-week-old bird from this chick program is from $.90 to $1.10 each. One of the main outlets for stocked birds is on the four public hunting areas around Chicago. Those areas, which are managed for game, must take the brunt of the gunning pressure from the Chicago region. On a "put and take" basis, about 25,000 mature cocks are released annually during a fifteen-day season. A given number of hunters are allowed on these public hunting grounds daily. A quota of cocks is released each evening after shooting hours to take care of hunters the following day. The fee per man to hunt the areas is $4.00, in addition to a regular license. About 70 percent of the birds released are recovered by the sportsmen. The cost per cock released is about $2.50. An official opinion of the Illinois program is expressed in a letter (Sept. 13, 1954) from John D. Montgomery, Supt. of game propagation for Illinois.

> "If it were not for our public shooting area program in Illinois, of which four of these areas are adjacent to the City of Chicago, it would create a highly explosive situation between our so called sportsmen and the farmers. These areas are designed to take care of such hunters who do not know a farmer or do not know where to go to hunt pheasants in Illinois. These areas have a purpose in holding to a minimum, as much as possible, certain trespass conditions that would arise if such an area were not available to the city hunter. We are of the opinion that public hunting in Illinois should be increased to some degree to try and take care of more of the city hunters. These public hunting areas are well advertised in the fall of the year through the columns written by several of our well-known daily newspaper sports editors. The Department does not advertise the areas itself."

He states further that this arrangement is "highly popular with the hunters in Illinois . . ."

Method of release

All states are attempting to improve their releasing methods to insure a healthy, stable population at the opening of the hunting season. Dumping pheasants directly from transportation crates into the wild produces less satisfactory results than does the gentle release method (Kozlik 1948). The latter implies that game-farm birds go through a period of acclimatization in the new habitat. In some instances, the late stages of rearing are in pens constructed on the edge of the release cover. At release time, the pen doors are opened and the birds are allowed to wander off at will. The pen doors frequently are kept open so that the birds can return for food and water if needed. Birds released by organizations rearing day-old chicks are liberated by the gentle release method in Illinois. The birds have enough of their flight feathers plucked at 6-7 weeks to prevent flying, thus holding them in the release area. This plucking takes place just prior to transfer into top-open pens. The birds gradually leave the pen when they are able to fly again, often returning for food and water. They return less and less frequently so that at about the time the hunting season arrives the birds are weaned completely from artificial conditions.

Most all states releasing pheasants use some modification of this gentle release principle.

Pheasant husbandry

Those whose charge it is to raise pheasants for releasing have long been interested in releasing the "best" bird possible This production often has been calculated by rules of thumb, some of which have been very effective, others of dubious value. Wisconsin and Ohio recently have become interested in scientifically producing a better game-farm bird. Wisconsin has set up a breeding program along the lines recommended by poultry breeders in order to select for desirable characteristics. The aim of this program (Stanz 1953) is to "explore possibilities of improving the quality of stocked birds by selecting the breeding for those characteristics which make for higher survival and increased reproduction." Five or six kinds of pheasants have been crossed to produce desirable traits and body size. Although this investigation is far from

TABLE 50. Wisconsin Hunter Returns on Summer-Released Game Farm and Wild Pheasant Cocks Personal Contact Check.

Year	Hunters Checked	Area	Date	Released Pheasants			Wild Birds Shot	
				Age (Weeks)	Number	Per Cent Recovered through Bag Check	Number	Per Cent of Total Bag
1940-42*	....	Jefferson	July 17 to Sept. 24	8-12	1,020	37	401	51
1948	1,534	Potter's Marsh	August	10	614	58	212	38
1949	1,478	Potter's Marsh	August	10-12	612	52	182	35
1949	446	Yellowstone	August	10-12	350	24	17	5
1950	580	Brodhead	Aug.-Sept.	11½-13½	580	48	385	58
1952	1,967	Mazomanie	Sept. 3	12-15	200	55	347	73
1953	2,629	Mazomanie	Aug.-Sept.	9-13	600	50	653	77
1954	2,958	Mazomanie	Sept. 16	16-18	400	68	397	48

*Buss (1946)

complete, there is (Stanz, *loc. cit.*) "a strong indication that many of these qualities may be inherited in such desirable combinations."

It is too early to predict results, but if game-farm birds are to be released, Wisconsin and Ohio hope eventually to liberate a large, wild bird that has an ability to survive well and reproduce adequately.

Hunter satisfaction and economy

No one set of conditions in the field satisfies all hunters. Even "good" hunting is relative. If one hunts in an area that produces excellent shooting (*e.g.* Pelee Island, or central South Dakota) where a legal limit virtually is assured in a day or less of hunting effort, anything short of the expected becomes annoying. Thus, a reduction in the bag to four on Pelee Island, where the limit has been about ten, undoubtedly would cause much disappointment, but a bag of four birds per day in the Lake States, where the daily bag limit usually is two birds, would, if warranted, because for rejoicing. Similarly in an area where there had been no previous open season any legal bag would be welcome.

Within each of the Lake States there are areas of low density or complete absence of birds. This is not disturbing unless one is obliged to hunt in such places. A stocking program might make these productive hunting areas, however. What we can expect is that a *small fraction* of the range be made huntable for those who have no ready access to naturally productive range. Since such a small part of the range is made available to only a limited number of hunters, one might ask, can we afford such a program? This question can be answered only by those who pay the bills. It is like asking a neighbor whether he can afford his home, his car or his cigar. A program of pheasant stocking benefits only a small segment of the hunting fraternity, but it is paid for by all license holders. It is the latter group which must agree or refuse to pay the bill.

The day-old-chick program

Many states maintain, as part of their game-farm program, the distribution of eggs and day-old pheasant chicks. Conservation organizations, 4-H clubs, schools and sportsmen's organizations of various kinds receive these eggs or chicks and continue to hatch and/or rear the young to release time (10 weeks). Those that survive are released on land that is not posted against hunting.

The states distributing day-old chicks suggest using the gentle release method, but do not require it. Methods of rearing, feeding, handling and release differ among clubs and among states. At present, Wisconsin is attempting to evaluate its day-old-chick program through cooperation with sportsmen's groups who rear the birds, and Wisconsin's pheasant hunters who bag them.

The value of rearing pheasants for the sake of recreation and education derived undoubtedly is great. How to assess these values in dollars and cents is difficult, if not impossible.

TABLE 51. Wisconsin Hunting Season Returns on Summer-released Game Farm Birds.

Year	Number of Birds Released	Method of Obtaining Hunter Returns	Percent Recovered
1948-1954*	3,356	*Personal Contact* (100 per cent hunter check by personal contact)	51
1940-1942	1,020	*Personal contact* (100 per cent hunter check by personal contact)	37
1951*	2,750	*Limited field contact* (Part of first weekend hunters personally contacted; direct solicitation with little or no personal contact for rest of season)	32.2
1950³	2,000	*Field station* (Voluntary check, direct solicitation with little or no personal contact) ..	12.8
1938**	80,600	*Mail report* (Hunters' reports were completely voluntary)	5.7

* The releases from 1940-1951 were made by conservation department personnel.
** All of the birds were raised from day-old chicks, banded, and released by sportsmen's clubs (Kellogg 1939).

Comments in Closing

It would be impractical in a publication of this kind to enumerate or summarize all the points covered in the Lake States chapter. There are, however, several points that warrant a final re-emphasis.

The ringneck pheasant is the most important game bird in the Lake States. The north-south limitation of the pheasant range lies within this geographic unit. The factors affecting range extension differ between the north and south boundaries as do the factors affecting density throughout. In each case, the causative agents have not been determined completely.

Climatic factors, predation, farm practices and illegal kill of hens all exert a drain on pheasant numbers, but no one agent can be regarded as causing state-wide or region-wide drops in population. Legal hunting of cocks does not affect the next year's numbers. The pheasant is a bird of farm lands. When farm commodity prices are high, there is a tendency for farmers to exploit agriculturally submarginal land. The resulting loss of habitat, particularly winter cover, is serious in many areas of the states. Certain farm practices can be harmful to pheasants (night mowing, marsh burning, mill cutting alfalfa); others can be beneficial (manure spreading in winter, windbreak plantings). One of the objectives of conservation education and game management is to coordinate the normal farming pursuits with the welfare of the pheasant.

The stocking of certain coverts with game-farm pheasants is a controversial issue among state administrations. The research facts indicate that there are times when stocking is a sound management technique, and others when it is not. No blanket stocking policy should govern all states, or all areas within a state.

The Lake States region has, for its size, the greatest number of hunters per capita anywhere in the United States. The population of the United States is expanding constantly (about 1.5 percent per year). Increased utilization of submarginal land has in most cases reduced game range. If the need is genuine, it would be foolhardy to insist upon game abundance at the expense of national welfare. If we project the sport of pheasant hunting 75 years into the future, what then will be the picture? In resolving our present-day problems concerned with pheasant hunting, we must not lose sight of future needs and demands. Pheasant hunting, expensive though it may be, still is within the range of the people. In order that it may remain so, and improve in both quantity and quality, will require the understanding, cooperation and action of all persons concerned with the ringneck pheasant as an object of the hunt.

CHAPTER 7

PELEE ISLAND PHEASANTS

By ALLEN W. STOKES

PELEE Island is a mere dot in the western end of Lake Erie. Yet to those few thousand sportsmen who have been on this 10,000-acre Canadian island it recalls memories of the most spectacular pheasant hunting in North America. This flat, fertile farmland derived from drained marshes has produced as many as five birds per acre, and in many years it has been necessary to shoot hens to prevent undue damage to soybeans and corn, the main sources of income for the 500 people on the island. The 1950 kill has had no equal— an average of more than two and a half pheasants were shot per acre during a four-day hunting season.

The drastic decline in pheasants during the mid-forties focused attention on Pelee. What are the conditions there that produce so many birds? Can such conditions be repro-duced elsewhere? The Pelee Island Pheasant Project, sponsored by the Wildlife Management Institute and the Ontario Depart-ment of Lands and Forests, was started in 1947 to seek answers to these questions. Information here is based largely upon studies from 1947 to 1950 (Stokes 1954).

Pelee Pheasant History

The liberation of three dozen Ontario ringnecks on the island in 1927 was the seeding of a crop, which in years to come, was to provide unexcelled sport to thousands of hunters and an important source of income to the islanders them-selves. Little attention was paid to the bird at first, and it is

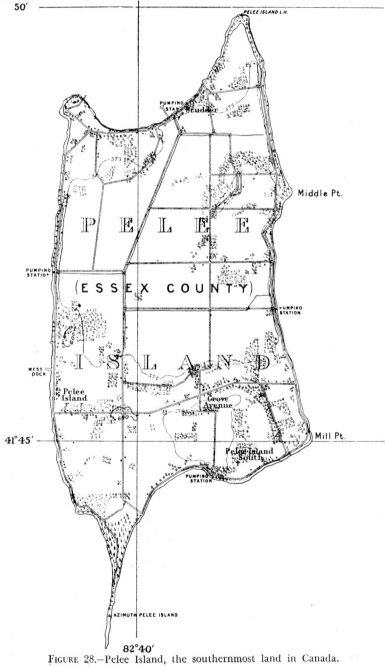

FIGURE 28.—Pelee Island, the southernmost land in Canada,

not until 1946 that accurate records were kept of the size of the population and of the annual kill. Prior to 1946, the history of pheasants has had to be reconstructed largely from records of hunting regulations, numbers of birds stocked, and from reports of the islanders.

Population trends, 1927 to 1950

The birds liberated in 1927 must have found conditions favorable. There are clues as to how fast they increased, for by 1932 there were complaints of crop damage, and hunting was permitted to relieve the situation. If farmers were as tolerant about crop damage at that time as they are now, there must have been about 20,000 birds on the island by the fall of 1932. Clarke (1947) estimated that there were between 50 and 100 thousand birds by 1934, or shortly afterwards, but farmers comparing the 1950 level of 38,000 birds with the earlier peak are inclined to think there never were more than 50,000 birds.

By that time, pheasants had become a pest, causing such damage to crops that farmers broke up nests whenever they found them. Although history is turning into legend, the islanders today say that during the first few years of hunting they brought back wagonloads of birds and that one hunter succeeded in shooting his limit from an armchair!

Judging from the records of hunting regulations, pheasants must have continued at high densities through 1938, for in every year, hunters were allowed a daily limit of at least one hen, and in some years, were obligated to shoot hens (Featherston 1949). In 1939 and 1940, numbers probably dropped somewhat, for in 1939, hens were protected completely for the first time and both the bag limit and season lengths were reduced. This decline evidently did not last, and by 1942 birds were numerous again (Fig. 29).

Despite the liberal bag limits in 1943, there is evidence that there was a decline that year. When game administrators have no precise information, they tend to base hunting regulations on the success of the previous season. Thus the liberal bag limits, extended season, and large number of hunters

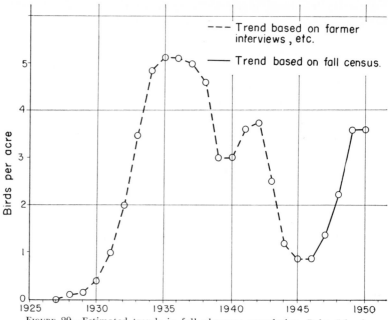

FIGURE 29.—Estimated trends in fall pheasant population, Pelee Island.

in 1943 may have reflected the good hunting of 1942; and the greatly curtailed regulations in 1944 probably are an indication of poor hunting in 1943.

In any case, the birds definitely were down in 1944 and still more so in 1945. In 1946, it was decided to make a tally of the kill for the first time. Hens, in that year, were granted belated protection from shooting for the first time since 1939. Clarke's (1947) estimate of the population that fall, based on the known kill and observed sex ratios, was a little over 10,000 birds. From that point on, the trend is well established and pheasants have increased steadily to a peak of about 37,000 birds in 1949 and 1950. By 1950, the birds were causing such extensive crop damage that it was necessary to shoot more than 12,000 hens to keep the population within bounds.

Thus, despite the over-all high population levels, pheasants dropped from a peak of an estimated 50,000 birds in about 1935 to a low of 10,000 in 1945. It is worth emphasizing, however, that this drop of 80 percent is as drastic as the decline in other regions (Kimball 1948).

Causes of the decline

The tremendous decline in pheasants across the country caused great concern. It is not possible to state what brought it about on Pelee, but certain factors can be ruled out and others suggested.

Predation definitely can be eliminated as a cause, for cats, dogs, squirrels, and rats are the only mammalian predators on the island. Their numbers have not changed appreciably in the past. The numbers of crows and snakes have, if anything, declined during this period.

There have been rapid changes in land use in the decade 1940-1950. Soybeans were planted first in 1934 and were so successful that by 1943 about 30 percent of the entire island was planted to beans. Corn and wheat were by then minor crops. Since pheasants now are thriving under this soybean economy, it seems unlikely that the shift from corn and wheat to soybeans could have caused the reduction.

Winter weather on Pelee generally is mild, with mean January temperatures of 24.9 degrees and average snowfall of 32 inches. Mean snowfall from 1938 through 1945, which covers the period of the decline, was 42 inches, while snowfall from 1945 through 1950, the period of recovery, was only 21 inches. The most severe winter was in 1942-43 when there were 56 inches of snow, of which 29 inches fell in January. The islanders still speak of this winter and of their efforts to feed the pheasants. Winter losses may well have been severe that year.

Unfavorable spring weather has been blamed quite commonly for the pheasant decline, and this may have been a contributing factor on Pelee. During the decade 1940-1950, rainfall in the critical months of May and June was above average in all years but 1944 and 1950. Although both the drop-off and recovery took place during this wet period, the greatest rainfall in the decade was in May, 1943, when 6.9 inches fell, a full 4 inches above normal. No doubt many nests were destroyed that year.

During the period 1935 through 1945, limited shooting of hens was permitted every year but 1939. Since pheasants had been too abundant for the good of the crops, shooting of hens undoubtedly was a wise measure even as late as 1942; but its continuance from 1943 through 1945 may have been a factor in driving numbers to the bottom in 1945. Non-residents were permitted a total of 3,000 hens in 1942 and 1943, 1,200 in 1944, and 1,600 in 1945. To this legal kill must be added the legal kill by islanders, crippling losses, and the generous quantity fed to hunters during their stay on the island. Many other hens were canned, and as a result of the economic depression of the early thirties, it had become accepted practice to shoot birds out of season. It is likely that the total kill of hens throughout the year was nearly double that permitted non-residents. In normal years this would make little difference in the ensuing year's population, but if other factors reduced breeding success, the population would suffer.

A piecing together of evidence gives ample reason why the decline should have started in 1943. The 1942 hunting season had been good, presumably with a large number of hens surviving. But the winter of 1942-43 was severe, with 56 inches of snow. This was followed by heavy rains in May (6.9 inches) and again in July (4.8 inches). Probably the population was at that time considerably below the 1942 level. Then came a liberal hunting season with a minimum of 3,000 hens shot—probably more like 5,000 when crippling losses and resident kill are included. The birds must have been far down at this point.

Weather was favorable in 1944 and the breeding success should have been good, but the decline continued. Killing of hens at this low level may have more than offset the increase from a good breeding season in 1944. Rain was heavy again in 1945 and, coupled with the legal and illegal kill of hens, may have caused the continued drop. The year 1946 was the wettest season of the decade (11.1 inches in May and June) and should have caused the birds to drop still further, since hens had been shot again the previous fall. Actually it was the consensus that the bottom had been reached in 1945. The rapid recovery period from 1947 through 1949 was associated with mild winters, favorable spring weather, and no legal shooting of hens.

Structure of the population

In terms of the bird itself, there are only two reasons why pheasants should decline in numbers from one year to the next. Either too few young have been produced, or too many mature birds have died in the previous 12 months. Had annual mortality and reproductive success been known during the early 1940's, the reason for the severe decline in pheasants on Pelee might be understood. A knowledge of these two quantities today permits a better understanding of how a population is maintained.

An excellent measure of reproductive success is the ratio of juvenile hens to adult hens in the fall. This ratio, when doubled gives the total number of young of both sexes per adult hen that survive until the hunting season. Female age ratios on Pelee have been determined from samples shot during the hunting season or trapped in early winter (Fig. 30). Young hens are more easily shot than adults, and hence these ratios are somewhat higher than actually existed in the entire population. By doubling the number of young females, we see that, in the years 1947-1950, there were from 3.0 to 3.6 young of both sexes brought to the hunting season by each surviving hen. Before evaluating the effect of these ratios upon population change, we first must know the adult survival rate.

Starting in 1946, fall populations were estimated by use of the Kelker Index, a formula from which the total cock or hen population can be calculated, if the sex ratios before and after the hunting season, and the kill, including cripples and illegal kill, are known (Kelker 1940). These population estimates are given in Fig. 30. The number of adult hens each fall was calculated from the total number of hens and the female age ratio. These adult hens are the survivors from the previous

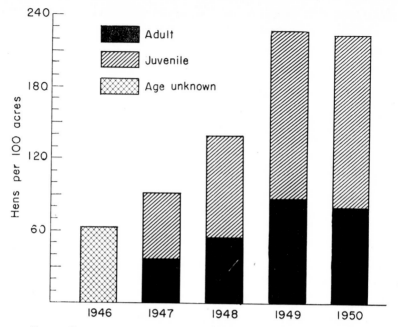

FIGURE 30.—Annual survival of hen pheasants, Pelee Island, 1946-50.

fall. Hence the survival rate is the ratio of adult hens alive one fall to the total number of hens alive the previous fall. The annual survival in the four years 1946-50 has been 52, 60, 63, and 35 percent. Disregarding the considerable error involved in this method of calculation, it appears that the large increases in the population between 1946 and 1949 were a result of high annual survival (53-63 percent) and good productivity (1.50-1.71 young per adult). In 1950, productivity also was good (1.81 young per adult), but the population failed to increase because of the much lower survival rate (35 percent).

Design for Abundance

Pheasants on Pelee have undergone the same tremendous fluctuation in numbers that has been evident elsewhere. Nevertheless once the island population became established, it never dropped below one bird per acre. An analysis of cover, food, predation, farming activities, and climate will disclose some of the reasons why the birds on Pelee have attained such high levels.

Land use is favorable

Pelee Island is one of Ontario's most prosperous farming communities. Half of the 10,000 acres is below lake level, derived originally from marshland that now is drained by a series of canals and tributary ditches that criss-cross the island. It is of interest that the heavy pheasant densities of Michigan's Thumb and northwestern Ohio are associated with clay soils almost identical with those on Pelee. About a fourth of the island consists of low-lying rock outcrops with soil too shallow for cultivation.

Seventy percent of the island is in crops, of which soybeans make up 75 percent, small grains 15 percent, corn 5 percent, tobacco 3 percent, and hay 2 percent. Farmers have found it difficult to market meat and dairy products, with the result that there is little need for hay. This is of prime importance to pheasant welfare, for nesting hens usually are spared the terrific destruction that occurs elsewhere during mowing operations. In the principal dairy states these losses run from 30 to 40 percent of all nests found. In addition, from 8 to 20 percent of all hens alive in the spring are killed or injured by the mowing machine (Randall 1939, Buss 1946, Baskett 1947, Dustman 1949). Nest studies on Pelee in 1949 and 1950, during which 2,360 nests were found, indicate that only 5.8 percent of the nests were in hayfields. Losses in those fields amounted to less than 2 percent of all nests found.

About one-fifth of the entire island consists of woodlots, wasteland, marsh, borders of fields, and roads, and lightly grazed or abandoned pastures. Most of this land is on rock outcrops, hence it provides pheasants with nesting, roosting, and loafing cover free from agricultural disturbance. This non-cultivated land is well distributed over the island and is interconnected by over a hundred miles of ditches and canals, the banks of which have been allowed to grow into grass, shrubs, and trees, providing superb travel lanes for pheasants.

The woods and brushy areas provide excellent winter retreats, and each morning the pheasants work out from this heavy cover to feed in surrounding bean fields. During the day, they withdraw to fencerows or ditchbanks where they can bask in the sun and be out of the wind. Following the evening feeding period, the birds return to roosting cover. The dispersion of good cover in relation to bean fields is such that pheasants rarely have to travel more than a quarter-mile to satisfy their daily requirements. Consequently there is minimum exposure to weather and enemies.

De luxe nesting

Safe nesting cover is provided by the extensive non-cultivated areas. This land has been classified on the basis of quality for nesting into five types:

Scrub-1: Woodlots, cut-over areas, fencerows, etc. with a good supply of shrubs or herbaceous cover providing good concealment for nests

Scrub-2: Woodlots with little or no herbaceous cover.

Abandoned Pasture: Pastures with grass a foot high and frequent shrubs.

Active Pasture: Grass short and very few shrubs.

Weeds: Abandoned marshland fields grown up to dense stands of weeds.

The use of these cover types, as well as wheat and hayfields, is shown in Table 52. Nesting densities in weed fields are spectacular, averaging 12.4 nests per acre. A single acre of weeds had 28 nests from which 195 chicks hatched, indicating that when good cover is available pheasants do not object to crowding. Somewhat less preferred was the scrub-1 type, with an average nest density of 8.3 nests per acre. Such cover was extensive and produced 50 percent of all nests. Scrub-2, abandoned pasture, and hay were favored about equally. Wheatfields are used relatively little for nesting, averaging only 1.5 nests to the acre, which was even less than active pasture, where cover was considerably inferior to that in wheat, as far as the eye could judge. Of all nests found, 94 percent were placed in cover that was almost entirely free from agricultural disturbance.

TABLE 52.   Relation of nest density to cover type, 1949-1950.

Cover Type	Mean Number of Acres	Mean Number Nests/Acre	Percent of Total Nests
Scrub-1	950	8.3	49.9
Scrub-2	340	5.1	10.9
Abandoned pasture	431	5.7	14.6
Active pasture	492	2.5	7.7
Weeds	80	12.4	6.2
Hay	149	6.2	5.8
Grain	613	1.5	4.9
Total	3,055		100.0

In most regions, when cattle are allowed to graze in woodlots, undergrowth is destroyed and the woodlot has little use for game. This is not the case on Pelee, for wherever woodlots on shallow soil have been pastured, one finds fragrant sumac (*Rhus aromatica*) growing profusely. This shrub is not very palatable to cattle and persists even under fairly high grazing pressure. It occurs as single bushes or in clumps up to 30 feet in diameter. The outermost branches usually bend close to the ground. At this rim is a heavy mat of grass protected from grazing by the branches of sumac. It is there that the hen pheasant frequently lays her eggs, and with good reason, for they are concealed perfectly.

Later in the season these bushes provide shelter from burning sun, chilling rainstorms, or predators. They also are used as roosting sites by young broods, and the berries rank high as summer food. In winter, thick clumps of sumac provide enough shelter so that the otherwise bare woodlots serve as important concentration areas. Fragrant sumac can tolerate some shade and persists in woodlots wherever there are openings. This shrub makes an important contribution to pheasant welfare throughout the year.

Diet among plenty

Food is an all-important item in the life of any animal. But for a population to flourish, food must be abundant in all seasons of the year. Winter generally has been considered the most critical period.

On Pelee, soybeans are the most important item in the pheasant diet, and the birds start eating beans as soon as the crop ripens in early September. Many waste beans remain in the field after the harvest, and these provide the chief item in the winter diet. Flocks of as many as 500 pheasants feed in the same fields day after day from November until April. In early winter, they forage in fields adjacent to excellent cover, and when nearby beans are cleaned up they move farther out, using the many fencerows as travel lanes. But the abundance of food is such that, even during winters when the land is supporting a density of two birds per acre, beans in the open expanses of drained marshes may be untouched.

It is possible for an abundance of food to be present but unavailable. This is not the case on Pelee, for winters are mild. There are several thaws during the winter, and the ground rarely is covered with snow for more than a week. Nor are there severe sleet storms to prevent birds from scratching down to the bean stubble. During stormy weather birds keep more to cover, where they find food furnished by grapes, burdock, sumac, and various weeds.

When pheasants first became numerous, no soybeans were grown and their place must have been taken by the greater amounts of corn and wheat planted at that time and by the seeds of foxtail grass and lesser ragweed. Very likely there always has been an abundance of winter food on Pelee.

It is possible that the most critical food problem comes in summer, a time when in recent years there have been from 3 to 5 birds per acre. For from late July to early September thousands of pheasants were caught in baited traps—over 6,000 birds in one year alone. Often the same bird was caught two and even three times in a single day. In one instance, a bird released from one trap was found in a nearby trap 15 minutes later. Adults were trapped almost as readily as young birds. In winter, on the other hand, trapping usually was unsuccessful unless snow covered the available food.

An additional indicator of food shortage was the fact that late-hatched chicks gained weight more slowly than those hatched earlier. Loughrey (1951) has shown the relation between availability of foods and their actual use by 251 juvenile pheasant chicks collected between June 19 and September 4, 1950. During the first three weeks, the young pheasant relies almost entirely upon insects and other animal foods. Mayflies *(Ephemerida)* make up over half of all insect matter eaten. These insects occur in such swarms in late June and early July that they give the appearance of a driving snowstorm as seen in the headlights of passing automobiles at night. During the day it is impossible to walk through tall grass without being covered by these insects. At the height of the swarming, a chick could no doubt secure a meal without moving more than two or three feet. However, these insects are available only to chicks hatched in the first half of the season.

Starting at 4 weeks, pheasant chicks turn rapidly to grain as the principal item in their diet, and by 6 weeks, almost 60 percent of their food is grain. Here again the early-hatched bird is at an advantage for it is able to shift from May-flies to abundant waste wheat. By the time later-hatched birds are old enough to eat seeds, much of the waste wheat has been eaten, plowed under, or has sprouted. Nevertheless, these chicks find grasshoppers, seeds of meadow grasses *(Poa* spp.), and many fruits, most important of which are grape, fragrant sumac, staghorn sumac *(Rhus typhina)*, bittersweet nightshade *(Solanum dulcamara)*, snowberry *(Symphoricarpos rivularis)*, hackberry *(Celtis occidentalis)*, and dogwoods.

In early September, pheasants suddenly stop entering the traps. This coincides with the ripening of soybeans and corn. From the evidence, it seems likely that pheasants will not enter traps during the May-fly season, and for the first two weeks after the grain has been harvested, because food is abundant then. But from late July, when waste grain disappears, until early September when soybeans and corn become ripe, pheasants are trapped easily. Wild foods presumably are not abundant enough to prevent an actual food shortage at that time.

Predation limited

Many people have assumed that predation is one of the important mortality factors of pheasants. Errington (1946) pointed out that extensive predation does not necessarily result in lowered populations. The bird that escapes predators may face other hazards of equal magnitude, and total mortality may be the same regardless of the intensity of predation. On Pelee, there are many pheasants and few predators. Is one condition a result of the other?

Pheasants on this island enjoy freedom from the fox, skunk, mink, weasel, raccoon, and opossum. This in large measure explains why only 9 percent of all nests found were destroyed by natural enemies. Of these unsuccessful nests, half were destroyed by crows and grackles, and most of the others by roving cats and dogs, with smaller losses from rats, fox squirrels, and fox snakes *(Elaphe vulpina)*. Losses from predation in other areas range from the 7-10 percent reported in Ohio (Dustman 1949) to 62.5 percent in South Dakota (Kimball 1948).

The only predators capable of killing adult pheasants, or chicks more than a few weeks old, are about a hundred dogs, 300 cats, and less than a dozen hawks (Cooper's, sharp-shinned, red-tailed, rough-legged, and marsh hawks) that are resident in winter or summer on the island. At times, large numbers of sharp-shinned hawks and much smaller numbers of other species of hawks migrate across Lake Erie and use Pelee Island as a stepping-stone. These hawks move almost exclusively along the east shore-line and seem to exert little influence on the pheasant population.

For a predator to increase in numbers along with abundant prey, it must be able to catch that prey throughout the year or have some alternative source of food in off seasons. Dogs and cats are the only animals which remain on the island throughout the year that can catch pheasants of all ages. Since their numbers have not been allowed to increase, the effect of predation has remained small.

It seems likely that the limited amount of predation on the island has had little effect on the size of the population. But conceivably, predation could have a depressing effect on the rate of recovery following a decline such as that of 1943 to 1946. The population that can recover rapidly from these periodic catastrophes will provide better hunting than one that requires a longer period, even though peak populations are the same. In this respect, Pelee Island may have an advantage over other areas with greater predator pressure.

Biology of Density

Several explanations for the abundance of pheasants have been presented: adequate cover, well-dispersed across the island; abundance of food throughout the year; a minimum exposure of birds to severe winter weather; abundant nesting cover almost entirely free from agricultural disturbance; and minimum predation. But isolation is in itself a factor in abundance.

In almost any population there are social intolerances that cause young animals in particular to move into less-populated areas with the effect of constantly diminishing the density in areas of most favorable environment. The extent of this movement must vary with circumstances, but it is doubtful if the pheasant densities of Pelee Island could be duplicated on any area where birds were free to move.

When any animal is first introduced into a favorable environment, the growth of the population after initial stages of adjustment is rapid, for reproduction far outweighs mortality. But as the population increases and more and more of the environmental accommodations are utilized, mortality begins to catch up with reproduction. Eventually these two quantities are in balance, and the population has reached its peak. While a population is increasing, there are many factors contributing to mortality and slowing up the rate of growth. But eventually, one of these factors becomes all important in limiting further increase. Only when this factor in the environment has been improved can the population rise still farther (Leopold, 1933). What is the factor on Pelee that eventually will limit population size?

In the spring of 1950, damage to sprouted beans was so severe near pheasant concentrations that some farmers had to plant portions of fields two and three times before getting a satisfactory stand. That same year, damage to corn, tomatoes, and strawberries was extensive. Valuable as the pheasant is as an additional source of revenue, the farmers were agreed that it was impossible to farm for profit when pheasants were so abundant. Spring densities have to be kept below one bird per acre if crop damage is to be minimized. Unless the revenue from the hunting season can be increased greatly, so that the farmer is willing to tolerate more crop damage, the limit to further population increase will be an economic one, rather than biological.

If pheasant numbers are not held down deliberately to limit crop damage, there is some indication of what biological factors might prevent further increase in the population. It has been mentioned that summer food may have been in short supply in recent years when growing-season populations were from 3 to 5 birds per acre. In 1949 and 1950, pheasant chicks were banded during the summer and returns collected in the hunting season. From an analysis of these records, it was estimated that about 60 percent of the chicks that hatch fail to survive to the hunting season. Dead or sick birds were not found in the field and it is not known what happened to them, but shortage of food may be involved.

An increasing rate of nest desertion by hens has been observed as the population level rises. This may be a still more important factor in limiting further increase. The greatest cause of nest failure by far has been voluntary desertion by hens. In 1950, 39 percent of 1,166 nests were abandoned before incubation began. Since there were no signs that these nests had been molested, it was concluded they had been left voluntarily by the hens.

Desertion was most frequent during the early part of the nesting season. Thus, of 85 nests begun in the last half of

April, only 14 percent were incubated. The incidence of incubation rose steadily until of 241 nests begun in the first half of June, 71 percent were incubated.

The reason for this high rate of desertion is not understood clearly. Buss, Meyer, and Kabat (1951) report high rates of desertion among penned birds and believe that this also occurs in the wild but has gone undetected. Their studies indicate that many nest failures have been attributed to mowing, predation, or other factors which occurred after the nests had been deserted. It appeared further that hens drop single eggs regularly and make abortive attempts at nesting early in the season, and only settle down later to incubate a clutch of eggs.

This may be the correct explanation, but the abandonment of nests seems to be related to breeding density. Only in areas of high population has the reported rate of desertion risen above 10 percent. On Eliza Island, off the coast of Washington, 37 percent of all nests were deserted when spring numbers reached 32 hens per hundred acres (Einarsen 1950). According to information from Chester M. Hart, of the California Division of Fish and Game, in that state where breeding densities of from 50 to 100 birds per hundred acres have been studied, desertion rates were from 25 to 45 percent. Similarly, on Pelee, with 100 to 150 hens per hundred acres in spring, from 35 to 39 percent of the nests have been left unincubated.

This contrasts with findings in Ohio (Dustman 1949), Iowa (Hamerstrom 1936, Baskett 1947), and Wisconsin (Buss 1946). Where nesting-season populations were under 15 hens per hundred acres, less than 10 percent of the nests were deserted before incubation started. If desertion increases with breeding density, as these data suggest, then the ultimate control of an expanding population may be a desertion rate so high that nesting success will not compensate for annual mortality.

On Pelee, the average nesting success in 1949 and 1950, when deserted nests are excluded, was 77 percent. Brood studies in these same years showed that 80-90 percent of hens seen in August had broods. Nesting success reported in other studies rarely has exceeded 40 percent (Buss, Meyer, and Kabat 1951), and seldom are more than 75 percent of the hens seen in August with broods. Therefore the high rate of nest desertion at the high breeding densities on Pelee has not prevented a nesting efficiency considerably greater than that reported in other pheasant studies.

The much lower survival of hens between the 1949 and 1950 hunting seasons (see Fig. 30) had the effect of stabilizing the population. If this increased mortality (of unknown cause) should prove a result of high population density, it would of itself constitute a limiting factor.

Today, pheasants on Pelee are held down to spring densities of about one bird per acre because of the extensive damage to crops that otherwise would occur in spring. Damage to crops in summer and fall never has concerned the farmers greatly. It appears to be the role of management to regulate the environment so that there will be the greatest possible gain in the population between spring and fall. At present, about 60 percent of all chicks die between hatching and hunting. If the causes for this tremendous loss can be ascertained and corrected, the harvestable surplus will be increased considerably without additional damage to crops in the spring.

The Hunting Season

The fame of the Pelee Island Hunt is spreading in ever-widening circles. The first season held in 1932 was limited to residents, but in 1934, the island was opened to nonresidents, who quickly spread the word of the superb shooting. As pheasants declined in numbers elsewhere, the island became more and more popular. Nor have hunters been disappointed; for nowhere else can they take home a limit of 8 to 12 birds with such little effort.

Management of the hunt

In favorable years, the fall population has increased two- or threefold over spring levels. The hunting season is the time for removing this harvestable surplus. Pelee Island offers un-excelled opportunities for regulating its hunting season, for not only is the size of the fall population known, but the hunting pressure also can be controlled.

Hunting is by special permit only. These are issued on a first-come-first-served basis to approximately 1,000 applicants, the maximum number the island can accommodate. These permits originally sold for as little as $3, but the cost, in step with inflation and the law of supply and demand, has risen steadily, until in 1951 they sold for $25. This high cost for the privilege of hunting on Pelee has not discouraged hunters, for in 1951 there were 3,500 applications.

Regulation of bag limits comes under the authority of the Province, but the wishes of the Town Council have been taken into consideration. This has worked well, for the Council has every reason to protect its valuable asset, and its recommendations have been, if anything, too conservative. In recent years, hunting has been limited to two days with season limits of from 8 to 12 birds.

The crop and the hunting

Official estimates of the kill started in 1946. The overseers secure an accurate tally of all birds leaving the island and of the much smaller number kept by the islanders. The kill since 1946 has kept pace with the steadily rising pheasant population (Fig. 31). Although hunters were satisfied with their average bag of 5.6 cocks in 1947, they were amazed at their success in 1949. It was an unforgettable spectacle to see hundreds of hunters trudge out onto the ferry dock with an even dozen birds slung over their shoulders and to hear the steady shout of the overseers as they called out the limits "Ten and two, ten and two, ten and two."

The limit of two hens and 10 cocks allowed in 1949 was a measure to prevent undue crop damage. Despite this legal kill of over three thousand hens, and removal of an additional thousand that were trapped and sold that winter for stocking, the population in 1950 was even higher than in 1949. Farmers

PLATE LXIX.—Passenger boats brought most of the thousand hunters who harvested the Pelee pheasant crop in 1948 (D. L. Allen).

agreed that pheasants must be reduced to forestall disastrous crop damage.

The two separate hunting seasons in 1950, totalling four days, produced perhaps the greatest hunting in the world. The event will go down in hunting history, for on this tiny, 10,000-acre island over 25,000 birds were shot—more than two and a half birds per acre. Most people feared that such a liberal hunting season had killed the proverbial goose, but after the smoke had cleared, there still remained a bird per acre.

The heavy hunting pressure on the island impresses any one who sees hundreds of hunters stream off the ferry as it docks, and again the following morning witnesses the barrage, so steady it is impossible to count individual shots for the first half hour. One might well ask if there is not danger of the cocks being overshot.

Although a maximum of 18 hours of hunting is possible in the two days, the average hunter from 1947 through 1950 spent only 8 to 10 hours in the field. Gun pressure in these years ranged from 83 to 186 gun-hours per 100 acres. Since two-thirds of the island was plowed land or bean stubble, and largely unhunted, the effective gun pressure was three times as great as that mentioned above. This hunting pressure compares with the 91 to 256 gun-hours per 100 acres at the Rose Lake Experiment Station and Prairie Farm in Michigan (Allen 1947); with 82-94 gun-hours on Potter's Marsh, a heavily shot public hunting ground in Wisconsin*; and 120-229 gun-hours on some of California's rice ranches (Harper, Hart, and Shaffer 1951).

It is evident that Pelee Island pheasants are exposed to about as high hunting pressure as occurs anywhere in the country. Studies at Rose Lake by Allen show that "hunting pressure of from 100 to 125 gun-hours per hundred acres will harvest the available crop of pheasants. Hunting above that intensity is largely unrewarded." This important principle of management has been substantiated on Pelee Island.

---

* Correspondence, Donald R. Thompson, 1951.

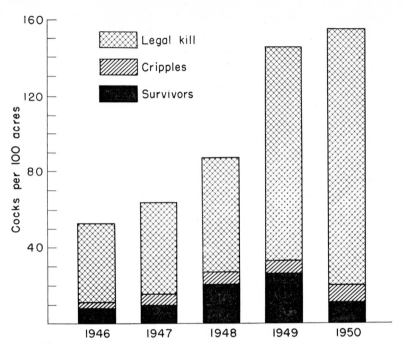

FIGURE 31.—Relation of kill to density of cocks, Pelee Island, 1946-50.

Diminishing returns

In 1947, it theoretically was possible for every cock on the island to have been shot, but actually only 86 percent were killed. In that year, an average hunter took home only 5.6 birds compared with the limit of 8 cocks. The kill on the first day had been heavy and by late afternoon there were many tired hunters who swore that there were no more cocks to be had. By noon of the second day, there were less than 10 percent of the hunters still afield. Yet, more than eight cock birds per hundred acres actually remained, the density level at which hunters in some states start their season.

The hunting in 1947 provided an excellent example of the law of diminishing returns. The average hunter knocked down his first rooster in the first 30 minutes of hunting, but took progressively longer to shoot each additional bird, until by the second morning, he spent several hours for every bird bagged. No wonder he was discouraged. But suppose a new group of hunters, who had been used to walking all day before shooting their first bird, had been exposed to the island. They would have continued to hunt with great enthusiasm at the level of eight cocks per 100 acres and would have succeeded in killing more cocks.

From this it follows that in years of low populations the cocks will be shot to a lower level than during years of higher populations. This is substantiated by records on Pelee. The low in the pheasant population on Pelee was about 1945. Following the hunting season that year Clarke estimated there could not have been more than 500 cocks surviving. In each succeeding year the population has risen and along with it the number of surviving cocks (Fig. 31). In 1949, the law of diminishing returns had little chance to operate, for hunting still was good by the time hunters had their limit. Had the bag limit been higher, there is little doubt that an additional thousand birds might have been shot.

In the 1950 season, 93 percent of all cocks were shot, leaving almost as few cocks as in 1947. How could such a high percentage of cocks be shot before hunters became discouraged? During the first 2-day season two-thirds of the cocks had been shot. This left the second thousand hunters fewer cocks than there had been in 1947. Having known nothing better, they were content to hunt at this lower density. Had it not been for rainy weather and the fact that hunters were allowed seven hens, the number of surviving cocks would have been even less.

Does such intensive hunting ever produce an unfavorable sex ratio? Following the hunting seasons for 1947 through 1950, the sex ratio has been from 7 to 10 hens per cock. The fertility of eggs, while slightly below that reported in other nesting studies, never fell below 86 percent and showed no relationship to changes in sex ratio during those years.

Pheasants and Pelee Prosperity

The traditional American philosophy that game belongs to the people is coming more and more into question. Wildlife, like other crops, requires fertile soils, and it is the landowner who is custodian of the soil's fertility. If the farmer can be encouraged to take care of his land, then there is a good chance that game to a large extent will take care of itself. It is not unreasonable that the Pelee Island farmer should be remunerated for raising game in such abundance. What is the cash value of pheasants to the residents of Pelee Island?

PLATE LXX.—*Above.* Hunter's view of Pelee when arriving. *Below.* Briefing the work crew of visiting biologists the evening before the hunt (D. L. Allen).

Most of the benefit from the pheasants comes at the hunt. In 1950, almost as much money was raised from the sale of licenses as from all other sources of municipal revenue combined. A balanced budget is no problem on Pelee. License fees have brought reduced tax rates and provided civic improvements as well. In 1950, the 2,100 nonresident hunters left an average $30 for room and board at the homes of islanders, for guide service, and purchases at stores. By the end of December, effects of the extra hunting season cash were evident everywhere. The store had installed electricity; a neighbor had traded his two-year-old car for a new one; there were new gas stoves and electric refrigerators. Entire bathrooms had blossomed in many a home. Pelee Islanders do not have to be told about the economic value of wildlife.

In 1949, the *net* income to the island from license fees, wages, room and board, guide service, and sales of goods at the stores amounted to over $36,000, or $3.63 an acre. In 1950, with twice as many hunters as in 1949, the net profit was $6.75 an acre. In comparison, the net income from farming, after all costs of farming have been deducted, is about $25 an acre. So, in 1950, the income from pheasants was almost a fourth the amount derived from farming. No wonder the farmer takes a personal interest in the welfare of the pheasants, putting out feed in winter, taking pains to avoid nests during farming operations, and being tolerant of damage to his crops. It is doubtful that anywhere else is the landowner so well repaid for the game crop produced on his land.

The Role of Management

The sportsman who participates in the hunt and sees the thousands of birds that are shot each year without benefit of stocking or refuges may well ask if any management other than regulation of hunting is needed on Pelee.

That is the first thought, but proper management on Pelee is a challenge of importance far beyond the interests of the island residents. Pelee Island is one of those rare show places where game in phenomenal numbers still can be hunted, or enjoyed throughout the year. Nowhere else are the conditions for the study of pheasant populations so perfect. Loss of this unique game-bird phenomenon would be a tragedy.

With the exception of the control of hunting, man can take little credit for the success of pheasants on Pelee Island. The island has been favored with a mild climate, fertile soil, and abundant waste land that cannot be farmed profitably. Land use has been determined by the economics of agriculture. Predators were removed long before pheasants were introduced. All of these factors have favored the pheasant—producing high nesting success, good survival of young chicks, and low annual losses. Under such conditions, the population has reached a peak of five birds per acre.

Despite the little-understood catastrophe that struck in the mid-1940's, the population was able to recover rapidly, as soon as this depressing influence was removed. The spectacle of thousands of pheasants on Pelee is an unplanned phenomenon, like most other wildlife resources.

The Future

There are, however, some rather ominous indications that bode ill for the future of pheasants on Pelee. Much of the waste land along the shores is being cleared for cottages. The power saw has made possible the clearing of woods and fence-rows that until now could not be cut economically. Improved drainage is doing away with remaining marshes, and permitting some of the drainage ditches that provide miles of superb travel lanes to be filled. Abuse of the land has caused decreased fertility, and with it lowered crop yields. The advent of weed killers may destroy much of the cover in pastures and along ditches, canals, and roadsides. It is difficult to measure the effects of these changes in advance, but they obviously are detrimental.

The islanders today would be almost unanimous in wishing to have the pheasants remain in their present numbers, not only for the economic return, but from a sense of pride in being guardian of something of such wide and spectacular

PLATE LXXI.—*Above.* On the flat, rich fields of Pelee Island, pheasants find abundant food, cover, and near freedom from mowing machines. *Below.* Dead birds and cripples picked up by Ontario officers using retrievers (D. L. Allen).

PLATE LXXII.—Few hunters failed to get their full bag of 10 cocks and 2 hens (D. L. Allen).

PLATE LXXIII.—Biologists checked every bird that left the island, recovering bands and tallying sex and age (D. L. Allen).

interest. Yet, as individuals, they follow their own interests, perhaps not realizing that a few hundred feet of cleared shoreline or a filled ditch only adds to many similar efforts elsewhere. Looking at the several thousand acres of good cover today, the landowner believes the elimination of 10 or 20 acres will have no effect. If not halted, this trend could mean the end of what makes Pelee North America's number-one pheasant range. It appears that only by uniting as a group, and making some decisions in the common interest, can island residents prevent such a deplorable ending.

No account of pheasants on Pelee would be complete without recognizing their esthetic value. Hunting is limited to a few, but the enjoyment of seeing a bird is free to all. After three years of studying pheasants on the island, the biologist is just as thrilled by them as on that first September morning when he drove about the island in wide-eyed wonder. The phenomenal abundance of nests in the weeds; the streaming of birds across snow-covered bean fields; the field of burned rye stubble, so cluttered with pheasants that it looked like a game farm; "Jean Harlow," the lovely blonde that for two years came out on the same stretch of road with her brood— all these are rewarding memories.

But the favorite scene always will be an October evening at the edge of a woods at dusk. Then it is that hundreds of pheasants return from feeding in fields to roost in the trees. They hurry home in the fading light, pausing here and there for a final morsel. On reaching the woods they begin to fly, heavily and with a great beating of wings, into the lower branches. Then higher and higher, until their outlines can be made out faintly against the sky in the last light of day. With each upward flight the cocks let out raucous squawks that can be heard a mile in the still evening air. As the watcher sits in darkness, listening to the last stragglers settle down, he feels himself in faraway Turkestan witnessing the primeval abundance of game. May it live forever on Pelee Island!

Plate LXXIV.—Moving out after two days of unexcelled pheasant shooting (D. L. Allen).

CHAPTER 8

THE PHEASANT IN THE NORTHEASTERN STATES

By ALLAN T. STUDHOLME AND DIRCK BENSON

T HIS chapter presents an account of the pheasant and its habitat in the northeastern states, including the Mid-Atlantic and New England regions. Pheasant biology and management are discussed at length in other chapters of this book, so no attempt is made to detail all features here.

In general, the northeastern states are inhospitable to pheasants. The only large areas of good productivity are the rich agricultural areas of New Jersey, Pennsylvania and New York. Some parts of this region have been as productive of pheasants as any in the United States, but throughout the remainder there are no outstandingly productive habitats. Since the bird lives almost exclusively on farmland, the hilly and wooded northeastern states offer little favorable range. Furthermore, productivity of this species is related directly to soil fertility; hence, fertile agricultural lands can support large populations, while marginal farms produce few if any pheasants.

With nearly 3 million hunters, most of whom probably like to hunt pheasants, the limited range is subjected to heavy pressure, as are the state game departments. Great demand and small supply have determined the course of pheasant management in the Northeast. Pheasant populations might possibly be increased on good agricultural lands through habitat improvement, but such work undoubtedly is expensive

388

for the number of birds added. With the limited funds available, it is impossible for any game department to manage much land intensively for pheasants. As a result, stocking is an annual event even though it may add little to the success of the hunt.

The bird has been here for only half a century, and biologists have been studying it for a much shorter time. It is not surprising that so little is known about pheasant management. With carefully planned and executed studies, game biologists eventually may come up with a system that can produce more cocks economically. Until then pheasant hunting in the Northeast will have to continue to provide—sport for many, and a bird in the bag for a few.

Pheasant History in the Northeast

By virtue of early settlement and their geographical relationship to Europe, the northeastern states have taken the lead initially in many fields. While credit for the first known successful stocking of pheasants in North America belongs to Oregon, the first attempt was made in New York. The earliest known record for introduction of the pheasant in North America is contained in Chapter 601 of the Colonial Laws of New York, passed November 1, 1733 and entitled, "An Act to preserve the breed of English Pheasants in This Colony."

In abstract, the Act indicated that the late Governor (Col. John Montgomerie, who died July 1, 1733, while in office) put "about half a dozen couple of English Pheasants" onto Nutten Island (now Governor's Island, not the Nutten Island on the South Shore of Long Island) after pinioning them. The pheasants increased and spread to nearby Nassau Island (now known as Long Island), so that later Governor William Crosby requested that they be protected for a period of five years to end December 1, 1738. A penalty of 10 shillings, or five days in goal, was to be enforced for disturbing or destroying birds or eggs, but the Governor could destroy or give away birds or eggs, and the recipients of his gifts could do likewise.

Col. Crosby died in 1736 and the law was not re-enacted, nor is there any further record of what became of this stock.

The next record of introductions shows that Richard Bache, son-in-law of Benjamin Franklin, obtained English pheasants about 1790 for his estate near Beverly, New Jersey (Phillips 1928). About 1800, another attempt was made in New Jersey by a landowner in the vicinity of Belleville. Both of these releases apparently failed.

It's understandable why these early settlers thought releases of pheasants in New York and New Jersey might succeed. The weather was comparable to that of England. There was less logic in attempts at stocking in northern New England, but try they did! In New Hampshire, a record of ringneck introduction was written in 1793. "The late Governor Wentworth brought several pairs of pheasants from England, and let them fly in his woods, at Wolfeborough; but they have not since been seen." (Belknap 1793).

Throughout the Northeast, the first pheasants were brought in by owners of estates interested in increasing recreational values on their lands. The success of some of those releases, through the sport provided on estates, and the overflow onto neighboring lands, stirred the minds of ordinary hunters. This was the stimulation that eventually brought about participation of state fish and game departments in the stocking program.

Private releases

Little is known of the success of early pheasant releases by private individuals. The following records are representative of the original establishment of this species in the Northeast.

The most complete history is available for New York. One of the earliest records of pheasants in that state included some 4,000 birds released between 1886 and 1891 on an estate in the lower Hudson Valley. Many of the birds were shot, but no record exists to show whether the stock became established (Bump 1940). The first known successful release involved some 300 hens and 275 cocks freed on 3,000-acre

Gardiner's Island lying at the east end of Long Island in 1892 and 1893. By 1900, the fall population was estimated at nearly 5,000 birds, and 300 to 400 cocks were said to be shot annually (Leffingwell 1928). During the early 1900's pheasants became established on Long Island through releases on various estates, though records are not available to show how this was accomplished.

Early pheasant stocking in western New York was primarily from two sources. At the Pleasant Valley Fish Hatchery, near Bath, something over 1,000 birds were reared between 1897 and 1904. This project, initiated by the hatchery foremen, later received financial aid from the state, but it finally was abandoned when the appropriation was cut. This stock was distributed through many western counties, the birds being sent out in small numbers for spring release. In 1903, pheasants were reared on the Wadsworth Estate in the Genesee Valley, near Geneseo. That year 350 birds were stocked by permitting the young to fly over the fence. According to verbal reports, pheasants from other sources were added to the population, and by 1905, it appears that they were well established throughout the fertile Ontario lowland of western New York.

In 1887, after two previous releases, a number of birds were brought from England for stocking the Tranquility Game Preserve at Allamuchy, New Jersey. Within a few years pheasants became well established in that region (Bennett 1945).

In Pennsylvania, during the early 1890's, private individuals purchased some hundreds of pheasants in England and released them in Lehigh and Northampton Counties. These plantings apparently had some success and furnished some of the forebears of the present population. In various parts of the state, other small private stockings were made from the late 1890's until 1915, when the Game Commision began releasing them (Gerstell 1937). Pheasants first were stocked in Massachusetts in the 1890's (Wandell 1945). By 1906, the bird was considered at least nominally established, and an open season was declared for that year and continued in 1907. The season then was closed until 1914, and during the interim, extensive stocking was carried on by the State.

In New Hampshire, an interested sportsman introduced some ringnecks in 1893. Two years later, a few more were stocked privately, and during the same year the first release was made by the Fish and Game Commission. The degree of success in these and other early releases is unknown. By 1912, pheasants were seen in numbers in the Mt. Vernon and Brookline area. The birds apparently prospered, because, in 1916, the Commissioner thought there should be a shooting season, and in 1918 the Fish and Game Department was buying grain for winter feed. The state began stocking in 1921, and gradually increased their output (Siegler 1949).

Maine's records go back to 1897, although some ringnecks probably moved into Maine even earlier from New Hampshire and Massachusetts (Palmer 1949). In 1897, five pairs were liberated, and young were produced during the next three seasons. They disappeared in the winter of 1899-1900. Pheasants gradually spread into Cumberland County, and after 1912, they were seen regularly around Portland. By 1920, they were becoming more numerous in the southern part of the state, and in 1926, people in York County were complaining of pheasant damage to their gardens. The state gradually increased stocking, and by 1931, ringnecks had been liberated in all coastal and some inland counties (Dorr 1951).

The same pattern of private, followed by state, releases is apparent in the history of pheasants in Rhode Island. The birds first were established as a private enterprise in 1894, and for the next 30 years stocking was a hobby of individuals or clubs (Wright 1953). In 1925, the state started liberating pheasants, and since that time the program has expanded to the present statewide annual releases.

Public hunting appears

Pheasants eventually took hold in the Northeast with varying success and even prospered on the richer agricultural lands. On poorer soils, more often than not, they failed. But sufficient numbers of this new, gaudy exotic were being seen to give the hunters itchy trigger fingers, and soon after the turn of the century, public hunting was permitted.

The first open season on ringnecks in the Northeast probably was held in Pennsylvania in 1902. There were no daily nor seasonal bag limits during the two-month season, but the kill was negligible. The Pennsylvania Game Commission began stocking in 1915. In the belief that the species could not withstand severe winters, the policy was to stock adult birds in the spring, let them raise their young in the wild, and shoot both hens and cocks in the fall. Under that arrangement, kills were smaller than releases during the first few years. But the birds proved to be hardier than was anticipated, and the population began to increase in size. Rapid growth, however, did not occur until the law restricting shooting to males only was enacted in 1923. Then the kill rose rapidly, reaching a peak of 294,000 in 1931 (Gerstell 1937). Since that time, pheasants have furnished Pennsylvania hunters an average annual kill of nearly a quarter of a million cocks, with the 1941 harvest estimated at twice that figure.

The first open season on pheasants in New York was held in 1908. Under a season limit of three cocks, in five western counties, a total of 4,169 cock pheasants was reported taken. Three eastern counties were permitted a shooting preserve season. Reports of the chief game protector indicated that the open season did not deplete the pheasant population seriously, and advocated a short open season over the entire state (New York Annual Report 1909). Actually, it was not until 1912 that such a general open season was declared. In subsequent years, only counties lying on the periphery of the pheasant range were closed occasionally, and after 1918, all counties were open until the period of extreme scarcity in the forties.

In northern New England, public hunting appears to have started a little later. New Hampshire had its first season in 1923, when three counties were open for a week, allowing a bag of two males a day and five in a season. By 1935, all counties except two were open, and the season was extended to eleven days. During 1945 and 1946, one hen pheasant was allowed in the two-bird daily limitation. There was a noticable drop in hunting success during that period. It was believed the decline might have been the result of hen shooting, and female pheasants have been protected since (Siegler 1949).

The State of Maine had its first shooting season in 1935, two years after the game department's first liberations of pheasants. From then until 1940, a five-day season, limited to coastal counties, permitted a bag limit of two a day and four a season. Shooting of both sexes has been permitted, and the regulations were liberalized steadily. By 1950, a two-week season was state-wide, excepting Aroostook County, and while the daily kill limit remained at two, the season limit was twelve (Dorr 1951). Maine officials evidently realized the shortcomings of their state's limited pheasant habitat and decided to operate on a put-and-take basis by permitting equal cropping of hens and cocks. The only other state in the Northeast allowing public shooting of both sexes of pheasants is Connecticut. There again, the productivity of the range is poor and hunting pressure is high.

State game farm stocking

Seeing this strange, oriental bird strutting in a cleanly mown field, or thrilling to the cock's staccato cackle as he burst from a weed patch, must have haunted hunters' dreams, stirred their imaginations, and whetted their appetites. After the first day of the first open hunting season, the pheasant was the number-one subject of discussion in the country hot-stove and cracker-barrel leagues. A new, exciting sport had been germinated. Now it was up to the state game departments to put a pheasant in every hunter's coat.

Pheasants had been raised artificially for centuries in Europe. It was only natural that public agencies turned to artificial propagation. In the Northeast, it was a new game management tool. State pheasant farms or hatcheries have at one time or another been operated in most of the Northeast, and today seven of the states raise birds on their own farms.

The first official game farm in New York was established at Sherbourne in 1909, and in 1910, some 6,500 pheasant eggs and 1,200 farm-reared birds were sent to sportsmen throughout the state. In the following years, the game-farm program was expanded, and by 1918, some 20,000 pheasants were being released annually from eggs sent to sportsmen, and from the game farms. In 1918, 59,318 eggs, 15 percent of which resulted in releases, and 11,415 farm-reared birds were distributed. At this time, and in subsequent years, releases commonly were made when the young were 10 to 15 weeks old, although the age varied and many of the chicks reared by sportsmen escaped at 7 to 8 weeks.

In the Annual Report of the New York Conservation Commission for 1918, it was pointed out that pheasants now were established in all suitable habitat, and that if there were not enough birds to permit hunting, the solution was not additional protection but rather abandonment of attempts to establish birds in the unsuitable environment.

From available records, it appears that the pheasant was established in New York by 1918. It seems probable that releases could have stopped at this time without affecting the population appreciably; but since stocking had proved a good thing, the feeling existed that more stocking might make the population even greater, or at least that it was essential to maintain the current level of abundance. Regardless of what might have been the wiser course in light of current knowledge, game-farm production was increased to an aggregate annual release of over 40,000 birds in 1930, and over 90,000 in 1940.

In 1929, Pennsylvania established two game farms whose annual production of range-reared pheasants never exceeded 30,000. They were released in the fall, before the gunning season, at ages of from 12 to 16 weeks. In 1933, with mechanical methods of incubation, the yearly production was jumped to approximately 40,000 pheasants, which were kept until six weeks of age, and released in the summer. Studies soon showed that liberations of six-week-old birds were nearly complete failures. The Commission, in 1935, changed its policy to one of releasing adult hens and cocks in the spring as breeders and limited numbers of twelve to fourteen-week-old hens in the early fall. Released cocks were placed with the large flocks of hens that were seen frequently in first-class range. In poorer portions of the range, both hens and cocks were released in an effort to increase the natural production of those areas. (Gerstell 1937).

That system was followed for several years, but the program gradually has swung to major emphasis on fall stocking and the supplying of six-week-old birds to sportsmen's clubs, and day-old chicks to other cooperators. According to plan, all birds are reared to 12 weeks of age before being stocked.

Pheasants evidently had reached the carrying capacity of the better ranges in Pennsylvania at about the same time the farms were established. An early peak in the kill was reached in 1931, although this was to be exceeded in the late thirties and early forties. It is doubtful that the stepped-up stocking program materially increased the total population of ringnecks within the state, as had been hoped. The range may have been extended somewhat, however, and stocking to the gun in the fall certainly afforded hunters whose "home covers" were poor pheasant habitat a chance to collect their favorite trophy.

Among other states in the Northeast which have in the past or are operating pheasant farms now, are Maine, New Hampshire, Massachusetts, Maryland and New Jersey. Their histories of ringneck raising, except for details, are similar to those of New York and Pennsylvania. They started with high hopes of establishing good ringneck populations throughout the state, but found that the birds did well only on fertile agricultural land. On poorer land, pheasants simply would not prosper. They also found that once they were in the propagation business it was impossible to get out! When hunters got a taste of pheasant shooting they fell in love with it and have insisted ever since that their favorite local gunning spots be stocked.

Source of stock

Relatively little is known of the original source of pheasants stocked in the Northeastern States. For the early releases, it appears that nearly all the stock came directly or indirectly from game breeders in England, Germany, and elsewhere in Europe. There are no available descriptions that record the characteristics of the birds.

Throughout the Northeast, today's pheasant is a hybrid. Gerstell's (1937) description for Pennsylvania exemplifies this. "The ringneck pheasant common to Pennsylvania today is a hybrid resulting from generations of various cross-breedings between the four pure line pheasants, the common, or English Pheasant *(Phasianus colchicus colchicus)*, the Chinese pheasant *(P. colchicus torquatus)*, the Mongolian pheasant *(P. colchicus mongolicus)* and the Japanese pheasant *(P. versicolor)*. A few melanistic mutants *(P. colchicus tenebrosus)*, are noted occasionally along with other birds of apparently true strains, but the total number of this type is negligible.

"The coloration and size of individual specimens vary widely. Some are noticeably 'Chinese' in appearance; others show pronounced Mongolian markings; a few evidence black-neck ancestry; while unusually light and even partial albinos are not uncommon. Cock birds legally killed by gunners during the month of November have been found to average 2.87 pounds in weight, the maximum recorded being 3.82 pounds, and the minimum 2.00 pounds."

An interesting observation in New York State shows the occurrence of two different strains of pheasants that developed as the result of different sources of stock—perhaps with natural selections, over the years, also playing a part.

At the newly established New York game farm in 1909, breeding stock from the West was used because the birds were of large size, with cocks weighing 3 to 3.5 pounds in contrast to the "smaller" pheasants which had been handled by private breeders. The possible significance of this is seen in studies of weights and measurements of pheasants collected in New York from 1939 through 1943.

Leg measurements from the tip of the longest toe (excluding the nail) to the articular surface of the proximal end of the tibiotarsus, were made on 614 pheasants. It was found that linear growth of the leg bones had reached its maximum by September and therefore leg measurements of fall, winter, and spring "first-year birds" for regional comparisons could be included with the adults. Based on a regional arrangement of these measurements, the Ontario lowland was shown to have the smallest bird, the periphery of the Adirondack Mountains the largest, and the Southern Tier of counties bordering on Pennsylvania and the Mohawk-Hudson Valley, a bird that fell in between, but nearer to the largest pheasant.

The range of measurements showed nearly the same maximum for all regions but indicated a minimum for the Ontario lowland below that for the other three regions. This was true for both males and females. Weights of 1,555 wild cocks taken on public hunting grounds during 1940, 1941, and 1942, including all ages together, showed a similar regional breakdown. The small Ontario-lowland cock showed an average leg measurement of 234 millimeters compared with 240 millimeters for the larger male, the females 205 millimeters compared with 211 millimeters. In weight, the smaller cocks averaged 1183 grams as against 1311 grams. This indicates that the larger cock had a 2.6 percent greater skeletal size and 10.8 percent greater body weight.

By far the best pheasant range in New York lies in the Ontario lowland, so that the smaller pheasant there does not seem to be the product of a deficient habitat. Rather, it appears that the size differences represent two different strains of pheasants. The pheasants of the Ontario lowland probably are descendants of the birds stocked before 1910. The presence of some birds with leg measurements and weights equal to the maximum reported for the state, however, indicates that later releases have been incorporated in the population. On the other hand, birds of the Adirondack periphery appear more likely to be the product of game-farm stocking since 1910, and the Southern Tier and Mohawk-Hudson regions probably show a blend of the two strains. An accumulation of miscellaneous verbal reports, and casual comments in the New York

Conservation Department Annual Reports, suggest that pheasants were established strongly in the Ontario lowland before 1910, only moderately so in the Southern Tier and Mohawk-Hudson regions, and very weakly so in the Adirondack periphery.

Population Fluctuations

There are few records from which to determine the extent of fluctuations in the pheasant populations of the Northeast. The best available indicator has been the "reported take of game," which most states maintained, although the methods used in gathering the data varied widely. In some places, the issuing clerk collected kill data when the licensee took out his license for the next year; elsewhere the hunter was required to file a report soon after the hunting season. In other places, state game protectors estimated the take, or various questionnaires were mailed to hunters. Thus the problem of how to interpret data is a real one, although in recent years a few specific pheasant studies have improved the situation.

After the establishment of an appreciable number of breeders in the better pheasant ranges, it ordinarily took from 15 to 20 years for available habitat to be populated fully. During that time, total numbers were building up steadily. In areas that were to prove "marginal" for pheasants, the birds increased slowly, or failed completely, according to local conditions.

By 1927 in New York, and 1931 in Pennsylvania, the species apparently reached the first peak of abundance, when 226,098 cocks were reported killed in the former state, and 294,000 in the latter. Following that there was a slump in the kill. No causative agent was apparent for the decline, and no direct correlation could be shown between the pheasant decline and the ruffed grouse, which reached a high in New York in 1923 and 1924 with the low point occurring in 1927 and 1928 (Gerstell 1937, Bump et al. 1947).

During the following years, populations apparently increased again with a new peak occurring in New York State in 1935, with a kill of 263,317 cocks. In Pennsylvania, the new high was reached in 1938, when 517,280 cocks were reported taken. In 1935, a peak year in New York, Tompkins County at the south end of Cayuga Lake and portions of the neighboring counties showed a decrease of nearly 10 percent in the reported take, apparently as the result of 9-odd inches of rain coming in a near cloudburst on July 6, 7 and 8.

In the fall of 1936, New York reported another decrease of about 20 percent in the pheasant population. A study of the effects of weather on pheasants indicated that this decrease was the combined result of blizzard conditions in January and February, climaxed by a severe ice storm in March, with ice glaze persisting as much as a week in much of the pheasant range (Benson 1948). Recovery from this low was rapid, and by 1938 an all-time high of 277,903 cocks was reported shot. Through 1939 and 1940, the pheasant population remained high, and it was estimated that annual harvests of 450,000 to 500,000 cocks were taken.

In Pennsylvania, after the 1938 high, the population remained high and produced a record kill of 537,990 in 1941.

The New England states, with their small amount of pheasant range, also apparently reached a high point in ringneck take in the early forties. In Massachusetts, the peak kill came in 1940, with a calculated kill of 45,166 cocks, while in Connecticut, the high of 44,873 pheasants bagged came in 1941 (Wandell 1945, Sondrini 1950).

The great decline

Through the twenties and thirties fluctuations in the kill of pheasants occurred, but even the lows did not reduce the hunter's bag enough to be thought of as periods of scarcity. In both sportsman and game administrative circles, the feeling existed that the pheasant was here to stay, and that if the birds were to be all killed off they could be replaced readily by stocking. For ten years, the sportsmen enjoyed a period of pheasant abundance. Hunters combing the coverts of good pheasant country found more birds than ever before. Even those hunting "fair" pheasant land were shooting a few more wild-reared birds than usual; but gunners pounding the brush and small isolated coverts of poor range still were depending largely upon stocked birds for their bag.

Suddenly, with no warning, tragedy struck the pheasant. Their numbers began dropping alarmingly where they had prospered before. The crash was real and was felt throughout the Northeast, severely in the first-class pheasant range, moderately in the secondary pheasant range, and little if any in the poorest range. The great decline started in the early 1940's and lasted till the late forties, when recovery appeared to be on the way.

Unfortunately, the decline came at a time when we were using every available man to save our human population, and could spend little time worrying about pheasants. As a result, research work was at a minimum and available data are meager on what happened to pheasants in the Northeast, and why.

In Pennsylvania, the slump in the pheasant population may have started in 1939. Randall (1940), who was studying ringnecks at that time in the heart of the best pheasant range in Lehigh County, found an 11 percent drop in the fall population of 1939 as compared to the previous fall. The decline was general throughout the good pheasant range. He attributed early summer drouth as being responsible, because haying operations ruined many nests nearly ready to hatch. Wetter weather would have held up mowing.

In the same state, evidences of a decreasing population were apparent in 1940, and the decline continued throughout the war years in spite of less hunting pressure. Studies showed a decrease of 77.1 percent in the amount of standing corn during the winter months in the best pheasant range (Lawson 1949). In Massachusetts, the population drop came during 1940-43, and indications were that poor reproduction was the cause. Fewer broods per hen, and smaller numbers of chicks in the broods, were observed (Wandell 1943). Rhode Island pheasant-kill figures in 1941 were 10,854, and in 1945, they had dropped to 4,415, even though in each year nearly the same number of cocks had been stocked. Perhaps more significant is the fact that 87 percent of the cocks taken in 1941 were wild-reared birds, while only 71 percent of the 1945 bag were wild produced (Wright 1953).

The data shedding most light on the drop in pheasant populations in the Northeast are found in records of what happened in New York State. For nearly ten years, through 1940, the sportsmen had enjoyed a period of pheasant abundance, which reached a peak in 1938. The reported take in 1939 showed a slight decline, caused by a 4 percent drop in the Ontario lowlands, which produces some three-fourths of New York's pheasants. The rest of the state remained about at the 1938 level. Again in 1940, the western portion of the state had a slight drop, while the eastern part, primarily the pheasant range of the Mohawk and Hudson Valleys, showed an increase to a new peak, though insufficient to offset the western decrease; so the total reported kill was about 3 percent below 1938.

In New York, the beginning of the real decline came in 1941, when the reported take showed a drop of nearly 18 percent. In 1942, the kill was down another 15 percent, and 1943 brought an additional slump of over 35 percent. Thus, the total decline from the 1938 peak was more than half, and the population was at its lowest point since 1922.

Hunting license sales for small game reached a high in 1941, and dropped only slightly in 1942, so the indicated decline was real. In 1943, the sale of licenses dropped about 15 percent, and the pheasant decline reported for 1942 probably includes the effect of those licensees who hunted in 1942, but did not buy licenses in 1943 due to the war, and hence did not report their take. By 1944 the sale of licenses had started to rise, so the decline in numbers of pheasants for 1943 appears real.

The severity of the pheasant decline was recognized in 1944 by reduction of the season to one week and the bag limit to one cock per day and four per season. The reported take in 1944 was approximately 20 percent below 1943, and in 1945 it was down another 20 percent, bringing the indicated accumulative decline from the 1938 peak to nearly 75 percent; by 1946 the reported kill was only 20 percent of that in the peak year.

The harvest figures for 1947 and 1948 are not comparable with preceding years, since during those two years the best pheasant range, the Ontario lowland, was closed to hunting and only the secondary ranges, where hunting success was considered primarily a product of stocking, were left open.

Following 1945, the decline of the pheasant population was studied by the farmer inventory method, in which selected farmers across the state were circularized annually with an April questionnaire for adult population reports, and in July for nest and brood reports. From the 1945 baseline, a further decline of nearly 70 percent was recorded through to the beginning of the 1947 breeding season. During this period the reduction was far greater in the Ontario lowland than in the secondary pheasant range. In 1945, pheasant densities in the Ontario lowland were about five times those of the Mohawk and Hudson Valleys; but in the spring of 1947 they were only two and one-half times.

In 1948, the farmer inventory indicated a slight upswing of perhaps 10 percent. Further increases were indicated in 1949 and the spring of 1950, bringing the population to almost double the 1947 low point. Just how low the low point was cannot be shown exactly, but it appears to have been about 10 to 15 percent of the density that existed through the years of pheasant abundance. This is corroborated to some extent by data from a 3,230-acre area in Wayne County, which in 1941 supported a spring population of 66 cocks and 185 hens and, in 1948, had a population estimated at 10 cocks and 10 hens.

Associated with the pheasant decline through the forties, was a marked change in the sex ratio. The most accurate figures available for New York indicate that during the late thirties and early forties sex ratios were about 2.5 to 3 hens per cock through most of the good pheasant range in late winter and the start of the breeding season. Reports of 5 to 7 hens per cock from areas of abundance may be true but appear to have been influenced by observations of large winter flocks of hens. In marginal pheasant range the cock:hen ratio frequently has been 1:1 or 1:2.

No reliable records are available to show just when the number of hens per cock began to decline, but by 1946 the ratio in the Ontario lowland was 1.5:1 and in the Mohawk and Hudson Valleys it was 1:1. At the extreme low point of 1947, a great deal of the pheasant range had nearly equal numbers of cocks and hens, and it was not infrequent for marginal areas to have more cocks than hens, though such conditions did not exist on breeding range adjacent to top quality winter concentration areas. With the gradual recovery of the population since 1947, has come an increase in the number of hens per cock in the eastern parts of New York that remained upen to hunting. In the Ontario lowland, an increase in the number of hens over cocks did not become apparent until the spring of 1950, following the reopening of the season in 1949. The change in the sex ratio probably was partly the product of the decreased removal of cocks by hunting, but it appears to have been associated otherwise with the general decline, either directly or indirectly.

The pheasant decline in the Northeast in the forties appears associated with adverse weather conditions, but an analysis of the records indicates that weather may not have been the only factor involved. In New York, Benson (1948a) made a study of the relation of weather to pheasant numbers, as shown by the reported take for the period from 1935 through 1945. The start of the pheasant decline came with semi-drouth conditions in the spring of 1941. A study in Albany County revealed nest and brood success above average, with a minimum of predation, but this area did not begin to reflect the pheasant decline until after 1943. The weather in 1942 can best be described as neither favorable nor unfavorable for pheasants. In 1943 and 1944, the winters were average and not adverse, but breeding season temperatures ranged slightly below average and precipitation above normal. In 1945, the winter was cold, the snowfall heavy and lasting, and the spring was both cold and wet.

Thus the pheasant decline in New York started when weather conditions could not be considered adverse, unless because of drouth, but the most rapid decline was associated with cold and wet springs, probably aggravated by a hard winter in 1945.

In 1946 the winter was average, and the spring was favorable in the Ontario lowland, but wet in the eastern part of the state; yet the population declined to a greater extent in the Ontario lowland than in the east. The 1947 winter was not adverse again, but the spring was both cold and wet; yet during the year some recovery in the pheasant population was observed. If cold and wet springs are interpreted correctly as being adverse for pheasants, then there must have been a higher than normal winter survival to the spring of 1948; and since that winter could be considered average to slightly adverse in terms of sleet and drifting snow, then it seems that other factors also must have been involved in the decline and recovery of the population.

The role of predation in the pheasant decline is rather obscure, and some of the data are conflicting. In New York, the fox population started a gradual increase in the middle thirties but did not reach a point of abundance to attract attention until 1943. The increase continued at least until 1947, and remained at a high at least through 1949 in some parts of the state.

The rabbit population reached a peak of abundance in 1938, and declined steadily until 1945, reaching a level that was only about a third of the peak, as judged by the reported take of game. Since 1945, the rabbit population apparently has been on the increase, as reflected by the damage complaints and increasing sight observations along highways.

In grouse, a minor depression occurred in 1936, but throughout New York and most of New England, grouse were at a good level in 1944. Pennsylvania and Maine suffered a decline in 1943 or 1944 (Bump *et al.* 1947). On the surface, it appears that grouse have followed their normal trends in cyclic abundance regardless of high fox populations, while pheasants and rabbits did decline with increasing fox numbers. On the other hand, rabbits and pheasants both started to increase while foxes still were abundant. Thus the obvious conclusion is that the pheasant decline might have been accelerated through fox predation, but the start of the decline, and the turning point from the low, must have been due to other factors.

The possibility that disease may have been involved in the pheasant decline was indicated by E. L. Cheatum's (unpublished) studies in New York. On a small island off Long Island, a rapid brood loss during the first weeks, resulting in the almost complete decimation of 66 broods by the end of their fourth week, was attributed to a severe infection of gapeworms and intestinal worms *(Syngamus* and *Dispharynx).* With pheasants at a relatively high density, disease could be expected to have a maximum effect and may have combined to bring about the rapid decline. Predators still were high and weather somewhat adverse in 1947, when the trend toward recovery began.

Hunting appears to have played no part in the pheasant depression. The sale of hunting licenses was at a peak in 1941 when the reduction started, but the further drop in numbers in 1943, 1944, and 1945, was associated with fewer licensed hunters and reduced hunting pressure resulting from the shortening of the season.

Distribution and Status

There is a wide variation in the quality of pheasant habitat in the Northeast—from excellent to poor. The number of birds each area will support is related directly to fertility of the soil, and to land use practices. The best pheasant range always is found only on rich agricultural land.

Fall concentrations on such areas approach 50 birds per 100 acres, but 20 to 25 birds per 100 acres is the rule. Before the great decline, a concentration area in Pennsylvania supported one bird for each acre (Gerstell 1937). According to standards for the Northeast, good pheasant habitat probably supports 10 to 15 birds per 100 acres in the fall throughout the bulk of the

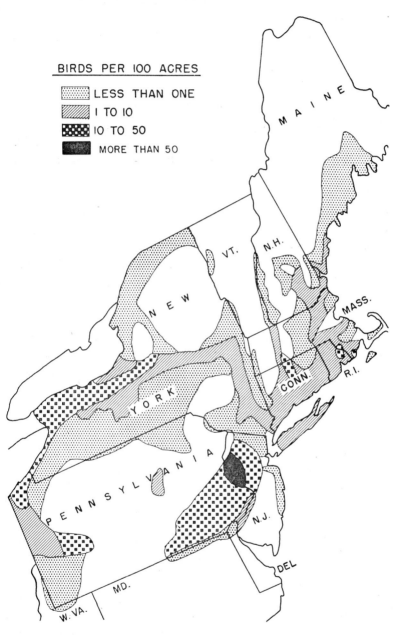

FIGURE 32.—Pheasant distribution in the Northeast, 1950.

range. The ringneck range classified as "fair" occupies likewise fair farm land and produces fall populations of 1 to 5 birds per 100 acres, while the poor range carries less than one bird per 100 acres.

Records used to compile the accompanying map of pheasant distribution and densities have been obtained through the courtesy of the various northeastern states and represent data that were collected in many ways. To permit evaluation of these records the situation in each state is discussed separately.

What caused the great pheasant decline in the Northeast? No one knows for sure. It probably was a combination of several factors. But among those of which we have knowledge, adverse weather, which limited nest and brood survival, appears to be the most important.

Maine

The only pheasant habitat in this state is along the coastal belt and in the major river valleys. The native fall population is less than one bird per 100 acres, except in limited areas of Cumberland County. The annual harvest runs less than 8,000 birds, of which over half are released stock. The Maine situation is a "put and take" proposition largely, with an open season on both cocks and hens (Dorr 1951).

New Hampshire

Pheasant hunting in this state is limited. The principal habitat is found in the Merrimack River valley, the coastal belt, and the narrow Connecticut River valley. A total of only 321,901 acres has been classed as possible pheasant cover, of which only 1,351 acres could be called "excellent." Over 90 percent must be rated "fair" or "poor" (Siegler 1949). In only a few limited places does the population exceed one bird per 100 acres in the fall of the year. New Hampshire stocks a few thousand birds annually, and released birds make up about 30 percent of the kill.

Vermont

The limited pheasant range in Vermont is confined to farmlands bordering Lake Champlain and here and there along the

Connecticut River valley. Practically nowhere does the fall population exceed one bird per 100 acres. Vermont no longer stocks pheasants, and the season is closed at the present time (Wallace 1937; Roger Seamans, personal communication).

Massachusetts

In recent years, this state's harvest has run about 25,000 cocks annually, of which some 80 percent are native stock. No direct estimate of the fall population has been made, but with over three-fourths of the available cocks being harvested (Wandell 1945) and a fall sex ratio only slightly favoring the hens, the total fall population probably is near 60,000 native birds.

Just over 17 percent, or nearly 900,000 acres, of the state is pheasant cover, indicating an overall average of about six birds per 100 acres. Studies carried on in Massachusetts (Pushee 1949) indicate that 15 percent of this range is good and probably carries over 10 birds per 100 acres, 40 percent is fair and carries from one to 10 birds per 100 acres, and 45 percent is poor and has a fall population of less than one bird per 100 acres. The bulk of the good range is located in Bristol County, and the Connecticut and Concord River valleys. The habitat is not continuous, but is composed of hundreds of small coverts often separated by woods.

Rhode Island

With a human population of over 100 per 100 acres it is a wonder there is any room at all for pheasants; but nearly 40 percent of the state is in farmland, and over a quarter of the land is cropped. In 1950, a calculated 2,210 game-farm cocks and 3,560 natives were shot (Wright 1951). No direct population estimates are available for the fall, but the harvest suggests that the native fall population may have been 10 to 12 thousand pheasants, or about 4 birds per 100 acres of farmland.

Connecticut

This state has its principal pheasant population in the Connecticut River valley. In 1948, about 35,000 cocks were shot, of which some 30,000 probably were native (Sondrini 1950). Calculated on the same basis as for Massachusetts and Rhode

Island, it appears that the total fall population probably was nearly 100,000 birds, or about 6 per 100 acres. Starting in 1949, the taking of both cocks and hens was permitted, and no methods of estimating the population changes to 1950 are available.

New York

The best state-wide records, showing pheasant abundance and distribution in New York, have been collected through the spring farmer inventory (Perry 1946), which shows relative numbers in various sections of the state and fluctuations from year to year. These records have been supplemented by population estimates made through crowing cock counts, and hen populations calculated from late-winter sex ratios and spring harem counts. Crowing cock counts on the basis of calls per 2-minute intervals have been made both on four areas where complete population estimates were made, and on a series of routes in Monroe, Orleans, Seneca, Ontario, and Yates Counties.

By use of these data it has been possible to determine the approximate population density in the spring. In the absence of reliable fall estimates, numbers have been based on a calculated 45 percent of the spring hen population bringing off broods averaging five young by fall and a loss through the breeding and summer season of 15 percent of the adult cocks and 20 percent of the adult hens. These figures were derived from studies carried out from 1939 through 1943, but appear in argeement with observations made on a lesser scale in recent years.

On this basis, no part of the state in the fall of 1950 had a population equalling 50 birds per hundred acres, although portions of the two northwest counties, Erie and Niagara, approached that density. Throughout most of the Erie-Ontario lowland, populations in the fall of 1950 ranged from 10 to 20 birds per hundred acres. In the Mohawk and Hudson valleys, fall populations ranged from one to 5 birds per hundred acres, except that in parts of Ulster and Dutchess Counties numbers may have approached 10 per hundred acres. In the rest of the occupied range, there was a residual population usually of less than one bird per hundred acres. These same areas 10 years ago probably had supported 5 birds per hundred acres or more in the narrow valleys, although pheasants were scarce there on the hill lands. The low point in pheasant populations in New York occurred in 1947, and the 1950 figures indicate nearly a doubling of the population in three seasons. However, this density probably was less than a fourth of the average from 1935 to 1940.

During the period when the population was declining, a change in the winter sex ratio favoring cocks was noted. Restrictions in hunting at least helped to bring about this condition, and in 1948, the sex ratio was nearly one to one throughout most of the state. In the spring of 1950, the cock population probably equalled the density of the peak years, but with a sex ratio still of less than two to one, the reproductive potential was well below that of former years, when the sex ratio occasionally exceeded three to one. The cock harvest in 1950 probably was about 100,000 but could have been greater. In the best pheasant range, only a two-day season was permitted, and only 30 to 40 percent of the available cocks were harvested. Judging by spring densities of three to five cocks per 100 acres in the better range of the Erie-Ontario lowland, a greater fall harvest could have been permitted.

Pennsylvania

Perhaps more than any other state in the Northeast, Pennsylvania offers sharp contrasts in pheasant populations, for one may go in only a few miles from areas with no pheasants to extensive sections that currently support upward of 50 birds per 100 acres in the fall. In 1950, over 350,000 cock birds were shot, an increase of more than 60 percent from the low year of 1946. With heavy hunting pressure, a 25-day season, and a bag limit of two cocks per day and 15 per season, Pennsylvania has succeeded in maintaining a pheasant population with a high reproductive potential, often 6 to 8 hens per cock. As a result, with a spring population of no greater density than in parts of New York, the harvestable crop for comparable areas has been two or three times as great.

The most important pheasant range is the rich agricultural area lying south and east of the Blue Ridge Mountains. The area west of York to the edge of the mountains, probably supported some 10 to 20 birds per 100 acres in the fall of 1950. East of York, to the New Jersey line and south to the border of the state, the population probably averaged 25 birds per 100 acres, and in spots, may have exceeded 50 birds.

A second important pheasant range involves the whole western edge of the state. A strip about 20 miles wide running south from Pymatuning Reservoir nearly to New Castle has supported close to 50 birds per 100 acres in the fall. Bordering this strip, and extending from the shores of Lake Erie south to the Ohio River, is an area that has averaged some 10 to 20 birds per 100 acres. East of that area, until the land becomes too mountainous for pheasants, and south to include Washington County, pheasants number one to 10 per 100 acres, and gradually taper down to nothing as one approaches the West Virginia line on the south. Immediately east of Pittsburgh, in the Conemaugh and Loyalhanna valleys, is another area supporting some 10 to 20 birds per 100 acres. In addition to the above mentioned areas, the Pennsylvania pheasant population is limited to occasional small agricultural valleys supporting small numbers. Only two of these approach importance—the river valley immediately south of Williamsport, to the point of junction with the main Susquehanna River, and that portion of the Susquehanna River from the New York line south to Scranton. In both cases, the fall populations are considerably less than 10 birds per 100 acres.

New Jersey

Pheasant distribution in New Jersey essentially is limited to the agricultural northern half. Three counties—Hunterdon, Somerset, and Warren—are an eastern extension of the rich southeastern Pennsylvania farm country, and probably support in excess of 50 birds per 100 acres in the fall. They provide the greater part of 250,000 to 300,000 cocks that are shot annually. The other northern counties, with the exception of hilly Sussex, carry 10 to 50 birds per 100 acres, except where the rapidly expanding human population has taken over. In the southern half of the state, a sprinkling of pheasants are found in the counties bordering Pennsylvania, and again along the coastal marshes, though not in sufficient numbers to warrant hunting.

Delaware, Maryland and West Virginia

These three states all have a few scattered pheasants in their northern tiers of counties, but not in numbers large enough for the birds to receive attention in the form of management. An interesting but unexplained feature is the very abrupt drop in population density about at the Pennsylvania line, from over 10 birds per 100 acres to less than one, in a few miles. There is no sharp change in agriculture, although the line of demarkation roughly parallels a change in soil type. From available information, however, it appears that the pheasant population follows more of an east-west line than the soil types.

Habitat Affinities

Every child in school learns that the Northeast is hilly, that much of the land is forested, and that only a small portion of the area may be cultivated intensively. Few probably grasp, however, how markedly the region differs agriculturally from other parts of the country. For example, over 90 percent of Iowa, Nebraska, and South Dakota, three of the more important pheasant states, is in farms, while less than 50 percent of the nine northeastern states included in this discussion is in farms. Cultivated lands, including hay, make up 44 percent of the three previously mentioned midwestern states, while less than 20 percent of the Northeast is cultivated, and nearly half of that is given over to hay. Iowa alone, which is one-third the size of the Northeast, has two million more acres under cultivation than all the Northeast together.

Land use

Since the pheasant primarily is a species of intensively farmed lands, it is necessary to visualize the distribution and characteristics of agriculture in the Northeast to understand fully the problems of pheasant management. In Table 53, a summary of the land use factors which might affect pheasant welfare are presented. For convenience, subtotals are given

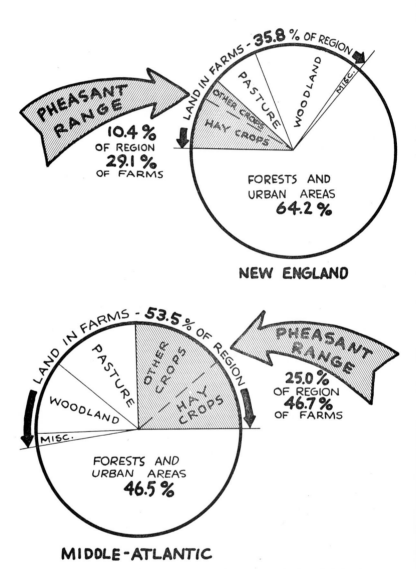

FIGURE 33.—Land use and pheasant range in New England and Atlantic States.

TABLE 53. Land Use in the Northeast*.

	Land Area Acres	Land in Farms		Land Use of Farm in Percent			Corn		Hay
		Acres	Percent	Wood-land	Open pasture	Crop-land	Percent Farm	Percent for grain	Percent Farm
Maine	19,865,600	4,613,175	23.2	53.1	11.1	30.7	0.2	19.8	19.7
New Hampshire	5,775,360	2,017,049	34.9	59.5	33.1	22.9	0.6	23.3	19.0
Vermont	5,937,920	3,930,514	66.2	39.5	28.4	30.2	1.6	5.4	25.7
Massachusetts	5,060,480	2,078,349	41.1	45.2	15.6	30.1	2.1	13.7	17.8
Rhode Island	677,120	264,734	39.1	41.5	19.3	26.7	3.3	10.8	12.6
Connecticut	3,135,360	1,599,169	50.8	42.6	21.5	28.7	3.0	17.6	17.9
NEW ENGLAND	40,451,840	14,496,990	35.8	47.8	20.8	29.1	1.3	12.7	20.6
New York	30,674,560	17,568,471	57.3	20.6	29.9	43.6	3.9	29.0	22.7
Pennsylvania	28,828,800	15,019,675	52.1	22.0	21.7	49.1	9.5	78.4	17.0
New Jersey	4,814,080	1,818,103	37.8	16.4	16.1	56.1	11.3	65.5	14.6
MID-ATLANTIC	64,317,440	34,406,249	53.5	21.0	25.6	46.7	6.7	59.8	19.8
TOTAL	104,769,280	48,903,239	46.7	28.9	24.2	41.4	5.1	56.3	20.0

* Data taken from U. S. Agricultural Census 1945.

for the New England and Mid-Atlantic states, since they differ in many respects agriculturally.

From Table 53 it may be seen readily that none of the New England States has the necessary attributes of pheasant country. Only 35 percent of the land area is in farms, with the bulk of the remainder in forests. Of the land in farms, nearly half is wooded and one-fifth is open pasture providing no food or shelter for farmland game species. The cropping of the remaining 30 percent of farmland reflects the needs of dairy farming. Some 70 percent is devoted to hay crops, and less than 5 percent to corn. Corn often has been given as an indicator of pheasant distribution, but here, nearly 90 percent of it goes into silos, leaving neither food nor cover for pheasants. Altogether, the New England States present an environment inhospitable to pheasants.

Now, pheasant populations in New England are restricted largely to the few fertile valleys devoted to general farming. Dairy farming still is on the increase, and even though pheasant numbers have increased from the period of scarcity in the forties, the population may never equal the density attained in the thirties. Since 1910, there has been a 25 percent reduction in farm lands, through reversion to forests and occupation by suburban developments. This trend may be expected to continue, and farm-game lands will be reduced further.

The picture for pheasants in the Middle Atlantic States, New York, Pennsylvania, and New Jersey, is more favorable, as shown by the foregoing table. For the region as a whole, over half the land is in farms and nearly half the farmland is cropped. In contrast to New England, only a quarter is devoted to open pasture. Of the three, New York is the most nearly comparable to the New England States, with large sections being devoted to dairying. Half of the cultivated land is in hay, only a small proportion in corn, and 80 percent of the corn goes into silos. The best pheasant range lies in the Erie-Ontario lowland of western New York, which provides three-fourths of the annual cock harvest. That region differs from the state average, as over 75 percent is in farms, and about 60

percent of the land in farms is cultivated. Though more livestock are carried per square mile in this region than the state
average, more fertile soil permits the land to be handled more
intensively. Only 25 percent of the cultivated land is in hay.
Nearly 10 percent of the cultivated acres is in corn, and 35
percent of that is permitted to mature for grain. The harvest
of small grains, too, makes the Lake Plains region more favorable, where nearly 25 percent of the cultivated land falls in
this category compared with the state average of 15 percent.

New York and Pennsylvania are the two most important
pheasant states in the Northeast, and it is of interest to contrast them in some respects agriculturally, while considering
that at the peak of pheasant abundance in 1938, it is estimated
that about 450,000 cocks were killed in New York and about
550,000 in Pennsylvania. Those estimates were made by adjusting the kill figures up by the percent of hunters who have
failed to report, and making allowances for unlicensed hunters,
so that the final figures are rough. While New York is larger
than Pennsylvania, and has more land in farms, as shown in
Table 53, the comparative acreages listed in Table 54 give
some indication of why Pennsylvania is able to harvest approximately 20 percent more cocks annually than New York.

TABLE 54. Comparative Acreages of Certain Crops in New York
and Pennsylvania.

Land Use	New York	Pennsylvania
Acres in State	30,674,560	28,828,800
Acres in Farms	17,568,471	15,019,675
Woodland	3,623,380	3,312,084
Pastureland*	5,254,779	3,266,718
Cropland**	7,661,293	7,372,838
Miscellaneous***	1,029,019	1,068,035
Hay (all types)	3,979,289	2,558,304
Orchards, Vineyards, Berries	280,309	191,693
Wheat	330,998	905,442
Corn (all purposes)	690,068	1,421,092
Corn for grain	136,983	1,113,877

* Pastureland—includes only open pasture. Excludes pastured woodland.
** Cropland—includes all hay but excludes that being used primarily for
   pasture.
*** Miscellaneous—includes farmyard zone, lanes, areas used for miscellaneous
   purposes and waste units not elsewhere included.

These two states have nearly identical acreages devoted to cropland, but the land use shown in Table 54 indicates rather clearly why the Pennsylvania range on the whole carries greater pheasant densities. Pheasants rely on the grain production of farmlands, and the weeds associated therewith, as their primary food source. Pennsylvania has nearly three times more wheat acreage and eight times more corn for grain production than New York, and can therefore be expected to carry greater pheasant densities.

Human populations

To visualize pheasant habitats in the Northeast, we must give adequate consideration to the human populations of the region. The New England States have an average of 149 people per square mile, and the Middle Atlantic States 300 per square mile, compared with 44.2 for the United States, and 21.9 for the combination of Iowa, Nebraska, and South Dakota. While less than a quarter of this northeastern population is rural, the rural population still exceeds that in the heart of the United States pheasant range. Rural populations in the Northeast exceed 50 people per square mile, compared with 13 in the previously mentioned states.

The significance of this concentration of people to the quality of pheasant hunting is difficult to determine. Obviously associated with it are more dogs and cats, more automobiles, better roads, and more high-speed traffic. While none of these factors causes much pheasant mortality, they do amount to greater year-around hazards than occur in less densely populated regions. On the other hand, there may be compensating factors in that farms are smaller and there are more miles of property lines affording waste areas for cover and, perhaps, even more farm gardens for pheasants to raid. That is a minor factor over the range as a whole, but it can be a major item in poor range. In much of New England, the pheasant is a "home garden" bird. On the whole, the range and density of pheasant populations in the Northeast are determined by fertility of the soil and the types of crops that the soils and

climate can grow, with the density of human population playing a relatively small part. Grain or general farming in fertile
soils is almost always associated with good pheasant populations. Truck gardening is favorable, but not on mucklands,
where the primary crops are tubers. Dairy farms, even on the
better lands, rarely are good pheasant habitat, and the fertile
farmlands of Aroostook County, Maine, where potato growing predominates, similarly offer little food or cover. Where
orchards are grown on good soil, and the intervening areas
are devoted to grains or truck gardening, pheasants do well,
but where land is less fertile and areas between orchards are
left idle, pheasants do not thrive.

Climatic relationships

The Northeast pheasant range has a continental type of
climate, which characteristically is cold in winter and hot in
summer. Many variations are induced by the varied topography, however. Western New York and Pennsylvania normally take the brunt of the cold air masses moving across the
continent, but they also are warmed by air masses moving up
from the south or from the Great Lakes. Southeastern Pennsylvania and New Jersey, because of their more southerly location, the shielding effect of the Blue Ridge Mountains and
Kittatinny Ridge, and the general tendency for cold air masses
to move northeasterly down the St. Lawrence Valley, are
endowed with a relatively mild climate. The coastal portions
of the New England States likewise have periods of mild
weather resulting from the tempering effect of the Atlantic
Ocean.

Average winter temperatures through the better pheasant
areas of the Northeast range from 20° to 30° (F), with average
minimums of 5° in southeastern Pennsylvania, and −20° in
the more northern areas, where temperatures of −30° occur
occasionally. In the summer months the temperature averages
70° to 75°, with hot spells reaching 90° to 100°. Occasionally
the thermometer records up to 105°.

Precipitation through the Northeast ranges from 30 to 50
inches annually, being influenced strongly by local topography.

PLATE LXV.—Wintering pheasants move boldly in the open fields to feed, yet they make good use of all available cover. Defining habitat requirements has been a complex problem in the East (R. M. Cady, Pennsylvania Game Commission).

The best pheasant areas in the Northeast average about 40 inches or less per year. Taken on a seasonal basis, the total rainfall is distributed rather uniformly throughout the year, the wettest months in New York being, in order, July, June, August, and May. Rains in May and June come most commonly in the form of all-day storms, accompanied by cool air, while July and August rains come in the form of thundershowers. In all four of those months, between 3.5 and 4 inches of precipitation are expected. Winter months from December through April have the least precipitation, averaging from 2.5 to 3 inches monthly. Through the best pheasant range of the Northeast 0.01 or more inches of precipitation may be expected on 120 to 140 days each year.

Average annual snowfall ranges from less than 20 inches in Southeastern Pennsylvania to 100 inches in other parts of the pheasant range. The best range in New York receives less than 80 inches of snow per year, with the greatest fall coming in January and February, when an average of 10 to 20 inches per month is expected. While snow increases the problems of the pheasant in obtaining food, little indication has been obtained to show that it has had much effect on populations in the occupied range. In snow storms, pheasants occasionally have been observed with chunks of ice or snow frozen to their feathers, often to the point that it impedes the bird's ability to take flight. Similar difficulties have been observed following sleet storms, but it is only the severe or prolonged storm that takes any appreciable toll of birds.

Research still has a long way to go to understand the role of climate in the pheasant's welfare, and this is discussed elsewhere in this book, but there are some weather features which should be considered even though their significance is not known. Through the late spring and summer months, relative humidity in the Northeast exceeds that of the plains and prairie states that support the greatest pheasant abundance. Similarly, the percent of possible sunshine both during winter and summer is lower in the Northeast than in the best pheasant range. At the same time, under ideal agricultural conditions, local pheasant populations in the humid Northeast sometimes have approached densities equal to the best in the Midwest.

Management Programs and Trends

Since the ringneck pheasant is confined almost exclusively to agricultural areas, it necessarily follows that any habitat work to improve its lot must be conducted on farmland. This complicates the problem in many ways. It involves biology, economics, and sociology, and any pheasant management plan not compatible with all these elements is doomed to failure. It is not merely a question of fulfilling the bird's daily, seasonal and yearly requirements, even if we understood them thoroughly, and knew how to do it. It is a problem of supplying these needs in a manner that fits in with man's way of life. To succeed on any sizable portion of the pheasant's range, management must mesh with good farming practices, fit into a sound land-use program, and be acceptable to the man who owns the land as well as to the hunter. We cannot expect a farmer to turn over valuable profit-making land to raise pheasants. Any birds he produces must be incidental to his regular farm crops.

Habitat development

Twenty years ago in the northeastern states, pheasant management was being carried out intensively by several states on publicly owned or leased lands. There was great hope that food and cover planting, establishment of refuges, and winter feeding would make pheasants abundant. On some of these areas, especially those having fertile soil, pheasants did prosper, but on marginal lands the birds did not respond. The costs of farming for pheasants proved excessive and it was evident that such practices could be justified only in those areas where shooting opportunity was limited and where hunting pressure was concentrated. Such shooting areas still are scattered throughout the pheasant range in the Northeast. They are important to urban hunters but the number of gunners they can accommodate is limited.

In an effort to help the mass of hunters (2,882,627 licensed in 1949), the states have turned more recently to state-wide farm-game habitat development projects. They are designed to establish management practices compatible with good farming on private lands. In return for the use of his land, usually

PLATE LXXVI.—The small-marsh program has been primarily for waterfowl, but it provides excellent winter retreats for the ringneck (D. L. Allen).

covered by an agreement or lease permitting public hunting and giving the game department control for five years, the farmer receives a variety of planting stock, services, and technical assistance. The creation of soil conservation districts has helped the game biologists' problem of getting work done on the land, and whenever possible they work through these organizations.

One of the most popular practices is that of supplying the farmer with trees and shrubs to be planted in waste areas adjacent to woodlots, or as fencerows. Some states merely supply the stock, while others actually also do much of the planting. A variety of game food and cover plants are used, but the most important are evergreens for clump planting and multiflora rose for fencerows. In Pennsylvania during 1951-52 the Game Commission furnished or planted nearly 2 million conifers and 1.5 million multiflora rose. In 1951, New York planted or supervised planting of more than 9.5 million evergreens and furnished or planted nearly three million shrubs. These are the two largest programs, but several other states in the region are doing the same type of planting.

It is well known that near woods borders or along fencerows grown up to trees, farm crops produce poorly. In a study in Delaware (Caulk 1951) it was found that farmers lost money on corn planted less than 15 feet from the woods border, and the yield was not normal out to 35 feet. Low-growing dense brush is much better game cover than trees, so in an effort to aid the farmer and at the same time help small game, several states are cutting 25-to 30-foot borders along the woods edge and felling trees in fencerows. This practice appeals to farmers and is growing. It costs about 25 cents a linear foot but the results in game food and cover production are much faster than when exotic stock is planted.

To furnish food and nesting cover, three states either purchase strips of standing crops or plant food plots in areas the farmer is not using.

Most of the states have a fencing feature in their program. Grazed woodlots are fenced to keep out livestock and make

PLATE LXXVII.—*Above.* Two Asians on a Pennsylvania farm—multiflora rose, and the pheasant (R. M. Cady, Pennsylvania Game Commission). *Below.* Research workers are after the answers, and some do not come easily (Daniel H. Chapman, U. S. Fish and Wildlife Service).

the area more suitable for game. Under some plans the farmer is furnished all or part of the materials; in others the fence is installed and the farmer pays part of the costs.

Some of the states have been building shallow ponds or marshes averaging about 5 acres each. New York has been the leader, and in 1951, completed 92 of those wildlife ponds. This phase of the program is designed primarily for the benefit of waterfowl and muskrats, but the areas must be fenced and support excellent cattail and other dense cover beneficial to all types of farm game. These man-made marshes have proved to be important to pheasants in good pheasant country. There they often become the "social center" for the birds and draw them to parts of farms that were not productive previously. In poor range, small marshes have not received the same pheasant utilization.

Some states set aside small refuges that are fenced or posted against shooting. In New York, all the wildlife pond areas are refuges, while in New Jersey and Pennsylvania, in addition to ordinary refuges, safety zones are established where no hunting is permitted within shooting distance of the farmer's buildings (Alpaugh 1951, Golden 1951).

Two states, New Jersey and Pennsylvania, operate intensive programs on private land that are worthy of mention. The former has a hunting-by-registration plan under which lands of 1,000 acres or more are registered and posted. Hunting can be done only after the gunner registers with the farmer. The shooting pressure is limited to one man per 20 acres per day. Approximately 10 percent of the area is in refuge which is managed through the planting of food and cover. Safety zones are provided and the areas are stocked (Alpaugh 1951).

The Pennsylvania plan, under which nearly a million acres of hunting rights have been leased, is the most intensive program on private land in the Northeast. In addition to the previously mentioned practices, the farm-game cooperators also receive technical advice and assistance with soil conservation operations, such as surveying for diversion ditches and contour farming, establishment of drainage ditches, locating sod waterways, recommending pasture management, and furnishing rye grass seed as winter cover crop (Golden 1951).

It is evident that these state-wide programs are designed to benefit small game in general. Approximately $1,085,000 was spent on such work in the region during 1951. It is not for pheasant management specifically, although certain practices may help pheasants on some areas. At the present time, game biologists are trying to evaluate the program, which will take time and careful study.

Habitat improvement operations can be successful only if full attention is given to the biological needs of each individual area. They cannot fulfill their purpose if carried out with the philosophy that all techniques are good everywhere. To get maximum benefits, the job must be approached as hundreds of small projects each having its own peculiarities, and biologists must evaluate each land unit from the standpoint of what is needed to help game animals prosper, and then put into practice that which applies.

Stocking

The releasing of pheasants is discussed elsewhere in this book, but stocking is such an important issue in the Northeast that a few remarks about its place in pheasant management should be made here.

For better or for worse, propagation and stocking of pheasants are here to stay, and this will remain so until research proves the fallacies to the hunter and comes up with pheasant management practices that will add more birds to his bag.

In this region, it is true of all but the best range, that pheasant carrying capacity is not high, and land that can grow any pheasants is quite limited in extent. As a result, there are 2 to 3 million hunters (2 million licensed) scrambling for birds produced on about 42 million acres of pheasant range—more than a hunter for every 21 acres!

The truth is that most land in the Northeast cannot be made to produce pheasants by known methods at any reasonable price; but hunters demand that they be provided with pheas-

PLATE LXXVIII.—Heavy human populations and limited pheasant range have brought about heavy demands for artificial stocking (R. M. Cady, Pennsylvania Game Commission).

ant shooting anyway. Thus, state game departments release birds for want of anything better. All of them have stocking formulas based on range quality and hunting pressures. Birds are freed as breeders or as shooting stock, according to local concepts and situations.

Research has shown that the proportion of liberated pheasants in the kill is inversely proportional to productivity of the land and that the closer to the shooting season birds are released the higher the returns (Benson 1948, Pushee 1948, Siegler 1949, Skiff 1948). With this as a background, cocks and hens are stocked in the spring only where the native population is not adequate to raise the number of pheasants up to the fall carrying capacity of the range. In the fall, stock is liberated as near to the gunning season as possible on fair or poor pheasant range where hunting pressure is high.

The accessibility of birds also plays an important role. In stocking banded birds, New York got good returns from birds placed near roads, but releases made in the center of a mile-square block provided few returns, even though field checks suggested equal survival. The harvest of cocks also dropped in areas removed from human population centers. Apparently, under those circumstances, the pheasant population was not being harvested amply. The problem is to determine how to get the hunter to the bird. With a little more effort the gunner could have better luck in working over the back forty.

In any stocking program it must be remembered that the number of birds that can be supported by any given area of habitat is determined by range quality. This is the inherent carrying capacity of the land. Any birds released after this population is reached are doomed before long. That is why, in spite of repeated stocking, results have been so poor on thousands of areas. Stocking can be a tool of pheasant management or simply public appeasement, according to its use.

Shooting

With large numbers of gunners combing the pheasant country, it is necessary to have restrictions on hunting. The birds could not withstand unlimited shooting, but they can stand a lot provided only cocks are killed.

Pheasants are prolific and, being polygamous, one cock can serve at least 9 or 10 hens (Shick 1952). In good pheasant range, heavy shooting pressure for periods of 20 to 30 days apparently does no damage, while too short a season actually may reduce productivity (Benson 1948, Shick 1952). A short shooting season also concentrates hunters, and as a result of this flood of champions of the chase, particularly near cities, more pheasant coverts are posted by irate and frustrated farmers.

On poorer range, it is possible that heavy hunting pressure can be a limiting factor. Where pheasant covers are small and widely scattered, constant combing of the areas by hunters apparently is harmful because the birds, cocks and hens alike, are harassed so much that they leave the cover with little hope of surviving in the unfit surrounding areas (Bishop 1949). Here the ill effects result from harassment and not actual killing. The shooting of hen pheasants can cause serious damage and probably is important in some places in the Northeast (Wandell 1942, 1943, 1949). In no place in this region where there is any hope for natural reproduction should hen pheasant shooting be permitted.

In summary, it appears that the heavy hunting of cock pheasants is not a limiting factor on good pheasant range. Harassment of pheasants caused by high hunting pressure can be important on poorer range. Actual overshooting of cocks in the Northeast under a two-cock daily bag limit and 30-day season has not been proved, although it might occur in isolated coverts.

CHAPTER 9

THE MANAGEMENT OUTLOOK

By DURWARD L. ALLEN

THERE are pheasants in North America because of a tremendous habitat management program. It was not carried out specifically for this bird, but the effect was the same. In the primitive state, you never could have established pheasants on river floodplains of the Northeast, or in the swamps and beaver meadows of Ohio and Southern Michigan. They would not have made the grade among herds of bison and flocks of prairie chickens on the northern plains, or in timbered valleys of Washington and Oregon. The Sacramento marshes would have been no place for them, and arid bottoms from Idaho to El Paso were fine for rattlesnakes or road runners, but not for pheasants.

We cut trees, drained wet soil, broke prairie sod, and irrigated dry valleys. We introduced some foreign weeds and began to raise corn, wheat, barley, soybeans, sorghum, and rice, As has been indicated in the foregoing regional accounts, we are far from understanding the precise adjustment of the ringneck to his agricultural habitats, but you will find him in areas mixed to grain and hay—almost everywhere but in the humid Southeast.

In the northeast quarter of the country you can take those regions that support pheasants and set up a fertility scale of farming areas, from the poorest to the best—and you also will have a scale of pheasant numbers from lowest to highest populations.

This implies that if it were possible to take nearly any unit of "fair" pheasant range, tip it up on edge, remove the old soil, and replace it with one of top fertility, we thereby would be improving that habitat for the gaudy bird from China.

Most pheasant specialists suspect it would work that way. Grade-A ranges typically put forth large yields of some favored food, such as corn or soybeans, but high densities of the bird appear to be associated more consistently with soil fertility itself than with any one crop. The high production of weed seed characteristic of such areas undoubtedly is a primary food source.

In western lands, where aridity is the rule, soils are almost invariably high in mineral content, awaiting only the addition of sufficient water to make them productive of both agricultural crops and pheasants. This seems to hold almost irrespective of latitude within the boundaries of the United States.

In the East, however, a different situation is evident. In the southern half of Michigan's Lower Peninsula, there are large pheasant concentrations on almost every area of highly fertile soil. Exceptions are a few islands of prairie in the extreme southwest. Likewise, below the state line the good prairie lands of Indiana, and their continuation on through Illinois, do not support large numbers of pheasants. To the west, through Iowa, numbers pick up again, and reach their maximum in the Dakotas. Low areas of the Kankakee Valley in northern Indiana resemble some of the better pheasant lands of Michigan, but like the adjacent prairies, they sustain only fair to poor populations.

A similar situation exists on the Pennsylvania-Maryland boundary. Pennsylvania's Lancaster Valley is proverbially a region of high crop-yields, and has been for more than 200 years under the knowing management of "Pennsylvania Dutch" farmers. Likewise, it is good pheasant country, but southward across the Maryland line the birds thin out rapidly to none at all, irrespective of crops or soil.

You can draw a line from the northern tip of Chesapeake Bay to Chicago, and nearly all the really good pheasant range will be to the north. The main exception is a tier of three counties (Allen, Hardin, and Marion) in the northwest quarter of Ohio.

Why do we have this limitation of range? What would need to be done in Indiana and Maryland to extend the distribution of pheasants southward? It is to be suspected that a slight over-hauling of the climate might be in order, but that is in the same category as starting over with a different soil.

As has been indicated elsewhere in this book, the specific reasons why pheasants do not get by in the humid South-east (as contrasted with the equally hot but dry Southwest) have not been defined. It might seem that research men are missing something big and obvious here, but the problem may be more difficult than that. There are spots in Mississippi, Florida, and probably elsewhere in the region, where by repeated stocking, this species has been maintained for a time, and some natural reproduction seems to have occurred. But the bird appears to fall short of replacing its annual losses and hence cannot persist. A little reflection affirms that if a breeding stock failed by only a small margin in keeping up with these losses, the population would diminish and disappear. At present there is no known management tech-nique which will put this species where it does not now exist.

With regard to soil fertility in presently occupied range, perhaps something can, and will, be done; but it will be slow and not primarily for pheasants. American agriculture has been characterized—at least since the aboriginal, fish-in-the-hill era—by the using up and washing away of available fer-tility. Primarily through the efforts of the Soil Conservation Service, the old, exploitive, row-crop-forever methods are giving way to practices that build and improve the land as they produce.

It is logical that this process, which we hope will be the *status quo* in years to come, should make the land more fruit-ful of pheasants along with other crops. This would be a

PLATE LXXIX.—Only the best live to fulfill their mission.

fortunate circumstance, but we could not credit it to any planned management for game.

Specific management measures for pheasants have shown variable results according to regional or local conditions. Much still is to be learned on the fine points, but the greatest usefulness and some of the limitations of certain techniques can be assayed.

Package Goods

The rearing and stocking of pheasants has long been a way of life for many workers in this field. It came down to us from feudal England, where the game keeper was a prominent staff member on large estates. Labor was cheap and the fiscal side of game management got little consideration. The self-respecting Nimrod held aloof from the rabble business of beating the brush. He enjoyed the sunshine of opening morning at some well-planned post while the range-reared or freshly liberated birds were driven toward him over some obstacle of proper height where the angle and light would be propitious.

In terms of our developing ideas of what constitutes sport, it is an anomalous fact that the semi-domestic bird sometimes was favored over his feral brethren. In his book on "Ten Years of Game-Keeping," Owen Jones (1909) remarked that "Wild birds are not nearly so easy to manage, and therefore to show, as so-called tame ones; and so the keeper naturally prefers the latter, since, as is so much the case in these days, the demand is for a concentrated show. I should say that a hundred tame birds are likely to make a better one-day show than half as many again of wild ones."

It was only natural that kindred ideas on pheasant shooting and management were imported to the United States. This was a happy situation to begin with, since the establishment of game farms and the far-and-wide distribution of reared stock assured the rapid establishment and dispersal of the pheasant in all suitable range.

The logic followed that if one game farm provided such

fine shooting in so short a time, then the building of more game farms would make the pheasant industry that much better. Twenty years ago such methods were about the only type of management that got recognition or even acceptance by the sportsmen. The building of a game propagation plant was sound evidence of where the money went, and oftentimes it was a patently efficient and businesslike establishment where inspection by the public was welcomed.

Similarly, the annual statistics on propagated birds were witness to accomplishment and highly reassuring to those who thought they understood them. Once a bird was stocked, he remained forever a statistic safely posted in the books. What happened to him in the flesh was a matter for assumption.

The assumptions came easily for most people who had no close acquaintance with the dynamics and ecology of animal populations. But in recent years, biologists have questioned on a purely logical basis the growth of artificial propagation programs. This is about how the matter reasons out:

The reproductive potential of the pheasant is geared to an average clutch-size of about 10 eggs per hen. Between incubation time and October, on many ranges it takes about two eggs to make one sub-adult bird. This means that Nature has overproduced by 100 percent to allow for a loss of half the crop between May and hunting season. One way to look at it is that by a drastic culling process a large, natural surplus is eliminated and the population reduced to a level determined largely by habitat conditions (which include weather) in the particular season.

Some such relationship undoubtedly exists, but it is a concept that must remain theoretical insofar as it implies an ability to measure summer carrying capacity. At that season, things are changing rapidly, including the requirements of a population of young birds whose ecological position is altered from week to week as they grow and modify their habits, and as they are thinned out. The habitat changes with the ripening of fruits and farm crops and the thickening of perennial weed cover. In the final synthesis, good environments consistently yield larger populations than poor ones. Under ordinary conditions we can assume that Nature does a large overstocking job and that natural limitations cut the annual production down to a size that will fit a given environmental pattern. This limitation of numbers is clear in Green's (1948) account of the build-up of pheasant populations on an area in Iowa following the heavy mortality that occurred during the winter of 1935-36.

In the spring of 1936, the sex ratio was 3 to 1 and the population was 25 birds per section of land. This breeding stock quadrupled its numbers to 100 per section by the fall of that year. The birds survived well through the following winter and the 1937 spring population was 60 pheasants per section with a sex ratio of 2 hens per cock. But in spite of the fact that there were 40 breeding hens compared with 18 the year before, fall numbers of pheasants were between 100 and 125 per section. In another year, breeders had increased to 70 with a sex ratio of 1 to 1 (35 hens). That fall the population was the same as before. In 1937 and 1938, there was an obvious surplus of breeders.

This raises the question of how much is accomplished when we release more breeders or more young birds in environments that are stocked to capacity already—and that probably is the usual condition. In many areas it may well be that production by such breeders or survival of such young does not represent a gain. Some or all of them probably are there *in place of* individuals originating in the wild population that would have made the grade otherwise.

That is how the stocking of breeders or young birds in spring and summer would seem, under ordinary conditions, to fit into the population mechanism of the pheasant or any other species. Naturally, research men have not dismissed the method on this basis but have carried out a considerable number of studies to get experimental results.

The first such jobs consisted of merely banding samples of young birds which were handled in accordance with customary stocking procedures. This meant that stocking was done principally where demand was greatest; the call for more pheasants was most vociferous in areas that had few birds; and that, of course, was in poor pheasant range. Usually poults of 8 to 10 weeks were taken out and dumped uncermoniously.

This probably accounts in part for the small number of recoveries from such stocking. In 1937, Gerstell (1938) liberated 3,000 banded cock pheasants in three classes of range in Pennsylvania. In first-class range he received reports on 35 percent, in second-class range slightly less than 16 percent were recovered, and in third-class range only 11 percent were reported.

Another factor governing survival and recoveries is the length of time between stocking and the shooting season. This is illustrated by an experiment carried out by Buss (1946) on Wisconsin shooting preserves from 1936 to 1940. Summarizing the records for 1,249 pheasants released from 35 to 110 days before the open season, he found that hunters bagged 11 percent, but for 1,027 birds turned out the day before shooting, returns were 41 percent. Buss called attention to a similar job by H. L. Kutz in New York in 1941, who stocked 1,794 banded pheasants on public hunting grounds between August 12 and 18 and received checking-station reports on 19.1 percent. But a sample of 1,583 released between October 16 and 26 yielded hunting recoveries of 39.6 percent. McNamara and Kozicky (1949) found similar trends in returns from pheasants stocked in New Jersey.

Poor survival undoubtedly is the primary reason for low banding returns, but the failure of hunters to return bands is an obvious source of error where all kills cannot be checked directly in the field. The thorough study which Buss (1946) made in Dunn County, Wisconsin, indicated actual recoveries of about 20 percent for stocking on a county-wide basis, but sportsmen voluntarily reported only a quarter to half of the bands. In a 4-year Massachusetts investigation, Pushee (1948) found that voluntary returns were less than 10 percent, but hunters actually bagged 37 out of every 100 cocks released.

The many possible combinations of these variables undoubtedly explain the wide variation in results obtained in different studies. Old shooting preserve records in Michigan showed that the owners accounted for about 16 percent of the birds stocked (Tubbs 1946). Ohio returns on 18,761 cocks stocked in July and August were 8.3 per cent (Olds 1940). Indiana biologists followed the fate of 4,000-odd club-reared cock pheasants distributed through 35 counties in the summer of 1942. Hunter reports indicated that 6.4 out of every 100 were taken in the open season (Ginn 1947). From 1945 to 1947, experimental releases were made on carefully checked areas in Utah. Low (1948) reported that average recovery was "not higher than 7.5 percent . . .", although about half of the wild cocks were taken from the stocked land. Exceptionally high returns obtained in Massachusetts averaged 37 percent (Pushee 1948). New Jersey band reports represented 8 percent of the 16,219 cocks distributed on "open lands" in the summer of 1946 (McNamara and Kozicky 1949).

Elsewhere in this book, individual projects or state-wide stocking have been discussed. Although returns have been incomplete in many studies, it seems evident that large-scale releases of young birds in summer frequently yield poor results, and it is only under the most favorable conditions that as many as half of the cocks find their way into the hunter's bag. Since half of the releases usually are hens, this means that it takes 4 to 8 birds of both sexes to put one male in the hunting coat in the fall. In most states a pheasant poult at 8 or 10 weeks of age probably represents an investment of at least a dollar, in which case the cost of one hunting target successfully recovered would range from about 4 to 10 dollars. That this estimate is conservative is indicated by McKean's (1951) figures showing that in Oregon the cost per cock harvested from summer-released birds was $18.44. When only adult cocks were stocked in the fall, the cost of a bird in the bag was $4.16. Of course, turning out the hens at that season would double the figure.

When pen-raised poults go out to make their own way in the world, their domestic beginnings obviously place them at a disadvantage. In the weeding-out of the less fit, the game-farm pheasant is likely to be converted into soil fertility long before the gun is added to the hazards of his career. The matter of low survival has had great emphasis in the published literature, and it frequently is pointed out that sport so produced is a luxury item that the average hunting-license fee falls considerably short of covering. Consequently, much consideration has been given to methods of increasing returns from the hand-reared product.

One expedient that has received much publicity is the "gentle release" pen, such as the one used by Kozlik (1948) on Wisconsin public shooting areas. This wire enclosure was designed to hold 50 pheasants and provided such accommodations as a watering device, mash and grain feeders, and an electric fence to repel inquisitive predators. After the pen is opened at both ends, the birds can return to it to feed at will. Results were considered "highly satisfactory." In a test of similar release pens in Montana, Roby (1951) found no significant difference in the survival of birds under the "gentle," as opposed to the "violent," method of stocking. About 14 percent of cocks from each group were killed by hunters.

Most states have not considered the extra investment in special handling to be worth while. Pushee (1948a) reported that out of 32 states that stock pheasants, only 2 used release pens exclusively and 27 depended entirely on "violent" methods.

For increasing returns it probably is more practical to hold birds at the game farm and turn them out immediately before shooting; and it is evident that this process could be intensified down to the point where nearly all stocked pheasants were being recovered. Such a method increases costs, but the percentage of recovery can be improved spectacularly by stocking large numbers of targets on small areas and then shooting heavily. The efficiency of this kind of "stocking for the gun" could be raised still more by allowing hens to be shot on such areas or by sexing the birds at hatching time and rearing only cocks.

What appears to be the most intensive development of public shooting preserves has been carried out by the State of Illinois in the vicinity of Chicago. Joe B. Davidson (1948) described it at the Midwest Wildlife Conference in 1948:

"Whenever anyone attempts to handle seven or eight hundred city hunters daily on limited areas, a definite land management procedure must be placed in operation if hunters are to have normal hunting successes, and if safety precautions are to be successful. We have worked out a definite plan for the dispersion of hunters into small groups of ten or less. These groups are placed in hunting areas from one-fourth to one-half mile apart from other groups. This is done by means of a number of parking areas where each individual small group will be allotted a certain parking area from which to start. A careful inventory is made of pheasants on the area, and nightly releases of game farm cocks are made to supplement the wild populations. Careful records kept of kill on the grounds have shown that we have been able to harvest and recover sixty-nine per cent of all game birds released on the grounds. We think that this is probably a record for recovery rate of game farm birds, and is one of the things in favor of the operation of the grounds under the system that we are using."

If the stocking of hand-reared birds is to be a part of the pheasant program, some such system undoubtedly is the way to get the most for money spent. In areas of highly concentrated urban populations it is conceivable that hunting of this kind may be about all that can be furnished the city shooter with no rural connections. Where hunting pressures tend to be excessive, standards of sportsmanship usually are low and trespass frequent. Farmers commonly react to the invasion of the opening day in the only way by which they can get any kind of control—the use of no-hunting signs. This puts the problem of where to hunt directly up to the state.

It would be difficult, and pointless, to attempt to assign a definite dollar cost to this kind of pheasant production. Both real and "hidden" costs vary widely from one part of the country to another. But it seems beyond question that by artificial methods, involving the handling of birds on a one-by-one basis, any reasonable license fee can cover only a fraction of one harvested game unit. Many hunters must pool their funds to operate the system and a few of them have something to show for it. Of course, even those who go home empty handed have had the benefit of hunting, but this value is difficult to appraise in terms of game-farm targets—the unlucky Nimrods could have hunted wild birds with no worse result!

Some of the justification for annual restocking frequently is alleged to be repopulation of areas where pheasants have been overshot or "depleted." But search of the literature fails to reveal an instance where it was demonstrated clearly that the shooting of cocks has limited the numbers of a pheasant population. Declines occur in response to changes in the environment—and the suspicion is strong that regional depressions, such as the one in the forties, have a climatic origin. Stocking may produce birds for a few hunters to shoot, but that is all.

The questionnaires which Pushee (1948a) distributed indicated that in the late forties about one and a quarter million pheasants were being stocked by 32 states. Eighteen years earlier, a note in American Game stated that 31 states were stocking about 174,000 (Anon. 1930). This implies a huge increase in such activity, but the figures do not give the whole story.

During the years of pheasant prosperity in the late thirties and early forties, stocking programs were receiving progressively less emphasis. However, the onset of the pheasant depression in or about 1943 raised a public hue and cry for any and all expedients to "save the pheasant." In the stark period from 1945 to 1948 the game biologist was a failure, and few remembered the "grand job" he had been doing 5 years before. The specialist wasn't saying much. He saw little reason for shortened seasons, and he had little faith that more propagation had an important relationship to public hunting, but his voice didn't carry well and he prudently waited the situation out.

Coincident with the upgrade of the small-game cycle that regularly affects such species as grouse and rabbits, pheasants showed signs of recovery, and populations generally were fair to good by 1950. Faith in game farms again was on the wane. In many places across the nation there was evidence that the responsible leadership in large sportsmen's organizations was questioning heavy expenditures for propagation, and in a few states the issue came into the open. Michigan's commission eliminated pheasant rearing for public hunting and turned the game farm to experimental uses. New York made a substantial reduction in the program in favor of farm habitat development. Both publicly and privately, many administrators were looking forward to stepped-up information and education services which would permit the tapering off of propagation activities.

The future trend probably will be in this direction. If the pheasant, like the Hungarian partridge, cycles with native grouse, then about every 10 years in the North and East we can expect a resurgence of sentiment in favor of artificial pump priming during the period of slump. On the other hand, the certainty of such ups and downs eventually may invade public consciousness. We may see a policy more nearly like that which now (necessarily) obtains in regard to the grouse—we hunt them when they are up and wait for them when they are down.

Regulated Shooting Areas

Public attitudes, geographic differences, and other factors have resulted in widely varying state policies with regard to the management of regulated, stocked, shooting lands. Some states have no provision for such reservations and in others, what are coming to be known as "regulated shooting areas" are encouraged, particularly in the vicinity of large population centers.

In general, establishments devoted primarily to pheasant

propagation and regulated shooting must have special provision in the form of liberal seasons and bag limits, or, from the standpoint of the private investor, the operation is hardly worth while.

Many hunters have been inclined to regard such regulations as a special privilege for the minority of gunners who are sufficiently solvent to belong to a club or to patronize a commercial preserve. Of recent years, however, a more general attitude seems to be that a man should be permitted to buy what he can pay for, and regulated shooting areas show a steady increase in regions of large urban populations. This is notable especially in the vicinity of cities like New York and Chicago.

Laws governing regulated "preserves" ordinarily provide that the operator must buy a license, liberate substantially more birds than he shoots, and tag all birds harvested. Safeguards have been such that there is little, if any, drain on wild pheasant populations. The removal of land from public hunting is of little consequence because the total acreage in such areas always will be small, and near large cities; much of the land would not be open to the public anyway.

Commercial preserves in New York are marketing penreared pheasants before the gun at about $5 each, the price depending upon accessory services rendered, such as the furnishing of guides and dogs, and how many birds a customer is required to take. From the standpoint of the general public, the chief significance of these preserves is in absorbing some of the hunting pressure that otherwise would add to competition on open land. The spill-over of pheasants stocked has been cited as a public benefit in some localities.

Laws which safeguard the public interest and at the same time permit regulated shooting areas to be operated in heavily populated districts provide several benefits. These areas offer good pheasant hunting whether the land will grow pheasants or not. To the city businessman, a club or commercial shooting area provides a place where he can get a few hours of dog and gun handling when more extended trips to other kinds of hunting would be impossible.

The problem of regulating private shooting establishments has had lengthy consideration in many states, and of recent years, particular attention has been paid to the farmer and landowner, whose interest is a major point. Raising birds and servicing a limited number of hunters is an attractive sideline for many individuals, and the man who trains dogs can make an especially good thing of it. He will need guidance in the management of his threefold—pheasant-dog-hunter—biological problem, and this guidance now is being supplied by the Sporting Arms and Ammunition Manufacturers' Institute, 250 East 43rd Street, New York City 17. In 1954 the institute added a number of trained technicians to its field staff for this purpose.

Previously, John M. Olin, of the Olin Mathieson Chemical Corporation, and chairman of the Institute's Committee on Game, established Nilo Farms near Brighton, Illinois, as a demonstration appealing directly to farmers and landowners.

The program at Nilo Farms was developed by Charles H. Hopkins, Director of Conservation of Olin Mathieson and a foremost authority on regulated shooting, with the active interest and cooperation of such agencies as the Illinois Department of Conservation and the U.S. Soil Conservation Service.

Nilo Farms simulates a cooperative effort by two farmers who own a total of 522 acres of land. This pheasant shooting enterprise is superimposed upon a modern farming program employing the most up-to-date cropping and soil conservation practices. Although Nilo Kennels is a separate project on this area, it has been convenient to use dogs from the kennels in lieu of dogs which might be kept for business purposes by the operators of a regulated shooting area.

Land improvements at Nilo Farms have included wildlife plantings such as food patches, strips of sericea lespedeza or sweet clover located with reference to brushy ravines and fence lines, and here and there a clump of shrubs or trees. The most important features of the agricultural pattern are "holding strips" of sericea or other herbaceous cover placed at field borders, in and near draw-heads, and on "odd areas." Beyond these holding strips, in the direction of the hunt, there is bare ground, and the birds hold to the dogs in the vegetation rather than break into the open.

Experience shows that one man should not attempt to take care of more than four hunters. Hence, with two farmers officiating, the maximum is eight hunters in two parties. One man receives and registers guests, and the other releases pheasants in the coverts to be hunted. Then each guides a party routed to different sections of the area.

The Illinois law, under which this project operates, is considered to be a model of its kind and its main provisions are similar to statutes in effect in New York, Pennsylvania, New Jersey, and other states. The State of Illinois permits the establishment of regulated shooting areas ranging from 320 to 1280 acres, and "hand-reared exotic game birds" of either sex may be hunted from October 15 to February 15. The state does not impose a daily limit, but regulated shooting areas are permitted to harvest no more than 70 percent of the number of birds liberated. A seasonal license is required, and any bird removed from the licensed area must bear a sealed leg tag furnished by the state. Full records are kept and an annual report made to the Department of Conservation.

At Nilo Farms, hunts are planned and birds are released so that each hunter has an opportunity to shoot at six pheasants. The average take is four, and experience shows that this recovery ratio of 66 percent will not be exceeded under most conditions. Thus, the limit of 70 percent, provided for in Illinois and some other states, is complied with automatically.

In general, the stocking technique ranges all the way from mass releases on large areas down to individual releases, where the birds are placed in stragetic spots. At Nilo, when a bird is placed in the field, its head is tucked under a wing and it is "dizzied" lightly to prevent it from taking wing and perhaps flying off the area. It then is placed in the cover, where it recovers quickly, reacting normally when roused by a dog. Holding cover is so alternated with bare "stopping strips," however, that the birds show little inclination to race a four-footed animal over bare ground. To this extent the hunting is different, for it eliminates the long runs and wide flushing so characteristic of wild ringnecks late in the season.

Farmers operating this kind of a shooting area can obtain grown birds by purchase from commercial breeders, or they can utilize their own labor by starting with either half-grown poults or day-old chicks. Particularly where some member of the family has had poultry raising experience, farmers will find the rearing of chicks to be most profitable. Usually, shooting and guiding will be done on Saturdays and Sundays, and there are 36 week-end hunting days in the open season permitted by Illinois. A full complement of gunners on each of these days would require the stocking of 1728 birds, but it has been learned through experience that it is impossible to operate a regulated shooting area at full capacity at all times. Accordingly, 1500 pheasants of both sexes has been found to be reasonable stock for a two-man operation.

Costs have been well worked out. It has been found possible to produce a grown pheasant, ready to hunt, for about $2, excluding labor. This includes 35 to 40 cents as the price of a day-old chick, brooding and holding losses, amortization of equipment, advertising, and other operating expenses.

If a hunter bags four of the six pheasants released before the gun, and pays $5 per bird, the cost of his day in the field, with four pheasants as his "take home" bag, amounts to $20. In many areas over the country, only three birds are liberated before each gun, and the cost of a take-home bag of two pheasants is from $10 to $12.50. Obviously, many a hunter spends more than that to harvest a brace of wild birds, particularly in heavily populated regions where it is necessary to drive long distances and where results are less certain.

It is evident that "made" shooting of this kind has little relationship to our big job of using the amazing fecundity of natural stocks to mass-produce pheasants for free public hunting. But good hunting of wild birds is out of the question for the vast numbers of hunters who are afield in the immediate vicinity of large population centers. There, regulated shooting areas will provide an orderly kind of hunting for those able to pay for it, and it is a strong point in their favor that they are self-supporting and no tax on public funds.

Limiting Factors and the Habitat Problem

It is almost a basic axiom in game management that mass public benefits must depend upon the natural productivity of favorable habitats. Pheasants are not exceptional in this respect, and much of the present research effort is aimed at defining and curing environmental deficiencies. In dealing with the major range limitations of this species, it probably is convenient and realistic to divide the objective into two phases: (1) to extend the present distribution of pheasants, and (2) to increase numbers in poor habitats within the occupied range.

Molding the bird?

As has been suggested previously in this book, there is a good probability that the ringneck is confined to its present holdings in North America by climatic checks. To the North, the operation of climate is obvious, but to the south it is more subtle, and probably is expressed in low breeding productivity.

In this connection, the findings of Ralph E. Yeatter (1950) of the Illinois Natural History Survey are likely to have a place in the final assemblage of facts which will explain the pheasant-distribution enigma. Yeatter observed that late pheasant nests at the southern limit of range in Illinois largely failed to hatch and contained partially developed embryos. This contrasted with the ability of the bobwhite quail to nest successfully throughout almost all of the deep South.

Accordingly, he set up a controlled experiment in which paired lots of pheasant and quail eggs were subjected to pre-incubation temperatures ranging from 62° to 88°F., from 8:00 a.m. to 5:00 p.m. for 7 days. The pheasant eggs showed a progressive decline in hatchability from 75 percent at the lowest temperature to 42.1 per cent at the highest. In contrast, the hatchability of quail eggs declined from 76.2 percent to 68.4 percent—a drop of only 7.8 percent.

To compare the heat tolerance of midwestern and far-western birds, Yeatter obtained ringneck eggs from the California Division of Fish and Game, and with a comparable supply of Wisconsin pheasant eggs, exposed experimental batches of both to pre-hatching temperatures from 62° to 88°F. He found that California eggs had a higher hatching success than Wisconsin eggs following exposure to high temperatures.

This suggests that speciation—the steady, natural selection of birds most fit to survive, and the culling out of those least fit— is showing its effect under the extreme California conditions. There is no doubt that this is taking place, not only there but elsewhere, and the result will be a progressive, slow improvement of pheasant stocks. Gradually, local strains will develop which are better suited to local conditions.

Of course, this has taken place widely in Asia, and the question sometimes arises whether the process could be speeded by deliberate selection in hand-reared stocks. To do so would require specific knowledge of adaptations that mean survival in various kinds of marginal range. There is little of such information available now, and the genetics of such characteristics are largely unknown. Of course, the production of a bird with "hybrid vigor" for stocking before the gun is a different problem, and one with its own complexities.

A major difficulty in any selection program with captive birds is the relatively small numbers that can be handled. It should be realized that on the edge of the pheasant range population pressure tends, year after year, to force birds into country unsuited to them. In each annual turnover there is a drastic regimen of selection in which the breeders of the next generation are chosen from a large number of candidates. This weeding out is taking place with complete realism and on a scale far beyond anything we could hope to achieve with captive birds. Conceivably, work with new strains could bring greater genetic variability to these border populations. Survival characters now absent, and even beyond our recognition, could make possible the occupation of new territory.

This is a field for future research, but it is of more immediate concern to determine key limitations in occupied range and find practical ways to improve habitats. Food and cover are obvious necessities, and problems of quantity, quality, and arrangement are not simple as they apply to the pheasant.

The food enigma

Within the many and variable regional ranges of this bird, it seems to be universally true that high pheasant densities never are reached on poor soils. Fertility is a common denominator among good habitats, even though conditions developing as a result of fertility may be widely different from Sacramento, California, to Saginaw, Michigan. It takes a prosperous agriculture to grow large numbers of ringnecks, and this almost always means an abundant food supply in the form of waste grain and weed seeds. From that we might conclude that a superabundance of food is a pheasant requirement—and maybe it is. But if so, it's somewhat inconsistent that investigators have not been able to demonstrate food shortage and privation in habitats that support only a few pheasants.

The opposite is the case, since the ringneck is notable in being able to survive on a minimum of food. When snow lies deep over northern states, and protruding tops of ragweed and lambsquarters have been stripped of their tiny but nutritious fruits, the hardy bird usually finds a next-best somewhere. If, a mile away, a farmer spreads manure from the barn or poultry house, a hundred pheasants may find it. Sometimes, lowland thickets will be strewn with gobs of balled-up burdock, from which these birds have been picking the seeds. It requires nearly a month to starve a captive ringneck in winter (Throckmorton 1952). In a Michigan experiment, the birds not only lived but did a good job of maintaining weight for 27 days on nothing but the hips of multiflora rose (Johnson 1951), and Oregon studies showed that a pheasant could live for three months in winter on "greens" alone (Uhlig 1948).

PLATE LXXX.—Above. Winter feeding seldom will be involved in state efforts to put more game in the bag but it may serve private purposes (D. L. Batcheler, Penna. Game Comm.). *Below*. Specifications for cover management must be determined locally, (R. M. Cady, Penna. Game Comm.).

Contrary to what many people assumed twenty years ago, pheasants rarely starve, although occasionally starvation does occur under prolonged conditions of deep snow on the northern plains (Nelson and Janson 1949). Actual starvation probably is not a criterion by which to judge food scarcity, and food quality may be as important as quantity.

Much more needs to be known about the relationship of minerals and food quality to the breeding and survival of pheasants, and nutrition research is progressing to that end. In the meantime we probably are less concerned about such obvious things as winter food supplies than we were twenty years ago. We have learned to be especially skeptical of the large-scale expenditure of public funds for winter feeding or annual foodpatch programs. These measures have certain types of usefulness, such as holding birds on small, private areas, but they seldom pay off sufficiently to be recommended in state efforts to put more birds in the game bag.

Present knowledge of the ringneck's dependence on fertile soils has application in a consideration of what we are to expect of public game areas. Many states in the East are buying large tracts of submarginal land for public hunting and other types of outdoor recreation. For the most part these are areas where farming has failed, and the ringneck fails there also. Here and there, where there are farms, or on the edges adjoining agricultural soils, a few pheasants will be found, but there is no reason to suppose that it ever will pay to work over these forest habitats and make them attactive to the pheasant hunter. Limited food patch plantings haven't done the job, and it appears to be sensible management to zone our hunting and decide that lands submarginal for agriculture are a good place to grow grouse, rabbits, squirrels, and deer—but not pheasants.

Weather and cover

It is well known that climatic extremes are one of the most critical environmental factors endured by pheasants and other game birds. From year to year, weather conditions seem to be the most obvious and uncontrollable determinant of habitat carrying capacity.

In particular, many workers have been impressed by the importance of the breeding season in the annual cycle of numbers. Whether hunting is to be good or poor is decided at that time of year, and a successful season is largely one of favorable weather. During the great bird depression of the forties, there evidently was a persistent trend toward cold, wet, spring weather in much of the East (Allen 1947, Carlson 1946, Ginn 1948, Perry 1946), and there were indications of something similar in parts of the West (Einarsen 1946). The reports gathered by Kimball (1948) and Wandell (1949) commonly referred to impaired reproduction and suggestive extremes of tempertaure and precipitation.

Exceptionally wet, or wet and cold, weather can have an unfavorable effect in the flooding of nests and destruction of broods. But curiously enough, rains can be beneficial if they come at the strategic time to delay hay cutting until the first hatch is off. In the interaction of two such variables as temperature and precipitation, there is an almost endless variety of conditions that can occur at different times through the spring and from one local area to another. We have no reliable way to measure the precise effect on pheasants, but in eastern United States it seems to be true that wet spring seasons, particularly when temperatures are low, tend to be unfavorable breeding years for the ringneck.

It is somewhat paradoxical that in the semi-arid West, it is the "wet" breeding seasons that produce maximum crops of birds. Of course, such terms as wet, dry, warm, or cold have different meanings in different parts of the country; but we undoubtedly have a gradation of conditions in which years characterized as wet are favorable on the western extreme of the range and unfavorable on the eastern extreme. This should give us, somewhere, a transition zone where weather effects are highly variable and difficult to pin down. It's a fair estimate that this zone is roughly the prairie region, and the situation probably accounts for widely differing observations and opinions on the effects of breeding-season weather.

A different kind of climatic extreme is clear-cut on the prairies. Blizzards and deep, persistent snows sometimes take heavy toll of wintering birds (Miller 1948, Nelson and Janson 1949). As a result of two hard winters in 1948-50, pheasants in north-central South Dakota declined about 80 percent.

PLATE LXXXI.—Over most of the range, protection of hens is a valuable management measure (E. P. Haddon, Fish and Wildlife Service).

Obviously, shelter in the form of well distributed thickets is a prime need in such habitats.

Agricultural areas of light rainfall, formerly characterized by a grassland climax, frequently offer plenty of food and most other attributes of good pheasant range. The big deficiency is woody vegetation, and farming trends are toward removal of what cover there is. In the decade of the forties, wheat subsidies placed a premium on the yield of every square yard of soil, and many a plains shelterbelt, planted during the dry thirties at public expense, was removed to make way for an interval of profit taking in grain. In the next period of drought there will be another job to do.

In the palouse region of Washington, what little woody cover remains among the miles of wheat and fallow is being torn out of the stream bottoms to provide a modicum more of pasture. In these loessal hills, come hunting season, pheasants flock up in the middle of extensive fields of broken ground, where they can see a hunter topping the rise half a mile away. These are sage grouse tactics, and they are necessary, for on the denuded land there is no place to hide.

As described in Chapter 2, it is this bare-earth trend that state habitat improvement programs are attempting to counter by stabilizing critical slopes, ditchbanks, and gullies with good wildlife cover. On the prairies (Kimball 1950), a systematic restoration of cover is the best answer to the blizzard problem. These are extreme conditions and the deficiencies are evident.

In pheasant ranges lying east of Lake Michigan, the problem is more difficult. These are regions of forest climax, and the natural succession produces shrubs, thickets, and woodlots wherever it is allowed to progress. The best agricultural lands frequently are "clean farmed" to an utterly barren condition; yet such areas may produce pheasants in abundance where there are adjacent stream bottoms, marshes, or brushy hills in which birds can flock up and winter. It is the ringneck's habit of moving a mile or more, as necessary, and flocking in winter cover that complicates the definition of minimum requirements.

In the East, winter storms seldom have the lethal ferocity of a prairie blizzard, and the problem of winter shelter for pheasants is less clear and urgent than on the plains. The best generalization is that the extent and nature of cover improvement for the ringneck must be decided by local studies.

Actually, habitat improvement for pheasants should not be considered out of the context of the entire small-game management program. We know that the durable ringneck can live with less woody cover than either the quail or rabbit, and plantings needed to fill out a given habitat will depend on what was there in the beginning. In point of people served, the rabbit is the most important small-game animal in the nation, and well distributed cover is its major need. If we do a reasonable job of rabbit management wherever possible in our farmland, we shall have met pheasant standards with plenty of margin to spare.

In practice, this is the way it is working out. Most of the northern states have cooperative habitat restoration programs aimed at increasing all wildlife on farmland. They do not need to justify every planting in terms of ringneck requirements, even though they know that pheasants will be benefited by much of the work.

The ecology of the pheasant is particularly complicated in its more humid ranges, and habitat problems are a real challenge to the field man. But good research is in progress, and each year adds its bit of new knowledge.

Harvest Time

At present, a realistic handling of the hunting season is perhaps the most constructive management that can be applied to the pheasant. Fortunately, information is available on which to build sound policies of this kind.

Time was when it was considered possible to shoot cock pheasants so heavily that in spring hens would be laying infertile eggs. There is frequent concern of sportsmen on this score, and states may be under pressure to stock cock birds because locally they have been "shot out." When hatches were poor in the early forties, California hunters were reporting harems of 15 to 20 hens and a shortage of breeding males. But state biologists who made roadside counts found an average of 3 hens per cock, and of 102 eggs examined, only one was infertile (Twining 1946). In such cases, investigation consistently shows that enough males remain for breeding even after the most intensive shooting. There appears to be no authentic instance in support of the myth of spinster hens and infertile eggs.

In Chapter 1, figures were quoted indicating that hen-cock ratios as divergent as 10:1 are satisfactorily productive, and that for practical purposes, there is no such thing as an "unfavorable" sex ratio. Work during the early forties showed that in Michigan's 22-day season it was impossible to shoot out cock pheasants by any gun pressure that could be attracted by good hunting on open land. In pheasant range of average quality, heavy hunting ordinarily accounted for about 75 percent of the cocks. In the state's best range, as many as 90 percent of the cocks would be taken (Allen 1947, Shick 1952).

This implies that in good range, not only will there be more pheasants present, but hunters can shoot a higher proportion of the cocks than they will be able to take in poor range. And consequently, that would leave more divergent winter sex ratios in the better range. It evidently works out that way:

Dale (1951, 1952) used figures published by Buss (1946) to show that in Wisconsin's six most productive pheasant counties the sex ratio averaged one cock per 8.99 hens. In three other groups of counties, in descending order of productivity for pheasants, the number of hens per cock was 3.85, 3.23, and 2.73, respectively. Where hens are protected, the winter sex ratio is a good measure of the extent to which male pheasants are being cropped in the hunting season.

It appears that the cover pattern of a given piece of land has a fairly consistent "carrying capacity" for cock pheasants in the face of heavy shooting. There is a point of diminishing returns beyond which further hunting is largely unrewarded. It is a phenomenon similar to Errington's (1945) "threshold of security," which represented a population level within which quail were relatively free from predation.

At Michigan's Rose Lake Wildlife Experiment Station, harvest figures showed that 125 gun-hours of hunting per hundred acres during the open season would take nearly as many pheasants from an average fall population as 250 gun-hours of shooting. Cock pheasants appeared to react with increased wariness directly as hunting pressure increased. The result was that about 70 percent of the season's kill was taken the first week, 20 percent the second, and only 10 percent in the last 8 days. As returns from hunting declined, the efforts of hunters also tapered off—percentages for the three weeks averaging about 50, 30, and 20 percent respectively. High pheasant populations attracted heavy hunting, and few pheasants meant few hunters (Allen 1942, 1947).

A problem faced by the Michigan Game Division in the mid-forties, when pheasants went down, probably will recur many times. Sportsmen were calling for a shortened season to prevent overshooting of the state's diminished stock of birds.

But it was evident that (1) with fewer pheasants on the ground on opening day, a lower percentage than normal would be shot, and (2) there would be no shortage of cocks for breeding. State biologists pointed out that even in the reduced population there undoubtedly were surplus cocks, and that by cutting a week off the season only about 10 percent of the males would be saved.

It is becoming increasingly clear that under most conditions hunting of cock pheasants is largely self-regulatory. Lauckhart (1946) summed up the situation in stating that "Game technicians generally agree that cock pheasants virtually cannot be overhunted in suitable habitat if illegal kill is held to a minimum."

The matter of illegal kill is not to be ignored. When pheasant populations were down, the reasoning behind many a shortened season (including Michigan's) was the supposition that with fewer cocks available, unscrupulous hunters might take it out on the hens. It may be most practical to meet this problem with a shortened season, although that reduces legitimate hunting for cocks, and hen-shooting can be regarded largely as an education and law-enforcement problem.

It almost goes without saying that preservation of hens probably is our most significant measure in producing pheasants—up to a certain point. One expression of carrying capacity in nearly all habitats will be the number of young birds that can

PLATE LXXXII.—Dog's Life. (D. L. Allen).

be produced on an area in a favorable breeding season. A given number of hens will be required to achieve this maximum production, and hens over and above that number are likely to be largely ineffective. Management of the harvest should assure that the new pheasant crop will not be limited by a shortage of breeding hens. But it probably is true that, where only cocks are shot, nearly all topgrade ranges are supporting an excess of hens that cannot be effective as breeders.

A recognition of this was behind limited hen shooting in South Dakota in the early forties and provisions for the cropping of females on Pelee Island. Large numbers of pheasants also may become a liability to crop-raising farmers; in which case the controlled harvesting of both sexes is a practical way of giving farmers reasonable protection and making use of the undesirable surplus. Where a bird population is held in this way at a level below carrying capacity, it may be just as productive for the hunter as a larger population from which only cocks are shot.

It is true of pheasants, as with other species, that any number of breeders approaching average for an area has the reproductive capacity to overstock the range. Through the year, this excess population is whittled away by environmental shortcomings that tend to increase from summer to winter to spring.

There must be some lag in these adjustments, and in terms of maximum security and comfort there probably are too many animals in most habitats at most times. We can visualize this situation as one of "population pressure," and it undoubtedly is what causes pheasants (or other species) to spread into all suitable range and to stock habitats up to that level where security falls off and mortality speeds up.

This is an important part of the modern concept of population dynamics; and if it is sound, then we can assume that nearly every area in occupied range is supporting about all the pheasants possible under existing conditions—including, of course, such variables as seasonal weather.

In terms of present knowledge, that appears to be the situation, and it probably explains why refuges for the most part, have been ineffective as a means of producing more pheasants. If shooting is not a limitation to the population, then protecting birds from the hunter during 3 or 4 weeks in the fall will not mean a higher density outside the closed area next year.

The chief significance of pheasant sanctuaries is in preventing the harvest of cocks that serve no useful purpose anyway. They are not necessary to a high breeding productivity and hence could easily be spared to swell the annual bag. It is true that in heavily shot-over territory, birds will collect on closed areas, and if refuges are provided with large food supplies such as fields of standing corn, concentrations can be held all winter.

Two thousand or more birds to the square mile (such as could be found in the late thirties on Michigan's Todd Sanctuary) make an impressive spectacle on winter snow, but it is likely that such concentrations are more vulnerable to certain types of losses (*i.e.* predation) than would be the case if they were allowed to scatter naturally. In spring the birds do scatter to breeding areas. Of course, the holding of such winter aggregations is largely a function of food supply rather than refuge signs.

Refuges do not overrun surrounding land with birds because, as we have seen, that land already is carrying all the pheasants it can support. The main purpose of unshot areas has been to produce more birds to hunt, and they have failed because we were treating a deficiency (over-shooting) that did not exist.

In common with the shortened season, pheasant refuges conceivably might be established to prevent the excessive illegal kill of hens. But this value too, is an elusive one when analyzed:

In assaying the state-wide effect of a pheasant refuge system, Dale (1951) showed how the ledger of pheasant production might tally out at the end of a season: "Since the most ambitious refuge programs seldom provide for more than 1 or 2 percent of the land in refuge, and many such areas do not result in any heavy concentration of pheasants, only a small percentage of pheasants on a state-wide basis will be affected by the program. For example, if 10 percent of the pheasants of a state were to be on refuges for the entire hunting season, and thus receive the maximum possible protection, and if the illegal hen kill off the refuges be estimated at 20 percent of the population, then the net saving of hens that could be credited to the refuge system would be 10 percent of 20 percent, or 2 percent of the state's hen population.

"If, under the same conditions, the legal kill of cocks be 70 percent, then the refuge system would result in reducing the legal kill by 10 percent of 70 percent, or 7 percent. Since these surplus cocks would be unnecessary for the production of the next year's crop they can be considered as 'drones,' competing for living space and food, and resulting in a net loss of a harvestable resource."

There may be good and valid reasons for closing many areas to shooting, but the biological function of increasing the game crop does not seem to be one of them.

Spring and summer surveys are becoming a routine part of wildlife management. It is good business for any agency concerned with such things to have an appraisal of the size of the game crop to be taken, and for some species under some conditions regulations will depend upon such knowledge.

For pheasants, however, it appears that proper regulations will develop as a matter of year-after-year experience and that in a year when the crop failed, hunting as usual would not constitute any particular danger to the resource. When the crop is short, the most significant result is that hunters have little to show for their efforts. Under heavy hunting, of course, a reduced daily limit would help distribute the "easy" kill of the opening day among more gunners. After that it would mean little.

It appears that the most valuable pheasant survey for regulatory purposes is likely to be the winter sex ratio count. As mentioned previously, unless there is some reason to suspect an excessive mortality of hens during the hunting season, the winter sex ratio usually will reflect the extent of harvest of cocks. If sex ratios indicate less than four hens per cock, the chances are good that a lengthening of the season or an increase in bag limit would be permissible. This might or might not be practicable, since pheasant regulations frequently must agree with laws on other species in order to expedite enforcement.

It should be recognized that the taking of a sex ratio count is an extremely critical job in many areas owing to an annoying and unpredictable habit of this species. At almost any time of year except the breeding season, the sexes may flock differentially. Technicians fully acquainted with local range and bird habits are the ones to get a reliable sex ratio, and sometimes even they will not back their figures too far.

From the above, it appears that getting the available surplus of cocks into the game bag is a much greater problem than preventing hunters from killing too many. Troubles resulting from large areas of posted land add to natural difficulties in many regions, and methods of increasing hunter access have been discussed in the regional accounts.

Facts Wanted

The Agricultural Yearbook for 1909 contained a discussion of the apparent possibilities in two species of exotic game birds that were being introduced into the Western Hemisphere. It is evident that some government authorities took a dim view of the proceedings at that time: "For more than twenty years determined and painstaking efforts have been made to establish these pheasants in America; but with the exception of a few regions, such as the Willamette Valley in Oregon, several circumscribed localities in Washington and British Columbia, the Genessee Valley in New York, and possibly one or two other places it is safe to say that the pheasants surviving in the United States and Canada not in private preserves have cost (on the basis of dividing all expenses of the experiments by the number of living birds) not less than $50 apiece. Furthermore, the few that are left will probably soon disappear if the stock is not replenished by fresh liberations.

"The unsatisfactory results of these ventures, together with one or two bad seasons for two of our principal native game birds, the bobwhite and the ruffed grouse, have turned attention to the European partridge; and this interest has been intensified by the inability of Northern States to procure bobwhites for restocking depleted covers, owing to the recent adoption of stringent nonexport restrictions by Southern States, the source of former supplies. But the failures of the past make it wise to consider carefully whether the partridge is better suited for acclimatization than were its predecessors in favor."

As it turned out, importations of the pheasant and Hungarian partridge were among those few introductions of exotic species that were profitable. Especially in the case of the pheasant, we struck it rich in finding a game species to fit an environment that, like the bird itself, was not native to the continent.

The foregoing quotation may have been a reasonable appraisal in 1909, and it illustrates the pitfalls that beset any attempt to look very far into the future. But our conservation record is a history of continuing failure to look ahead, and it is well to do so in spite of obvious limitations.

It seems evident that we are narrowing down the field of unknowns and that we must continue the process as rapidly as possible. As with other wildlife problems, the shortest way to more efficient management would be to put more of our total effort into high-quality research now. The federal aid program has benefited pheasant research and management tremendously, but it should be kept in mind that all the funds going into "surveys and investigations" should not be considered as part of the research account. The greatest present need is to expand basic work in the fields of nutrition, bioclimatics, and physiology. What happens during the breeding season in various range types and how year-to-year variations occur are questions on which progress should be speeded up. Seasonal population changes are better understood now than ever before, thanks to work of the past decade, but the excellent techniques developed could well be applied more widely. Frequently it is the differences between regions that make interpretation possible.

A comparison of wildlife research with basic inquiry in other scientific fields reveals an impressive difference. The greater part of our investigational work is being done by young men, recently out of school, who get by for a time at the low salaries offered. As their economic need increases, they move into other types of employment and their experience is lost to research.

We have reached the point in pheasant studies where probing into the unknown requires long-term attention by teams of well-trained and experienced specialists. If we could bring to bear on the pheasant the kind of cooperation and scientific talent now employed in hundreds of medical and other laboratories across the country, important barriers probably could be broken. To bring this about it would be necessary in a few strategic places to put the same kind of money into research that we have been willing to pour into our game farms in the past. It is reasonable to expect that the results would be more beneficial to the average hunter.

Managing pheasants in this country might be easier if we could study the various races on their native Asian ranges. And in addition to facts that could be learned, there are strains of birds that offer possibilities. From the Caucasus to Japan there are 42 recognized subspecies of *Phasianus colchicus*. As has been suggested elsewhere, it is possible that an infusion of blood from some of these might serve to extend ranges in this country—especially in the humid Southeast.

In a world at peace, we could recommend things that are not possible at present. The time may come when we can do further intelligent experimenting with other subspecies of pheasants. But it should be kept in mind that the Chinese ringneck, the basic stock in North America, undoubtedly is the best of the original races for our purpose. In its native land it was distributed more widely than any other in man-dominated habitats. Many strains have been tried in North America but disappeared or were submerged in the successful ringneck characters.

Certainly we must recognize that this is no field for the kind of irresponsible boondoggling that has characterized previous experience with exotics. The introduction of disease and inferior stocks always is a possibility. Further importations should be undertaken only as part of a carefully planned and thoroughly scientific program.

Although we should not eliminate the possibility of new pheasants for new ranges, it appears that for the present the ringneck has sought its level in North America and found the ranges where it is to be a part of the fauna from now on. In such case, it is in the same position as many native game animals.

We recognize the limitations in putting ruffed grouse or prairie chickens in everyone's backyard, and we appreciate that in certain ranges it would be too expensive even to increase existing stocks. Sooner or later, we shall grant that these same premises must apply to the ringneck. The best management investment on nearly any piece of land will be aimed at the species to which that area is adapted naturally and which can be produced there most economically. Nothing is to be accomplished by the sheer weight of expenditure.

There is no hazard in asserting that 50 years hence biologists will understand the nature and requirements of the ringneck far better than they do now. But likely enough, hunters still will be going where the birds are and finding them on the same kind of land. As today, the pheasant crop will be a function of basic factors—climate, soil, vegetation, and agricultural pattern.

LITERATURE CITED

This bibliography includes only references cited in the text. For a more complete listing of works on the pheasant, see *Wildlife Abstracts,* 1935-51, U. S. Fish and Wildlife Service, 1954, compiled by Neil Hotchkiss. The same agency publishes *Wildlife Review,* which contains a relatively complete listing of current references on the pheasant and other game species.

Albrecht, William A.
  1944 Soil fertility and wildlife—cause and effect.
        9th N. Amer. Wildl. Conf. Trans., 19-28.
  1946 The soil as the basis of wildlife management.
        8th Midwest Wildl. Conf. (mimeo), 8 pp.
Albrecht, William A. and G. E. Smith
  1941 Biological assays of soil fertility.
        Soil Sci. Soc. Amer. Proc. 6:252-258.
Allen, Durward L.
  1938 Some observations on fall and winter food patches for birds in
        southern Michigan.
        Wilson Bul. 50 (1):42-46.
  1942 That season limit.
        Michigan Cons. 11 (2):4-5.
  1942a A pheasant inventory method based on kill records and sex ratios.
        7th N. Amer. Wildl. Conf. Trans., 329-352.
  1946 What happened to the pheasant?
        Michigan Cons. 15 (1):6-8.
  1947 Hunting as a limitation to Michigan pheasants.
        Jour. Wildl. Mgt. 11 (3):232-243.
  1950 Problems and needs in pheasant research.
        Jour. Wildl. Mgt. 14 (2):105-114.
Alpaugh, George N.
  1951 Farm game in the State of New Jersey.
        N. E. Fish and Wildl. Conf. Proc. (mimeo), 7 pp.
Anon
  1930 States liberate much game.
        Amer. Game 19 (4):61.
  1941 Fifty million pheasants in South Dakota.
        South Dakota Dept. Game & Fish, 90 pp.
Arnold, David A.
  1951 The relationship between ring-necked pheasant and red fox popu-
        lation trends.
        Michigan Acad. Sci. Papers, 37 (part 2):121-127.
Bach, Roy N.
  1944 Population fluctuations of the North Dakota pheasant, 1938-43.
        North Dakota Outdoors 6 (7):8-9.

Ball, Chester C., Norman P. Knott and J. Burton Lauckhart
    1941 Upland game bird study, Whitman Co., Washington, 1940.
          Washington Dept. Game Biol. Bul. 6.

Barnes, William B.
    1946 The sportsman's questionnaire method of estimating the game kill
          in Indiana.
          11th N. Amer. Wildl. Conf. Trans., 339-348.
    1947 Is artificial propagation the answer?
          Outdoor Indiana 14 (2):8-10.

Baskett, Thomas S.
    1947 Nesting and production of the ring-necked pheasant in north-
          central Iowa.
          Ecol. Mon. 17 (1):1-30.

Baumgras, Philip S.
    1943 Winter food productivity of agricultural land for seed-eating birds
          and mammals.
          Jour. Wildl. Mgt. 7 (1):13-18.

Beebe, William
    1926 Pheasants, their lives and homes.
          Doubleday, Doran, Garden City, N. Y. 2 vol.

Belknap, Jeremy
    1793 The history of New Hampshire.
          Ed. 1812, Vol. 3.

Bellrose, Frank C. and Elizabeth B. Chase
    1950 Population losses in the mallard, black duck, and blue-winged teal.
          Illinois Nat. Hist. Survey, Biol. Notes 22, 27 pp.

Bennett, Logan J.
    1936 The ring-necked pheasant as a nesting parasite of other game birds.
          Iowa State Coll. Jour. Sci. 10 (4):373-375.
    1945 The pheasant in Pennsylvania and New Jersey (in McAtee, W. L.,
          The ring-necked pheasant and its management in North America).
          Amer. Wildl. Inst., 11-31.

Bennett, Logan J. and George O. Hendrickson
    1938 Censusing the ringneck pheasant in Iowa.
          3d N. Amer. Wildl. Conf. Trans., 720-723.

Bennitt, Rudolf and Harold V. Terrill
    1940 Possible temperature factors in north central pheasant distribution.
          5th N. Amer. Wildl. Conf. Trans., 428-432.

Benson, Dirck
    1948 Pheasant management research.
          New York Cons. Dept., PR Quart. Rept. 26-R (mimeo), April.
    1948a Pheasant management research.
          New York Cons. Dept., PR Quart. Rept. 26-R (mimeo), October.

Bergeson, William R.
    1949 State-wide pheasant checking station data.
          Montana Dept. Fish & Game, Unpub. Rept.

Bissonette, Thomas Hume
    1938 Experimental control of sexual photo-periodicity in animals and
          possible applications to wildlife management.
          Jour. Wildl. Mgt. 2 (3):104-118.

Blouch, Ralph I. and L. L. Eberhardt
    1953 Changes in pheasant populations and land use on the Prairie Farm.
        15th Midwest Wildl. Conf. (mimeo), 8 pp.
    1953a Some hatching curves from different areas of Michigan's pheasant
        range.
        Jour. Wildl. Mgt. 17 (4):477-482.

Boeker, Harold M.
    1951 Farmer-sportsmen relationships and small-game trends on farms in
        northern Colorado.
        Colorado Coop. Wildl. Research Unit (Unpub. Rept.)

Brodell, Albert P. and Joseph A. Ewing
    1948 Use of tractor power, animal power and hand methods in crop
        production.
        U. S. Dept. Agr., Bur. Agr. Econ., Rept. FM 69, 32 pp.

Brown, E. Kliess
    1948 More pheasants from Federal Aid.
        Colorado Cons. Comments 10 (8):3-4.

Browne, C. A.
    1938 Some relationships of soil to plant and animal nutrition—the major
        elements.
        U. S. Dept. Agr. Yearbook, 777-806.

Bump, Gardiner
    1937 Game scarcity—some causes and cures.
        Amer. Wildl. 26 (4):51-52, 58-61, 64.
    1940 The introduction and transplantation of game birds and mammals
        into the State of New York.
        5th N. Amer. Wildl. Conf. Trans., 409-420.

Bump, Gardiner, Robert W. Darrow, Frank C. Edminster, and Walter F. Crissey
    1947 The ruffed grouse.
        New York State Cons. Dept., 915 pp.

Buss, Irven O.
    1946 Wisconsin pheasant populations.
        Wisconsin Cons. Dept. Publ. 326, A-46, 184 pp.

Buss, Irven O., Roland K. Meyer and Cyril Kabat
    1951 Wisconsin pheasant reproduction studies based on ovulated follicle
        technique.
        Jour. Wildl. Mgt. 15 (1):32-46.

Buss, Irven O. and Carl V. Swanson
    1950 Some effects of weather on pheasant reproduction in southeastern
        Washington.
        15th N. Amer. Wildl. Conf. Trans., 364-378.

Cahn, A. R.
    1938 A climographic analysis of the problem of introducing three exotic
        game birds into the Tennessee Valley and vicinity.
        3d N. Amer. Wildl. Conf. Trans., 807-817.

Carlson, C. Edward
    1946 Status of pheasants, 1946.
        Conservation Volunteer 9 (54):30-33.

Caulk, Elizabeth T.
    1951 An economic use for the woods edge.
        N. E. Fish and Wildl. Conf. Proc. (mimeo), 6 pp.

Clarke, C. H. D.
    1947 Pelee Island pheasant shoot.
        Sylva. 3 (4):45-55.
Clarke, C. H. D. and R. Braffette
    1946 Ring-necked pheasant investigations in Ontario 1946.
        Ontario Dept. Lands and Forests (mimeo).
Craighead, Frank C., Jr. and John J. Craighead
    1950 The ecology of raptor predation.
        15th N. Amer. Wildl. Conf. Trans., 209-222.
Crawford, Bill T.
    1950 Some specific relationships between soils and wildlife.
        Jour. Wildl. Mgt. 14 (2)115-123.
Dale, Fred H.
    1951 The refuge in pheasant management.
        Jour. Wildl. Mgt. 15 (4):337-346.
    1952 Sex ratios in pheasant research and management.
        Jour. Wildl. Mgt. 16 (2):156-163.
    1954 Influence of calcium on the distribution of the pheasant in North
        America.
        19th N. Amer. Wildl. Conf. Trans., 316-323.
    1955 The role of calcium in reproduction of the ringneck pheasant.
        Jour. Wildl. Mgt. 19 (3):325-331.
Dalke, Paul D.
    1945 Food habits of adult pheasants (in McAtee, W. L., *The ring-necked
        pheasant and its management in North America*).
        Amer. Wildl. Inst., 139-142.
Davidson, Joe B.
    1948 Pheasant hunting in Illinois on a put and take basis.
        10th Midwest Wildl. Conf. (mimeo), 4 pp.
Dawson, William L.
    1903 The birds of Ohio.
        Wheaton Publ. Co., Columbus, Ohio, 2 vol.
Delacour, Jean
    1945 Classification and distribution of the game, or true, pheasants (in
        McAtee, W. L., *The ring-necked pheasant and its management in
        North America*).
        Amer. Wildl. Inst., 6-10.
Denney, Arthur H.
    1944 Wildlife relationships to soil types.
        9th N. Amer. Wildl. Conf. Trans., 316-323.
Dorr, Donald E.
    1951 Maine pheasant investigation.
        Maine Dept. Inland Fisheries and Game, Game Div. Bul. 2, 47 pp.
Dustman, Eugene H.
    1949 Nesting and production of the ring-necked pheasant in northwestern
        Ohio following a population decline.
        Ohio State Univ., Unpub. Thesis, 305 pp.
    1950 Pre-hunting season wildlife survey in northwestern Ohio, August.
        Ohio Coop. Wildl. Research Unit, Release 204 (mimeo), 9 pp.
    1950a Effects of alfalfa mill cutting on pheasants and other wildlife in
        Wood County, Ohio, 1946-1947.
        Jour. Wildl. Mgt. 14 (2):225-234.

Einarsen, Arthur S.
 1942 Specific results from ring-necked pheasant studies in the Pacific northwest.
 7th N. Amer. Wildl. Conf. Trans., 130-138.
 1945 Some factors affecting ring-necked pheasant population density.
 Murrelet 26 (1):3-9; 26 (3):39-44.
 1945a The pheasant in the Pacific Northwest (in McAtee, W. L., *The ring-necked pheasant and its management in North America*).
 Wildl. Mgt. Inst., 254-274.
 1946 What about pheasants?
 Oregon State Game Comm. Bul. 1 (6):1, 5, 7.
 1950 The fourth annual field day of the Oregon Cooperative Wildlife Research Unit.
 Oregon Coop. Wildl. Research Unit (mimeo), 5 pp.

Ecklund, Carl R.
 1942 Ecological and mortality factors affecting the nesting of the Chinese pheasant in the Willamette Valley, Oregon.
 Jour. Wildl. Mgt. 6 (3):225-230.

Erickson, Arnold B., David B. Vesall, C. Edward Carlson and Clair T. Rollings.
 1951 Minnesota's most important game bird—the pheasant.
 Flicker 23 (3):23-49.

Errington, Paul L.
 1936 Differences in nutritive values of winter game foods.
 1st N. Amer. Wildl. Conf. Proc., 356-360.
 1937 Food habits of Iowa red foxes during a drought summer.
 Ecol. 18 (1):53-61.
 1939 The comparative ability of the bob-white and ring-necked pheasant to withstand cold and hunger.
 Wilson Bul. 51 (1):22-37.
 1945 Some contributions of a fifteen-year local study of the northern bobwhite to a knowledge of population phenomena.
 Ecol. Mon. 15:1-34.
 1946 Predation and vertebrate populations.
 Quart. Rev. Biol. 21 (2):144-177.

Errington, Paul L. and Frederick N. Hamerstrom, Jr.
 1937 The evaluation of nesting losses and juvenile mortality of the ring-necked pheasant.
 Jour. Wildl. Mgt. 1 (1-2):3-20.

Faber, Lester A.
 1946 The history of stocking and management of the ring-necked pheasant in the State of Iowa.
 Iowa Cons. 5 (10:73, 75, 78; 5 (11):81, 84; 5 (12):93; 6 (1):97, 103.
 1948 The effect of farm crops on the production of the ring-necked pheasant in Iowa.
 Iowa Acad. Sci. Proc. 55:109-113.

Feast, Cleland N.
 1948 Co-ordination of agricultural and wildlife practices.
 Internat. Assoc. Game, Fish & Cons. Comm. Proc. 38:111-117.

Ferrel, Carol M., Harold T. Harper and Jack Hiehle
 1949 A progress report on pheasant hunting season studies for the years 1946, 1947 and 1948.
 California Fish and Game 35 (4):301-322.

Ferrel, Carol M., Howard Twining and Norman B. Herkenham
  1949 Food habits of the ring-necked pheasant *(Phasianus colchicus)* in
        the Sacramento Valley, California.
        California Fish and Game 35 (1):51-69.

Fetherston, Kathleen E.
  1949 A study of the ring-necked pheasant on Pelee Island, Ontario.
        Cornell Univ., Unpub. Thesis, 170 pp.

Fisher, Harvey J., Robert H. Hiatt and William R. Bergeson
  1947 The validity of the roadside census as applied to pheasants.
        Jour. Wildl. Mgt. 11 (3):205-226.

Fried, Louis A.
  1940 The food habits of the ring-necked pheasant in Minnesota.
        Jour. Wildl. Mgt. 4 (1):27-36.

Garren, Henry W. and C. S. Shaffner
  1954 Factors concerned in the response of young New Hampshires to
        muscular fatigue.
        Poultry Sci. 33 (6):1095-1104.

Gerstell, Richard
  1937 The status of the ringneck pheasant in Pennsylvania.
        2d N. Amer. Wildl. Conf. Trans., 505-509.
  1938 An analysis of the reported returns obtained from the release of
        30,000 artificially propagated ringneck pheasants and bob-white.
        3d N. Amer. Wildl. Conf. Trans., 724-729.
  1942 The place of winter feeding in practical wildlife management.
        Pennsylvania Game Comm. Research Bul. 3, 121 pp.

Ginn, William E.
  1947 Band returns from Indiana club-reared pheasants.
        Jour. Wildl. Mgt. 11:226-231.
  1948 Pheasants in the rain.
        Outdoor Indiana 15 (5):4-5.

Golden, M. J.
  1951 The man with the land—how to reach him.
        N. E. Fish and Wildlife Conf. Proc. (mimeo), 4 pp.

Gordon, Seth
  1950 California's fish and game program.
        Wildl. Cons. Board Rept., 246 pp.

Gordon, Seth, Jr.
  1941 A sampling technique for the determination of hunters' activities
        and the economics thereof.
        Jour. Wildl. Mgt. 5 (3):260-278.

Gower, W. Carl
  1939 The use of the bursa of Fabricius as an indication of age in game
        birds.
        4th N. Amer. Wildl. Conf. Trans., 426-430.

Graham, Samuel A. and Gene Hesterberg
  1948 The influence of climate on the ring-necked pheasant.
        Jour. Wildl. Mgt. 12 (1):9-14.

Green, William E.
  1938 The food and cover relationship in the winter survival of the ring-
        necked pheasant, *Phasianus colchicus torquatus* Gmelin, in northern
        Iowa.
        Iowa State Coll. Jour. Sci. 12 (3):285-314.

1948   The development of experimental management areas for the ring-necked pheasant, *Phasianus colchicus torquatus* Gmelin, in northern Iowa.
Iowa State Coll., Unpub. Thesis, 168 pp.

Greenhalgh, Clifton M.
1951   Utah upland game bird investigation and survey.
Pittman-Robertson Quart. 11 (1):89.

Grinnell, Joseph, Harold C. Bryant and Tracy I. Storer
1918   The game birds of California.
Univ. California Press, Berkeley, 642 pp.

Gubser, Cecil E.
1942   A correction factor of ring-necked pheasant sex ratios for application in census methods.
Oregon State Coll., Unpub. Thesis, 70 pp.

Hamerstrom, Frederick N., Jr.
1936   A study of the nesting habits of the ring-necked pheasant in northwest Iowa.
Iowa State Coll. Jour. Sci. 10 (2):173-203.

Harper, Harold T., George H. Metcalfe and John F. Davis
1950   Upland game cooperative hunting areas.
California Fish and Game 36 (4):404-432.

Harper, Harold T., Chester M. Hart and Dale E. Shaffer
1951   Effects of hunting pressure and game farm stocking on pheasant populations in the Sacramento Valley, California, 1946-1949.
California Fish and Game 37 (2):141-176.

Harris, Bruce K.
1950   Water requirements of pheasant chicks in North Dakota.
North Dakota Outdoors 13 (6):12-13.

Hart, Chester M., Fred L. Jones and Dale E. Shaffer
1951   Pheasant cooperative hunting area results, 1950.
California Fish and Game 37 (4):395-437.

Hart, Chester M., John F. Davis, and Wilbur E. Myers
1952   Pheasant cooperative hunting area results, 1951.
California Fish and Game 38 (4):597-604.

Hicks, Lawrence E.
1938   History of the importation and naturalization of the ring-necked pheasant in the United States.
Ohio Wildl. Research Sta., Release 67 (mimeo), 3 pp.

Hill, Russell G.
1940   Some observations on farm game management cooperatives in Michigan.
Jour. Wildl. Mgt. 4 (4):383-391.

Hjersman, Henry A.
1947   A history of the establishment of the ring-necked pheasant in California.
California Fish and Game 33 (1):3-11.
1951   The 1948 surveys of California's hunting take and their significance.
California Fish and Game 37 (1):77-95.

Hubbs, Earl L.
1951   Food habits of feral house cats in the Sacramento Valley.
California Fish and Game 37 (2):177-189.

Hunter, Gilbert N.
    1949 The personal interview method of obtaining information on game
          and fish resources.
          Colorado Game and Fish Dept. Federal Aid Proj. 36-R, Rept. 24,
          56 pp.
Hunter, J. S. and Donald H. Fry, Jr.
    1941 Trends in California's game kill 1935-1938.
          California Fish and Game 27 (1):13-28.
Janson, Reuel G.
    1946 Automobile sight record analysis.
          South Dakota Pittman-Robertson Quart. Prog. Rept., Proj. 14-R
          (mimeo), 18-27.
Johnson, Herbert E.
    1951 Multiflora rose hips as pheasant food.
          Jour. Wildl. Mgt. 15 (2)221-222.
Jones, Owen
    1909 Ten years of game-keeping.
          Edward Arnold, London, 306 pp.
Jones, Paul V., Jr.
    1950 Pheasants in the panhandle?
          Texas Game and Fish 8 (11):4-7, 27.
Kabat, Cyril, Irven O. Buss and Ronald K. Meyer
    1948 The use of ovulated follicles in determining eggs laid by the ring-
          necked pheasant.
          Jour. Wildl. Mgt. 12 (4):399-416.
Kabat, Cyril, D. R. Thompson, and Frank M. Kozlik
    1952 Recent Wisconsin pheasant stocking studies.
          Wisconsin Cons. Dept. Bul. (mimeo), 16 pp.
Kelker, George H.
    1940 Estimating deer populations by a differential hunting loss in the
          sexes.
          Utah Acad. Sci. Proc. 17:65-69.
    1944 Sex ratio equations and formulas for determining wildlife popu-
          lations.
          Utah Acad. Sci. Proc. 19-20:189-198.
Kellogg, H. B., Jr.
    1939 Pheasant banding statistics.
          Wisconsin Cons. Bull. 4 (12):49-50.
Kimball, James W.
    1944 Age gauge for pheasants.
          Jour. Wildl. Mgt. 8 (3)263-264.
    1948 Pheasant population characteristics and trends in the Dakotas.
          13th N. Amer. Wildl. Conf. Trans., 291-314.
    1949 The crowing count pheasant census.
          Jour. Wildl. Mgt. 13 (1):101-120.
    1950 South Dakota pheasant management—past, present and planned.
          3d No. Rocky Mountain Wildl. Conf. (mimeo) 1-4.
Kirsch, Leo M.
    1951 Our winter storm losses.
          South Dakota Cons. Digest 18 (4):2-3, 7, 12.
Knight, John Alden
    1947 Ruffed grouse.
          Alfred A. Knopf, New York, 271 pp.

Knott, Norman P., Chester C. Ball and Charles F. Yocum
    1943 Nesting of the Hungarian partridge and ring-necked pheasant in
          Whitman County, Washington.
          Jour. Wildl. Mgt. 7 (3):283-291.
Kozicky, Edward L.
    1951 Juvenile ring-necked pheasant mortality and cover utilization in
          Iowa, 1949.
          Iowa State Coll. Jour. Sci. 26 (1):85-93.
    1952 Variations in two spring indices of male ring-necked pheasant
          population.
          Jour. Wildl. Mgt. 16 (4):429-437.
Kozicky, Edward L. and George O. Hendrickson
    1951 The production of ring-necked pheasants in Winnebago County,
          Iowa.
          Iowa Acad. Sci. Proc. 58:491-495.
Kozicky, Edward L., George O. Hendrickson, P. G. Homeyer and E. B. Speaker
    1952 The adequacy of the fall roadside pheasant census in Iowa.
          17th N. Amer. Wildl. Conf. Trans., 293-304.
Kozlik, Frank M.
    1948 Gentle release method of stocking pheasants.
          Wisconsin Cons. Bul. 13 (5):1-3.
    1949 Effect of starvation on penned pheasants.
          Wisconsin Wildl. Research Prog. Rept. (mimeo) 8 (1):59-62.
    1949a The 1948 hunters' check on Potter's Marsh.
          Wisconsin Cons. Bul. 14 (3):16-18.
Kozlik, Frank M. and Cyril Kabat
    1949 Why do pheasant populations remain low?
          Wisconsin Cons. Bul. 14 (10):7-10.
Latham, Roger M.
    1947 Differential ability of male and female game birds to with-
          stand starvation and climatic extremes.
          Jour. Wildl. Mgt. 11 (2):139-149.
Lauckhart, J. Burton
    1946 Habitat areas and their relation to pheasant management.
          Western Assoc. State Game & Fish Comm., 26th Ann. Conf. Proc.
          (mimeo), 120-123.
Lawson, W. D.
    1949 Pheasants in trouble.
          Pennsylvania Game News 18 (6):11, 38-39.
Leach, Howard R., Carol M. Ferrel, and Ernest E. Clark
    1953 A study of the food habits of the ring-necked pheasant on irrigated
          pasture in California.
          California Fish and Game 39 (4):517-525.
Leedy, Daniel L. and Charles A. Dambach
    1948 An evaluation of Ohio's wildlife resources.
          Ohio Div. Cons. and Nat. Resources Wildl. Cons. Bul. 5, 16 pp.
Leedy, Daniel L. and Lawrence E. Hicks
    1945 The pheasants in Ohio (in McAtee, W. L., The ring-necked
          pheasant and its management in North America).
          Amer. Wildl. Inst., 57-130.
Leffingwell, Dane I.
    1928 The ring-neck pheasant—its history and habits.
          Chas. R. Connor Mus., State Coll. Washington, Occ. Pap. 1, 35 pp.

Leopold, Aldo
   1931 Report on a game survey of the north central states.
        Sporting Arms & Ammunition Manufacturers' Institute, Madison, Wisconsin, 299 pp.
   1933 Game management.
        Charles Scribner's Sons, New York, 481 pp.
   1940 History of the Riley game cooperative, 1931-1939.
        Jour. Wildl. Mgt. 4 (3):291-302.

Leopold, Aldo, Elwood B. Moore and Lyle K. Sowls
   1939 Wildlife food patches in southern Wisconsin.
        Jour. Wildl. Mgt. 3 (1):60-69.

Leopold, Aldo, Theodore M. Sperry, William S. Feeney, and John A. Catenhusen
   1943 Population turnover on a Wisconsin pheasant refuge.
        Jour. Wildl. Mgt. 7 (4):383-394.

Linduska, Joseph P.
   1943 A gross study of the bursa of Fabricius and cock spurs as age indicators in the ring-necked pheasant.
        Auk 60 (3):426-437.
   1945 Age determination in the ring-necked pheasant.
        Jour. Wildl. Mgt. 9:152-154.
   1947 Keeping tab on pheasants.
        Michigan Cons. 16 (7):6, 7, 10; (8):8, 9, 14.

Loughrey, Alan G.
   1951 A food habit study of juvenile ring-necked pheasants on Pelee Island, Ontario.
        Univ. Western Ontario, Unpub. M.S. Thesis, 60 pp.

Low, Jessop B.
   1948 A summary of the restocking of pheasant habitat in Utah with farm-reared birds.
        Utah Coop. Wildl. Res. Unit Spec. Rept. (mimeo), 43 pp.

Luttringer, Leo A., Jr.
   1938 Outlaws of the air—or are they?
        Pennsylvania Game News 9 (4):10-11.

Lytle, Horace
   1935 Under church auspices.
        Field & Stream 40 (8):36-37, 63-64.

MacMullan, Ralph A. and L. L. Eberhardt
   1953 Tolerance of incubating pheasant eggs to exposure.
        Jour. Wildl. Mgt. 17 (3):322-330.

MacNamara, Lester G. and Edward L. Kozicky
   1949 Band returns from male ring-necked pheasants in New Jersey.
        Jour. Wildl. Mgt. 13 (3):286-294.

McClure, H. Elliott
   1945 Comparison of census methods for pheasants in Nebraska.
        Jour. Wildl. Mgt. 9 (1):38-45.
   1948 Factors in winter starvation of pheasants.
        Jour. Wildl. Mgt. 12 (3):267-271.
   1949 The eyeworm, *Oxyspirura petrowi*, in Nebraska pheasants.
        Jour. Wildl. Mgt. 13 (3):304-307.

McKean, John W.
   1951 Oregon's pheasant propagation program.
        Oregon State Game Comm. Bul. 6 (9):1, 3-5, 8.

Metcalf, George
  1953 Pheasant cooperative hunting areas, report for 1952 season.
        California Dept. Fish and Game, Unpub. Rept.
Miller, J. Paul and Burwell B. Powell
  1942 Game and wild-fur production and utilization on agricultural land.
        U. S. Dept. Agr., Circ. 636, 58 pp.
Miller, Wilford L.
  1948 Pheasants killed by blizzard.
        North Dakota Outdoors 10 (9):4-6, 10.
Mohler, Levi L.
  1943 Pheasant weights and time of season in relation to meat produc-
        tion in Nebraska.
        8th N. Amer. Wildl. Conf. Trans., 210-213.
  1949 Foods of pheasants in Nebraska.
        Wildl. Mgt. Notes 1 (7):27-30.
Mohr, R. W., H. S. Telford, E. H. Peterson and K. C. Walker
  1951 Toxicity of orchard insecticides to game birds in eastern Wash-
        ington.
        Washington Agr. Exp. Sta. Cir. 170, 22 pp.
Moore, Paul J. and Archibald B. Cowan
  1947 Results of a two year study on typical Illinois pheasant range.
        9th Midwest Wildl. Conf. (mimeo), 8 pp.
Moreland, Raleigh
  1948 First-year survival of different age groups of game farm-reared
        pheasants as indicated by shooting returns.
        Washington Game Dept., Unpub. Rept.
Morse, John S.
  1941 Foods of the ring-necked pheasant on Protection Island, Washington.
        Oregon State Coll., Unpub. Thesis.
Nelson, Bernard A.
  1946 Population characteristics of South Dakota pheasants.
        8th Midwest Wildl. Conf. (mimeo), 3 pp.
  1948 Pheasant data from a two-year bag study in South Dakota.
        Jour. Wildl. Mgt. 12 (1):20-31.
  1949 Pheasant bag check—1948.
        South Dakota Pittman Robertson Quart. Prog. Rept.
        Proj. 17-R-3 (mimeo), 14:55-77.
  1950 Pheasant nesting studies—1946-1949.
        South Dakota Pittman Robertson Quart. Prog. Rept.
        Proj. 17-R-4 (mimeo), 4-39.
Nelson, Bernard A. and Reuel G. Janson
  1949 Starvation of pheasants in South Dakota.
        Jour. Wildl. Mgt. 13 (3):308-309.
Nestler, Ralph B.
  1946 Vitamin A, vital factor in the survival of bobwhites.
        11th N. Amer. Wildl. Conf. Trans., 176-192.
Norris, L. C.
  1934 Some studies of the nutritive requirements of pheasants.
        20th Amer. Game Conf. Trans., 304-310.
Norstog, Knute J.
  1948 Hunter success, 1947.
        South Dakota Pittman-Robertson Quart. Prog. Rept.
        Proj. 17-R-2 (mimeo), 8:4-11.

Olds, Hayden W.
  1940 Ohio pheasant banding results 1930-1939.
        Ohio Div. Cons. and Nat. Res. Bul. 191, 44 pp.
Perry, Robert F.
  1946 Appraisal of pheasant abundance in New York State during 1945
        and some factors responsible for the recent decline.
        11th N. Amer. Wildl. Conf. Trans., 141-152.
Petrides, George A.
  1949 Viewpoints on the analysis of open season sex and age ratios.
        14th N. Amer. Wildl. Conf. Trans., 391-410.
Phillips, John C.
  1928 Wild birds introduced or transplanted in North America.
        U. S. Dept. Agr., Tech. Bul. 61, 63 pp.
Pushee, George F.
  1948 Summary report, pheasant banding studies 1943 to 1948.
        Massachusettts Dept. Cons., Div. Wildl. Res. and Mgt. (mimeo),
        22 pp.
  1948a A survey of pheasant stocking in the United States.
        Massachusetts Dept. Cons., Bur. Wildl. Res. and Mgt. (mimeo), 10 pp.
  1949 Massachusetts farm game investigations—pheasants.
        Massachusetts Dept. Cons., PR Quart. Rept. 3-R (mimeo), Jan.
Randall, Pierce E.
  1939 Nesting habits and causes of nest mortality of the ringneck pheasant.
        Pennsylvania Game News 10 (9):6-7, 30.
  1940 The ecology and management of the ring-necked pheasant in
        Pennsylvania.
        Pennsylvania State Coll. Unpub. Thesis, 141 pp.
  1940a The life equation of the ringneck pheasant in Pennsylvania.
        5th N. Amer. Wildl. Conf. Trans., 300-320.
Riordan, Lawrence E.
  1948 The sexing of deer and elk by airplane in Colorado.
        13th N. Amer. Wildl. Conf. Trans., 409-430.
Rasmussen, D. Irwin and William T. McKean
  1945 The pheasant in the intermountain irrigated region (in McAtee,
        W. L., *The ring-necked pheasant and its management in North
        America*).
        Amer. Wildl. Inst., 234-253.
Robbins, Chandler S. and Robert E. Stewart
  1949 Effects of DDT on bird populations of scrub forest.
        Jour. Wildl. Mgt. 13 (1):11-16.
Robbins, Otis and George O. Hendrickson
  1951 Productivity of the ring-necked pheasant in southeastern Iowa, 1950.
        Iowa Bird Life 21 (2):30-32.
Roby, Edwin F.
  1951 A two year study of pheasant stocking in the Gallatin Valley,
        Montana.
        Jour. Wildl. Mgt. 15 (3):299-307.
Sandfort, Wayne W.
  1951 Ring-necked pheasant production in north-central Colorado.
        Colorado A and M Coll., Unpub. Thesis.
  1951a Missing legs and broken eggs.
        Colorado Cons. March:3-6.

Schorger, A. W.
  1947 The introduction of pheasants into Wisconsin.
         Passenger Pigeon 9 (3):101-102.
Schultz, Vincent
  1948 Vitamin A as a survival factor of the bobwhite quail (*Colinus v. virginianus*) in Ohio during the winter of 1946-47.
         Jour. Wildl. Mgt. 12 (3):251-263.
Schwartz, Charles W. and Elizabeth R. Schwartz
  1949 A reconnaissance of the game birds in Hawaii.
         Bd. of Commissioners of Agr. and Forestry, Territory of Hawaii, 168 pp.
Scott, Thomas G.
  1947 Comparative analysis of red fox feeding trends on two central Iowa areas.
         Iowa State Coll., Agr. Exp. Sta. Bul. 353:427-487.
Scott, Thomas G. and Thomas S. Baskett
  1941 Some effects of the 1940 Armistice Day storm on Iowa's wildlife.
         Iowa Bird Life 11 (2):22-29.
Selye, Hans
  1949 Textbook of endocrinology.
         Acta Endocrinologica Inc., Montreal, 914 pp.
Severin, Harry C.
  1933 An economic study of the food of the ring-necked pheasant in South Dakota.
         South Dakota State Coll., in coop. with South Dakota Dept. Game and Fish (mimeo), 252 pp.
Sharp, Ward M. and H. Elliott McClure
  1945 The pheasant in the Sandhill region of Nebraska (in McAtee, W. L., *The ring-necked pheasant and its management in North America*).
         Amer. Wildl. Inst., 203-233.
Shick, Charles
  1947 Sex ratio-egg fertility relationships in the ring-necked pheasant.
         Jour. Wildl. Mgt. 11 (4):302-306.
  1952 A study of pheasants on the 9,000 acre Prairie Farm, Saginaw County, Michigan.
         Michigan Dept. Cons., 134 pp.
Siegler, Hilbert R.
  1949 The ring-necked pheasant in New Hampshire.
         New Hampshire Fish and Game Dept., Survey Rept. 5, 82 pp.
Skiff, J. Victor
  1948 Is there a place for stocking in game management?
         13th N. Amer. Wild. Conf. Trans., 215-227.
Smith, Eldon H.
  1948 Factors influencing the validity of pheasant census methods, Sevier County, Utah.
         Utah State Agr. Coll. Unpub. Thesis.
Sondrini, William J.
  1950 Estimating game from license reports.
         Connecticut State Board of Fisheries and Game, PR Proj. 7-R, Bul. 3.
Stanz, Harry E., Jr.
  1953 Pheasant breeding research.
         Wisconsin Conservation Bull. 18 (10):15-17.

Stiles, Bruce F. and George O. Hendrickson
  1946 Ten years of roadside pheasant censuses in Iowa.
        Jour. Wildl. Mgt. 10 (3):277-280.

Stokes, Allen W.
  1948 Status of Pelee Island pheasants, 1947-1948.
        10th Midwest Wildl. Conf. (mimeo), 3 pp.
  1954 Population studies of the ring-necked pheasants on Pelee Island,
        Ontario.
        Ontario Dept. Lands & Forests, Wildl. Ser. 4, 154 pp.

Swenk, M. H.
  1930 The food habits of the ring-necked pheasant in central Nebraska.
        Nebraska Agr. Expt. Sta., Research Bul. 50, 33 pp.

Swift, Ernest F.
  1951 Report to the people of Wisconsin on cover destruction, habitat
        improvement and watershed problems of the state in 1950 (com-
        piled by Walter E. Scott).
        Wisconsin Cons. Bul. 16 (2):1-78.

Taber, Richard D.
  1949 A new marker for game birds.
        Jour. Wildl. Mgt. 13 (2):228-231.
  1949a Observations on the breeding behavior of the ring-necked pheasant.
        Condor 51 (4):153-175.

Taylor, D. J.
  1942 Game management in Ontario.
        7th N. Amer. Wildl. Conf. Trans., 361-365.

Taylor, Ernest W.
  1950 Summary Report of pheasant studies conducted in the municipality
        of Delta, British Columbia.
        Univ. British Columbia, Unpub. Thesis.

Temple, J. Lawrence
  1948 Pheasant hunt in review.
        Oklahoma Game & Fish News 4 (11)3-4.

Thompson, Donald R. and Carl A. Baumann
  1950 Vitamin A in pheasants, quail and muskrats.
        Jour. Wildl. Mgt. 14 (1):42-49.

Thornthwaite, C. Warren
  1948 An approach toward a rational classification of climate.
        Geog. Rev. 38 (1):55-94.

Throckmorton, Michael
  1952 How many pheasants starve?
        Idaho Wildlife Review 4 (3):10-11.

Trautman, Carl G.
  1950 Determining the age of juvenile pheasants.
        South Dakota Cons. Digest 17 (8):8-10.
  1952 Pheasant food habits in South Dakota and their economic signifi-
        cance to agriculture.
        South Dakota Dept. Game, Fish and Parks, Tech. Bul. 1, 89 pp.

Trautman, Milton B., William E. Bills and Edward L. Wickliff
  1939 Winter losses from starvation and exposure of waterfowl and up-
        land game birds in Ohio and other northern states.
        Wilson Bul. 51 (2):86-104.

Tubbs, Farley F.
   1946   Pen-reared birds don't help sport.
          Michigan Cons. 15 (3):10-11.

Twining, Howard
   1946   Pheasant management problems.
          Western Assoc. State Game and Fish Comm., 26th Ann. Conf. Proc.
          (mimeo), 110-113.

Twining, Howard, Henry A. Hjersman and Wallace MacGregor, Jr.
   1948   Fertility of eggs of the ring-necked pheasant.
          California Fish and Game 34 (4):209-216.

Uhlig, Hans G.
   1948   Experimental feeding of ring-necked pheasants in the Willamette
          Valley, Oregon.
          Jour. Wildl. Mgt. 12 (3):272-279.

Wadkins, Laurence A.
   1948   Testing of winter pheasant foods.
          Washington State College, Unpub. Rept.

Wallace, George
   1937   Vermont's pheasant situation.
          2d. N. Amer. Wildl. Conf. Trans., 340-345.

Wandell, Willet N.
   1942   Progress report of the ring-necked pheasant investigation in the
          Connecticut River Valley.
          Massachusetts Dept. Cons., Research Bul. 5, 118 pp.

   1943   Ringnecked pheasant research
          Massachusetts Dept. Cons., PR Quart. Rept. (mimeo), January.

   1945   An appraisal of pheasant stocking in Massachusetts.
          Massachusetts Dept. Cons., Wildl. Research and Mgt. Bul. 111
          (mimeo), 32 pp.

   1948   Agricultural and wildlife values of habitat improvement plantings
          on the Illinois black prairies.
          13th N. Amer. Wildl. Conf. Trans., 256-270.

   1949   Status of ring-necked pheasants in the United States.
          14th N. Amer. Wildl. Conf. Trans., 370-386.

Wandell, Willet N., Charles L. McLaughlin, Carl F. Nelson, and James J.
          McDonough
   1942   Progress report of the ring-necked pheasant investigation in the
          Connecticut River Valley, Massachusetts.
          Massachusetts Dept. Cons., Div. Wildl. Research and Mgt. Research
          Bul. 5 (mimeo), 118 pp.

Warvel, Harold E.
   1950   The flushing bar, a valuable game saver.
          Ohio Cons. Bul. 14 (2):4-6.

Weston, Henry G., Jr.
   1950   Winter behavior and spring dispersal of the ring-necked pheasant
          (Phasianus colchicus torquatus Gmelin) in Emmet County, Iowa.
          Iowa State Coll., Ph. D. thesis 1104, 146 pp.

Wight, Howard M.
   1933   Suggestions for pheasant management in southern Michigan.
          Michigan Dept. Cons., 25 pp.

Wight, Howard M., Jr.
    1950   Nesting loss—the pheasant bottleneck.
           Pennsylvania Game News 20 (12):10-11, 25, 28.
Wright, Thomas J.
    1951   Estimate of game populations.
           Rhode Island Dept. Agr. and Cons., Div. Fish and Game, PR
           Quart. Rept. 6-R (mimeo), October.
    1953   A study of the pheasant banding program.
           Rhode Island Dept. Agr. and Cons., Div. Fish and Game Pamph.
           4, 8 pp.
Yeager, Lee E.
    1950   Burning: it's farm-game's enemy.
           Colorado Cons. Comments 10 (15):3-8.
Yeager, Lee E., Wayne W. Sandfort, and L. Jack Lyon
    1951   Some problems of pheasant management on irrigated land.
           16th N. Amer. Wildl. Conf. Trans., 351-367.
Yeatter, Ralph E.
    1950   Effects of different preincubation temperatures on the hatchability
           of pheasant eggs.
           Science 112 (2914):529-530.
Zorb, Gordon L.
    1950   Too much of a good thing?
           Utah Fish and Game Bul. 9 (4):6-8.
    1951   Application of pheasant census methods in Cache County, Utah.
           Utah State Agr. Coll., Unpub. Thesis.

INDEX

Unless otherwise indicated, all subject entries in this index apply to the pheasant.